Mathematics for Teachers of the Middle Grades

J. Maurice Kingston
Associate Professor of Mathematics, University of Washington

John Wiley & Sons, Inc., New York — London — Sydney

Copyright © 1966 by John Wiley & Sons, Inc.
All Rights Reserved

This book or any part thereof
must not be reproduced in any form
without the written permission of the publisher.

Library of Congress Catalog Card Number 65-26847
Printed in the United States of America

TO MY WIFE

Mathematics for Teachers of the Middle Grades

Preface

This book is designed to provide the minimum amount of background material needed by mathematics teachers in junior high school and the middle grades. I do not claim that it contains everything that these teachers should know. It is intended simply to provide assistance in an area that until now has been largely neglected.

Recent curriculum developments in elementary and secondary school mathematics have greatly enhanced the role of mathematics in the middle grades and junior high school. Instead of texts that concentrate on reviewing arithmetic computations, teachers in these grades now have available a body of material designed to bridge the gap between elementary school and senior high school mathematics. Often college and university undergraduate students who are aiming at teaching mathematics in these intervening grades will complete considerably less than a mathematics major and, for this reason, it is most desirable that teaching materials be prepared with these particular people in mind.

A central theme which runs continuously through the mathematics of grades 4 through 9 is the structure of the number system. This structure is examined in ever-increasing depth as the grade level rises, and one main purpose of preparing this material has been to enable teachers to be more effective in presenting the development of this basic concept. The emphasis on informal geometry is bound to have, as one consequence, the possibility of teaching in senior high school a much better course in geometry than has heretofore been offered. Hence it is most desirable that teachers in the middle grades have a clear understanding of the place of geometry in the mathematical hierarchy.

In addition to the exercises that have been placed at the end of almost every section, a considerable number of questions are scattered throughout the body of the material. These are designed to help the reader to obtain a firm understanding of the material presented. In effect, they are the questions that I believe the reader should be asking himself. It is intended that the reader should not be content with a "Yes" or "No" answer to a question, but should, at least, think through a solution to the problem. Some of the complete solutions require more than a reasonable amount of labor and have been inserted for the purpose of providing a basis for class discussion.

It should be emphasized again that this material has as its sole purpose the improvement of the background knowledge of the teacher and is not intended to be exhaustive in the treatment of the topic. This purpose reflects my belief that it is more desirable to treat a wider variety of subject matter in moderate detail.

There is probably sufficient material for a year's course of three hours a week. If less time is available Chapters 5 and 10 could be omitted without destroying the continuity of the presentation, as could Chapters 4 and 8 also, if desired.

I am particularly indebted to Professor Roy Dubisch for his unfailing assistance and advice during the various stages of preparation of the manuscript. I would like to express my appreciation to Mr. Wayne Peterson, Mr. Harry Iverson, and Miss Marjorie Lortz for their valuable suggestions and to the editorial consultants for the publisher, whose criticisms were most useful. I am also grateful to the many students and teachers in my classes whose comments and encouragements have been exceedingly helpful.

Finally I would like to thank the National Science Foundation for making possible the development of preliminary written material which was made available to all interested persons; and to the Committee on the Undergraduate Program in Mathematics of the Mathematical Association of America for printing and distributing that material.

J. MAURICE KINGSTON

Seattle, Washington
November 1965

Contents

Chapter 1. Concept of Natural Number 1

1.01 Basic Meaning, 1
1.02 Subsets, 3
1.03 Compound Sets and Venn Diagrams, 4
1.04 Addition of Natural Numbers, 7
1.05 Role of Numeral, 9
1.06 Multiplication of Natural Numbers, 10
1.07 Exponents, 11
1.08 Distributive Property, 12
1.09 Whole Numbers, 15
1.10 Order, 16
1.11 Subtraction, 17
1.12 Inverse Operation, 18
1.13 Division, 19
1.14 Prime Numbers, 20
1.15 Greatest Common Divisor, 21
1.16 Least Common Multiple, 22
1.17 Significance of Number Base, 23
1.18 Mathematical Systems, 28
1.19 Mathematical Induction, 31

Chapter 2. Elementary Logic 36

2.01 Propositions and Truth Tables, 36
2.02 Truth Sets, 43
2.03 Logical Truth and Logical Falsity, 45
2.04 Valid Arguments, 48

Chapter 3. Extension of the Whole Numbers 56

3.01 Sentences, or Why Is Extension Necessary? 56
3.02 The Concept of Negative Number—the Integers, 57
3.03 Absolute Value, 61
3.04 Relations and Equivalence Classes, 65

x   Contents

3.05   Rational Numbers, 67
3.06   Decimal Fractions, 78
3.07   Irrational Numbers, 80
3.08   The Algebraic Field, 84
3.09   Real Numbers Are Not Sufficient, 85

Chapter 4.   Basic Geometric Concepts   **90**

4.01   Geometry Is All Around Us, 90
4.02   Euclid's Strengths and Weaknesses, 91
4.03   Why Postulates? 92
4.04   What Should We Look for in Postulates? 93
4.05   Is Geometry True? 95
4.06   Geometric Figures, 95
4.07   Betweenness and Definitions, 96
4.08   Measure, 99
4.09   Coordinates, 100

Chapter 5.   Measurement and Approximation   **104**

5.01   Exact Values and Measured Values, 104
5.02   Precision and Accuracy, 105
5.03   Significant Digits, 109
5.04   Addition and the Rounding of Numbers, 112
5.05   Significant Digits and Multiplication, 113
5.06   Short Multiplication and Division, 115

Chapter 6.   From Arithmetic To Algebra   **118**

6.01   Where Does Algebra Begin? 118
6.02   Graphs, 118
6.03   Linear Equations, 123
6.04   Quadratics and Factoring, 132
6.05   Mathematical Induction Applied to Series, 139
6.06   Equivalent Sentences, 141
6.07   Progressions, 144
6.08   Binomial Theorem, 148
6.09   Permutations, 149
6.10   Combinations, 152
6.11   Probability, 154

Contents   xi

Chapter 7. Fractions and Fractional Exponents   **159**

7.01 Number and Numeral, 159
7.02 How Many? 161
7.03 Countability of Rational Numbers, 162
7.04 More about Decimal Fractions, 164
7.05 Noncountability of the Set of Irrational Numbers, 168
7.06 Radicals and Fractional Exponents, 170
7.07 Per Cent, 173

Chapter 8. More Informal Geometry   **175**

8.01 Congruence, 175
8.02 Existence of Parallel Lines, 178
8.03 Do We Have Rectangles? 181
8.04 Euclid's Parallel Postulate, 182
8.05 Area of a Triangle, 184
8.06 Similarity, 185
8.07 The Theorem of Pythagoras, 187
8.08 Constructions, 189
8.09 Volumes of Solids, 193

Chapter 9. More Algebra   **197**

9.01 The Division Algorithm, 197
9.02 The Concept of Function, 199
9.03 The Remainder Theorem, 201
9.04 Synthetic Division and Synthetic Substitution, 203
9.05 Factoring and the Distributive Property, 206
9.06 Casting Out b-1's, 208
9.07 Rational Zeros of Polynomials, 212
9.08 Simultaneous Inequalities, 215

Chapter 10. Statistics   **219**

10.01 Meaning of the Term, 219
10.02 Frequency Distribution, 220
10.03 Graphs, 221
10.04 The Normal Distribution, 224
10.05 Descriptive Measures, 225

xii   Contents

10.06   Measures of Dispersion, 230
10.07   Sampling, 233
10.08   Hypothesis Testing, 234

Appendix A   Example of a Geometric Sophism (or Fallacious Argument), 239
Appendix B   Determinants, 240
Appendix C   Some Elementary Facts about Matrices, 244
Appendix D   Proof of the Binomial Theorem for Positive Integral Exponents, 250
Glossary, 253
Answers to Odd-Numbered Exercises, 259
Answers to Questions, 271
Index, 319

Mathematics for Teachers of the Middle Grades

1 *Natural Numbers*

1.01 BASIC MEANING

It is possible to investigate the structure of our number system in almost any desired amount of detail. We wish to begin our study by examining the familiar properties of the "counting" numbers 1, 2, 3, ..., usually referred to as the natural numbers. If we wished we could accept the natural numbers as existing by assumption or, on the other hand, we could obtain them by a formal development based on more fundamental assumptions known as the Peano postulates. We wish to adopt what might be termed a "middle-of-the-road" approach, which makes use of certain elementary properties of the concept of *set*, a term which we wish now to introduce.

Whenever we are faced with the need of presenting a new concept, such as set, great care must be taken to avoid an unsatisfactory sequence of words attempting to define other words. This is the situation we encounter if we attempt to define the word set. Therefore let us accept the word set and the clause "is a member of" as undefined terms and draw on our experience to give them meaning. For the purpose of illustration we may say that any collection of objects (or elements, as we often speak of them) is an example of a set, provided that there is a clearly established rule for determining whether or not a given object is one of the objects of the set. For example, Seattle is one of the cities of the set of cities of the state of Washington. We say that Seattle *belongs to* the set of cities of the state of Washington. We often describe a set of elements in what is sometimes referred to as the *set-builder* notation, that is, a symbol for the element, followed by a vertical bar (or sometimes a colon) and the restricting condition on the symbol with the whole expression enclosed in a pair of braces. Thus the above set of cities of the state of Washington may be described as $\{x|x$ is a city in the state of Washington$\}$. When it is convenient, we may simply list between braces the complete set of objects, for example, {chair, table, lamp}. If x is a member of a set A, we write $x \in A$; hence, Seattle $\in \{x|x$ is a city in the state of Washington$\}$ and chair $\in$ {chair, table, lamp}. The symbol, $\notin$, will mean "is not a member of," and, for example, desk

2   Natural Numbers

∉ {chair, table, lamp}. Then it is evident that all sets consisting of a single element have a common property which can serve to define a number to which we give the name "one." However, it should be emphasized that there is a definite distinction in every case between the object and the set consisting of that object; that is, q is not the same as $\{q\}$. A good example would be a club whose membership has dwindled to one member. The club may be dissolved without the same fate befalling the person himself.

In a similar fashion, consideration of all possible sets, such as {Washington, Oregon}, {□, △}, {blue, green}, {car, boat}, leads us to abstract their only common feature and use it to define the number to which we give the name "two." The essential characteristic of each of these particular collections of sets is the fact that the elements of any one set may be made to correspond exactly (but not in a unique way) with the elements of any other set of the collection, that is,

$$\text{Washington} \leftrightsquigarrow \square \leftrightsquigarrow \text{blue} \leftrightsquigarrow \text{car}$$
$$\text{Oregon} \leftrightsquigarrow \triangle \leftrightsquigarrow \text{green} \leftrightsquigarrow \text{boat}$$

We refer to this type of correspondence as one-to-one, often written 1:1 or 1–1, and the symbol ↭ merely indicates which elements are thought of as corresponding to each other. The variety of available sets is so great that the only possible common property of such sets stands out and makes unmistakable the concept of the natural number which we wish to define. The historical development of the most convenient symbols to use to represent these natural numbers is a story* in itself.

We say that two sets are *equivalent* when a 1 : 1 correspondence can be established between their elements. Hence the sets {□, △} and {blue, green} are equivalent sets. When the elements of two sets are the same, we say the sets are *equal*. Hence $\{a,b,c\} = \{b,c,a\}$.

Questions. 1. Are all equal sets equivalent?
  2. Are any two equivalent sets necessarily equal?

It should be noted that it is customary to think of a set as consisting only of distinct elements. Hence $\{a,a,b,c\} = \{a,b,c\}$.

For our purposes, then, we shall think of a natural number as associated with a collection of equivalent sets. That is, $n(A)$ is the natural number associated with the set A or with any set equivalent to A. For example, $n(\{a,b\}) = 2$, $n(\{a,b,c\}) = 3$, etc. Therefore, if

---

*See *An Introduction to the History of Mathematics*, by Howard Eves, New York, Rinehart, 1953.

$n(A) = n(B)$, it follows that A and B are equivalent sets. We shall refer to the set of natural numbers as N.

We shall use the common symbols for natural numbers and define the process of *counting* as merely the determination of the largest natural number n needed in the sequence $1,2,3,\ldots,n,\ldots$ so that the set $\{1,2,3,\ldots, n\}$ may be put in $1:1$ correspondence with the set of objects we wish to count. The sets we have encountered so far are all examples of *finite sets*, that is, sets consisting of a finite number of elements. However, we shall have occasion to deal with many sets which contain an infinite number of elements. By this we mean that there is no natural number large enough to indicate how many elements belong to the set. Such sets are called *infinite sets*. The set of all natural numbers is an example of an infinite set.

EXERCISES

1. Are the following valid examples of sets? Explain.
   (a) {Mt. Baker, Mt. Hood, Mt. Rainier, Mt. Shasta}.
   (b) {The ten most important residents of Seattle in 1962}.
   (c) {The states of the United States of America, whose names begin with the letter W}.
   (d) $\{\{a\},\{b\}\}$
2. Let J denote Mr. Jones, a man who lives in Seattle, Washington. Let S denote the set of all people who live in Seattle. Let W denote the set of all people who live in the state of Washington. Is it true that:
   (a) $J \in S$? (b) $J \in W$? (c) $S \in W$?
3. Let E denote the set of Evenfellow Clubs in Illinois. Let E_1 denote the Evenfellow Club of Springfield, Illinois. Let S denote Mr. Smith who is President and sole surviving member of E_1. Is it true that:
   (a) $E_1 \in E$? $S \in E$? $\{S\} \in E$?
   (b) $S \in E_1$? $S = E_1$? $\{S\} = E_1$?

1.02 SUBSETS

Whenever set A contains no members which are not members of set B, we say that A is a *subset* of B and we write $A \subseteq B$. For example, $\{1,3,5\} \subseteq \{1,2,3,4,5\}$ and also $\{w\} \subseteq \{w\}$. When $A \subseteq B$ we sometimes say that set A *is contained in* set B. As we have seen, when $A \subseteq B$ this does not make it impossible to have $A = B$. In fact frequently the most effective way of proving that $A = B$ is to prove that both $A \subseteq B$ and $B \subseteq A$.

It should be emphasized that there is a basic distinction between the meaning of the symbols, $\in$ and $\subseteq$. For example, $3 \in \{1,3,5\}$ and

4 Natural Numbers

$\{3\} \subseteq \{1,3,5\}$ and it is incorrect to write $\{3\} \in \{1,3,5\}$ or $3 \subseteq \{1,3,5\}$.

It is customary to accept as a valid set the set which contains no element. We call this set the *empty* or *null set* and it is usually denoted by $\emptyset$. It is consistent with our definition of subset to agree that $\emptyset$ is a subset of every set.

EXERCISES

1. State which of the following statements are correct and which are incorrect:
   T (a) $\{1,3\} \subseteq \{1,3,5\}$ F (b) $\{\{1\},\{3\}\} \subseteq \{1,3,5\}$
   F (c) $\{1\} \in \{1,3,5\}$ F (d) $\emptyset \in \{1\}$
   T (e) $\emptyset \subseteq \{1\}$ F (f) $\{\emptyset\} \subseteq \{1\}$
2. Do the same for the following statements:
   (a) $\emptyset \subseteq \emptyset$ (b) $\emptyset \in \emptyset$ (c) $\emptyset \subseteq \{\emptyset\}$
   (d) $\emptyset \in \{\emptyset\}$ (e) $\emptyset = \{\emptyset\}$
   (f) $\{\emptyset\} \subseteq \{\emptyset\}$ (g) $\{\emptyset\} \in \{\emptyset\}$
3. How many different subsets can be formed from the elements of each of the following sets?
   (a) $\emptyset$ (b) $\{1\}$ (c) $\{1,2\}$ (d) $\{1,2,3\}$ (e) $\{1,2,3,4\}$
   (f) $\{k | k$ is any of the natural numbers $1,2,3,\ldots,n\}$

1.03 COMPOUND SETS AND VENN DIAGRAMS

It is convenient to be able to think of all the elements which appear in the sets we deal with in a given situation as belonging to a *universal set* or *universe* which we shall label U. In what follows we shall describe an effective way of picturing sets which can be helpful in clarifying relations between sets. We may think of the elements of set U as represented by points within a rectangle and the elements of set A as points within a circle contained within the rectangle. Such a representation is known as a *Venn diagram*. A is a subset of U, and the subset represented by points inside the rectangle but outside the circle is known as the *complement* of A, which we shall designate as $\overline{A}$.

Question. What set is equal to $\overline{\overline{A}}$, by which we mean $(\overline{\overline{A}})$?

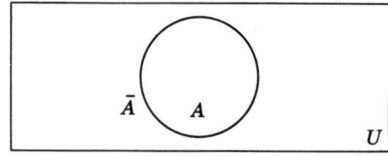

Very often we shall have occasion to construct a new set from given sets. This can be accomplished in several ways. If we are given sets A

and B, one easily constructed set is the *union* of A and B, denoted by $A \cup B$ and read "A union B". In symbols, $A \cup B = \{x | x \in A \text{ or } x \in B\}$ and, in words, the union of sets A and B is the set of those elements which belong either to set A or to set B or to both sets. For example, if $A = \{a,b,c\}$ and $B = \{a,c,d,g\}$, then $A \cup B = \{a,b,c,d,g\}$.

Another set which is immediately describable is the set of elements which belong to set A *and* to set B. This new set is known as the *intersection* of sets A and B and is written $A \cap B$ and read "A intersect B". If A and B are the sets described in the previous paragraph, then $A \cap B = \{a,c\}$.

Question. Can you express $A \cap B$ in set–builder notation?

When there is no element which belongs both to set A and set B we say that A and B are *disjoint* sets and we write $A \cap B = \emptyset$. Hence the intersection of any two sets exists in all cases. The thatched regions in the following Venn diagrams will represent the indicated sets.

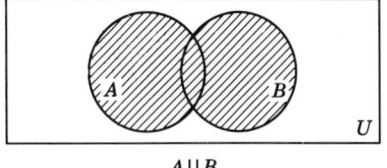
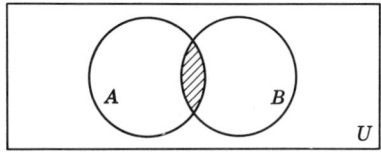

$A \cup B$ $A \cap B$

We may think of union and intersection as two *operations* applied to the sets A and B. We call such operations *binary* since they are applied only to a pair (A,B) of sets. When we apply either operation to (A,B), we do not know automatically that the same result is obtained when the operation is applied to (B,A). Hence we refer to (A,B) as an *ordered pair* of sets and write

$$(A,B) \xrightarrow{\cup} A \cup B$$
$$(A,B) \xrightarrow{\cap} A \cap B$$

Let us verify, in fact, that the order in which the sets occur is immaterial as far as the operation of union is concerned; that is, $A \cup B = B \cup A$. We observed earlier that an effective procedure in establishing the equality of two sets is to show that each is a subset of the other. This may seem a bit trivial in this case but let us proceed to show that $A \cup B \subseteq B \cup A$. We know that $x \in A \cup B$ if and only if $x \in A$ or $x \in B$. However, if $x \in A$ or $x \in B$, then certainly $x \in B$ or $x \in A$. Hence $x \in B \cup A$ as a result of belonging to $A \cup B$. Therefore $A \cup B \subseteq B \cup A$. An exactly similar argument leads to the conclusion that $B \cup A \subseteq A \cup B$. Accordingly we have established that $A \cup B = B \cup A$. When this is true of an operation we say that the operation (union of sets in this case) is *commutative*.

Question. Can you prove that the operation of intersection of sets is commutative?

EXERCISES

1. Is it true that
   (a) $\{a\} \cup \{b\} = \{a,b\}$?
   (b) $\{\{a\}, \{b,c\}\} = \{a,b,c\}$?
   (c) $\{\{a\}, \{b,c\}\} = \{\{a\}, \{b\}, \{c\}\}$?
2. Is it true that
   (a) $2 + 3 \in \{1,2,3,4\}$?
   (b) $5 \in \{5\}$?
3. Is it correct to say $123 \in \{1,2,3\}$?
4. Are the following correct statements:
   (a) $a \in \{a,b,c,d\} \cap \{a,b,c,g\}$?
   (b) $d \in \{a,b,c,d\} \cap \{a,b,c,g\}$?
   (c) $\{b\} \in \{a,b,c,d\} \cap \{a,b,c,g\}$?
   (d) $\{a,b\} \in \{a,b,c,d\} \cap \{a,b,c,g\}$?
   (e) $\{a,b\} \in \{a,b,c,d\} \cap \{a,b,f,g\}$?
   (f) $\{b\} \in \{\{a\}, \{b\}, \{c\}\}$?
5. Is it possible to have two sets C and D such that $C \cup D$ and $C \cap D$ are equal sets? Explain.
6. Identify the following sets:
   (a) $\overline{\varnothing}$ (b) $\overline{U}$ (c) $A \cup \overline{A}$
   (d) $A \cup \varnothing$ (e) $A \cap \varnothing$ (f) $A \cup U$
   (g) $A \cap U$ (h) $A \cap \overline{A}$
7. (a) When $A \subseteq B$, what set is
       (i) $A \cup B$?   (ii) $A \cap B$?
   (b) Verify by drawing Venn diagrams.
8. (a) If we define the *difference* of sets A and B, viz., $A - B$, to be the set consisting of those elements of A which do not also belong to B,
       (i) obtain the Venn diagram for $A - B$,
       (ii) describe $A - B$ in set-builder notation,
       (iii) obtain an alternative expression for $A - B$ in terms of A and B and their complements.
   (b) Verify the following equalities of sets by comparing their Venn diagrams:*
       (i) $(A - B) - C = A - (B \cup C)$
       (ii) $A - (B - C) = (A - B) \cup (A \cap C)$
       (iii) $A \cup (B - C) = (A \cup B) - (C - A)$
       (iv) $A \cap (B - C) = (A \cap B) - (A \cap C)$

*When making a Venn diagram involving three sets, the circles representing each set should be permitted to intersect in the most general manner, resulting in seven sub-regions in addition to the region within the rectangle and exterior to all three circles.

9. Construct the Venn diagram for three subsets A, B, and C of the universal set U and give a set description of each of the eight subregions appearing in the diagram.
10. Identify the equal sets among the following eight sets by comparing their Venn diagrams:
    (a) $A \cup (B \cup C)$
    (b) $(A \cap B) \cup (A \cap C)$
    (c) $(A \cap B) \cap C$
    (d) $A \cup (B \cap C)$
    (e) $A \cap (B \cap C)$
    (f) $(A \cup B) \cap (A \cup C)$
    (g) $(A \cup B) \cup C$
    (h) $A \cap (B \cup C)$
11. Prove that
    (a) $P \cup (Q \cap R) = (P \cup Q) \cap (P \cup R)$
    (b) $P \cap (Q \cup R) = (P \cap Q) \cup (P \cap R)$
    (These two equalities comprise what are known as the distributive properties of union and intersection of sets.)

1.04 ADDITION OF NATURAL NUMBERS

Now that the natural numbers are well established we need to consider how best to define operations on them. Particularly we would like to set up the binary operation of addition (+) which would permit us to add two numbers, say, $n(A)$ and $n(B)$. In view of our definition of counting (see Section 1.01), it would seem natural to form $A \cup B$ and consider the natural number $n(A \cup B)$ associated with this set. This agrees with our intuitive notion of addition provided that A and B have no element in common. Therefore we shall adopt the definition: $n(A) + n(B) = n(A \cup B)$, provided $A \cap B = \emptyset$, and we shall refer to $n(A \cup B)$ as the *sum* of $n(A)$ and $n(B)$. For example, since

$$2 = n(\{a,b\}) \text{ and } 3 = n(\{c,d,g\})$$

then

$$2 + 3 = n(\{a,b\} \cup \{c,d,g\}) = n(\{a,b,c,d,g\}) = 5$$

Clearly, if we thought of $2 = n(\{a,b\})$ and $3 = n(\{a,c,d\})$, then

$$n(\{a,b\} \cup \{a,c,d\}) = n(\{a,b,c,d\}) = 4$$

but in this case $A \cap B = \{a\} \neq \emptyset$ ($\neq$ is read "is not equal to"). We may represent addition as a binary operation on the ordered pair (a,b) of natural numbers a and b in symbols: $(a,b) \xrightarrow{+} a+b$.

Incidentally we might note that, in general, a *function* or *mapping* of a set A into a set B is a rule by which a particular element of B is assigned to a given element of A. The correspondence thus established may or may not be 1:1. Thus the previously described addition operation

8 Natural Numbers

is an example of a function or mapping of the set of ordered pairs of natural numbers into the set of natural numbers, that is, a rule by which a particular natural number is assigned to a given ordered pair of natural numbers. Clearly this correspondence is not 1:1 but rather many-to-one, for example, $(1,5) \to 6$, $(2,4) \to 6$, and $(3,3) \to 6$. It is important to note that the result of the operation is a unique number in every case.

Question. Do you think addition of natural numbers is commutative?

In case the reader might begin to believe that all operations are commutative, let us create the artificial binary operation ($*$) on the ordered pair (a,b) of natural numbers by writing $(a,b) \to a + (b + b)$ or, in equivalent symbols, $a*b = a+(b+b)$. Then $b*a = b+(a+a)$. That $a*b \neq b*a$ in general is established by showing one particular ordered pair for which the equality fails to hold. Suppose we let $a = 2$ and $b = 3$. Then $2 * 3 = 2 + (3 + 3) = 8$ and $3 * 2 = 3 + (2 + 2) = 7$.

When any operation is applied to members of a set, if the result belongs to the set in every case, we say the set is *closed* with respect to the operation. Evidently the set of natural numbers is closed with respect to addition. (Incidentally it is also closed with respect to the above $*$ operation.)

We have been working with ordered pairs of elements and we shall continue to do so in the material which follows. This concept is so important that it might be instructive and interesting to examine another way of considering it. The statement $(a,b) = \{\{a\}, \{a,b\}\}$ is an elegant way of employing set notation to describe the ordered pair, (a,b). Thus the ordered pair $(2,5) = \{\{2\}, \{2,5\}\}$. If, for the ordered pairs $(2,5)$ and (a,b), we know that $(a,b) = (2,5)$, then $\{\{a\}, \{a, b\}\} = \{\{2\}, \{2,5\}\}$. But if $\{a\} = \{2,5\}$, then $2 = 5$, which is a contradiction. Hence

(1) $$\{a\} = \{2\}$$

and

(2) $$\{a,b\} = \{2,5\}$$

Therefore, from (1) we obtain

(3) $$a = 2$$

and, from (2) and (3) we obtain

$$b = 5$$

Question. If (a,b) and (c,d) are two ordered pairs such that $(a,b)=(c,d)$, can you show that $a = c$ and $b = d$?

The question might well be asked at this point: Can we add three numbers? Technically the answer would have to be "no" in view of the fact that addition is purely a binary operation. However the idea of adding one number to the sum of the other two numbers immediately suggests itself, and we see that there are two ways of grouping for this purpose, namely $(a+b)+c$ and $a+(b+c)$. It would make no sense to adopt one of these results as the answer unless the two expressions are equal. When both ways of grouping always give the same result we say the operation is *associative* and when the result is not the same the operation is *nonassociative*.

Question. Can you show that addition of natural numbers is associative? [*Hint:* Can you demonstrate that union of sets is associative, that is, $(A \cup B) \cup C = A \cup (B \cup C)$?]

Whenever a binary operation is associative, we customarily define the operation for three elements by inserting parentheses giving one of the two equivalent ways of grouping, for example, $a + b + c = (a + b) + c$. The definition can be extended then to the sum of as many numbers as we wish, that is,

$$a_1 + a_2 + \cdots + a_{n-1} + a_n = (a_1 + a_2 + \cdots + a_{n-1}) + a_n$$

EXERCISES

1. Prove that the operation of intersection of sets is associative, that is, $A \cap (B \cap C) = (A \cap B) \cap C$.
2. Let us suppose that the binary operations denoted by Q, L, and $\#$ have the following meanings:
    $a \, Q \, b = a + (b + b)$
    $a \, L \, b = a$ (that is, take the number on the left)
    $a \, \# \, b = (a + a) + (b + b)$
    (a) Is the operation Q both commutative and associative?
    (b) Is the operation L both commutative and associative?
    (c) Is the operation $\#$ both commutative and associative?
3. (a) Describe each of the operations in Exercise 2 in symbols as a correspondence between the set of ordered pairs of natural numbers and the set of natural numbers.
    (b) Are the respective correspondences one-to-one or many-to-one?

1.05 ROLE OF NUMERAL

Whereas any given number, for example, the number 6, is a definite abstract concept, we shall use the word *numeral* as a name for a number. The operation of addition provides us with many numerals for a number, for example, "$1 + 5$," "$2 + 4$," "$3 + 3$" are numerals for

10   Natural Numbers

the number, one of whose numerals is "6." In fact when we write the numerical sentence $2 + 4 = 6$ we are merely stating that "$2 + 4$" and "6" are numerals for the same number. We shall encounter many more numerals that name the same number that "6" does.

When we write $a = b$ we cannot say that "a" and "b" are numerals in the strictest sense, since they are not names for a particular number. However it is extremely useful to be able to represent the result of an operation performed on two numbers in terms of general symbols, treating them as if they were numerals. The word *pronumeral* has been suggested as an excellent name for quantities like a and b, as they are used in this paragraph.

EXERCISES

1. If $a = b$, show that $a + c = b + c$, where a, b, c are natural numbers.
2. If $a = b$ and $b = c$, show that $a = c$.

1.06 MULTIPLICATION OF NATURAL NUMBERS

Let us consider the set A of colors {red, green}, and the set B of cities {Chicago, Fairbanks, Portland, Reno}. There are eight possible color and city combinations of the type, for example, "green, Portland." They may be displayed in a table as follows:

	C	F	P	R
r	(r,C)	(r,F)	(r,P)	(r,R)
g	(g,C)	(g,F)	(g,P)	(g,R)

We call this set of eight ordered pairs the *Cartesian product* of sets A and B, written $A \times B$, and read "A cross B." In a more formal way, we could define $A \times B = \{(a,b) | a \in A \text{ and } b \in B\}$, by which we mean the set of all ordered pairs, (a,b), where a is an element of set A and b is an element of set B. We may use the number of pairs occurring in such a rectangular array as the basis for multiplication according to the definition: $n(A) \times n(B) = n(A \times B)$. In our example, therefore, $2 \times 4 = 8$. Of course it is very necessary to keep in mind the particular meaning assigned to each of the symbols, $\times$ and $\mathbf{X}$ in the above definition. Thus multiplication also appears as an operation on an ordered pair (c,d), of numbers with a unique result which could be symbolized as follows: $(c,d) \rightarrow c \times d$.

Question. Can you show that $1 \times b = b$?

Since it is true that $1 \times b = b$, the number 1 is given the name *multiplicative identity;* in other words it is a number which, when multiplied with any number, leaves the latter unchanged.

Question. Is the set of natural numbers closed under multiplication?

Again the multiplication of three numbers has no meaning until we define $a \times b \times c = (a \times b) \times c$ or $a \times (b \times c)$. We often find it more convenient to write $a \times b$ as $a \cdot b$ or ab.

EXERCISES

1. (a) (i) Is multiplication commutative?
    (ii) Is multiplication associative?
   (b) On what properties of sets do the questions in (a) depend?
2. Use the commutative and associative properties of multiplication to establish the truth of the following statements:
   (a) $7 \times 5 \times 2 = 5 \times 2 \times 7$
   (b) $a \times b \times c = c \times a \times b$, $a, b,$ and c being natural numbers.
3. Do there exist natural numbers $a, b,$ and c such that $a \cdot b \cdot c = a + b + c$?
4. If $a = b$, show that $ac = bc$, a, b, c, being natural numbers.
5. Prove that 1 is unique as a multiplicative identity. (*Hint:* Suppose that there is another number, $1'$, which does the work of 1. Examine $1 \times 1'$.)

1.07 EXPONENTS

When we multiply numbers we refer to them as *factors* and to the result of the operation as the *product*. When several of the factors of a product are the same it is needlessly laborious to write each one separately. Instead we express the product of n factors of b as b^n; that is, $b^n = \underbrace{b \cdot b \cdot b \cdots b}_{n \text{ factors}}$

In this *power* of b, n is called the *exponent* or *index* and b the *base* of the power. For example, we have $1125 = 3^2 \times 5^3$.

It follows from the definition that the product of two powers of the same base, that is, $b^n \times b^m$ is expressible as a power of that base in which the exponent is the sum of the original exponents, that is, $b^n \times b^m = b^{n+m}$.

EXERCISES

1. Give an equivalent expression for $b^3 \times b^2$ and for $b^7 \times b^{10}$.
2. How many factors b are present in the power $(b^3)^5$? in $(b^4)^7$? and in $(b^n)^m$, where m and n are natural numbers? Hence what is an equivalent expression for $(b^n)^m$? Give an equivalent expression for $(b^2)^3$ and for $(b^5)^8$.
3. How many a's and b's are present as factors in the product $(ab)^3$? in $(a^2b^3)^{10}$? in $(ab)^n$ if n is a natural number? Hence what other expression equals $(ab)^n$? Give an equivalent expression for $(ab^2)^5$ and for $(a^3b^5)^7$.

1.08 DISTRIBUTIVE PROPERTY

Now that we have the ability to construct addition tables and

+	1	2	3	4	.	.	.
1	2	3	4	5	.	.	.
2	3	4	5	6	.	.	.
3	4	5	6	7	.	.	.
4	5	6	7	8	.	.	.
.	.	.	.	.	.	.	.
.	.	.	.	.	.	.	.
.	.	.	.	.	.	.	.

×	1	2	3	4	.	.	.
1	1	2	3	4	.	.	.
2	2	4	6	8	.	.	.
3	3	6	9	12	.	.	.
4	4	8	12	16	.	.	.
.	.	.	.	.	.	.	.
.	.	.	.	.	.	.	.
.	.	.	.	.	.	.	.

multiplication tables for the natural numbers as far as they are needed, the question may be asked: Is there any relation between the two operations? In Section 1.06 we made use of set $A = \{$red, green$\}$ and set $B = \{$Chicago, Fairbanks, Portland, Reno$\}$ in order to illustrate the multiplication $2 \times 4 = 8$, in the form

$$n(A) \times n(B) = n(A \text{ X } B)$$

Now let us consider the set D of colors, $\{$yellow, blue, white$\}$. Then

$$n(D) \times n(B) = n(D \text{ X } B) \text{ indicating } 3 \times 4 = 12$$

An examination of sets A and D makes it evident that $A \cap D = \emptyset$ and hence $n(A \cup D) = n(A) + n(D)$, which means in this case that $5 = 2 + 3$. We would like to examine in some detail the expression $(2 + 3) \times 4$. This requires us to consider $(n(A) + n(D)) \times n(B) = n((A \cup D) \text{ X } B)$. The array of elements of $(A \cup D) \text{ X } B$ is the following:

$$\left.\begin{matrix} A \text{ X } B \begin{cases} (r,C) & (r,F) & (r,P) & (r,R) \\ (g,C) & (g,F) & (g,P) & (g,R) \end{cases} \\ D \text{ X } B \begin{cases} (y,C) & (y,F) & (y,P) & (y,R) \\ (b,C) & (b,F) & (b,P) & (b,R) \\ (w,C) & (w,F) & (w,P) & (w,R) \end{cases} \end{matrix}\right\} (A \cup D) \text{ X } B$$

Evidently the twenty ordered pairs belonging to $(A \cup D) \text{ X } B$ consist of the original eight pairs of $A \text{ X } B$ combined with the recently added twelve pairs of $D \text{ X } B$. Hence, at least in this case,

$$(A \cup D) \text{ X } B = (A \text{ X } B) \cup (D \text{ X } B)$$

Therefore

$$n((A \cup D) \times B) = n((A \times B) \cup (D \times B))$$
$$= n(A \times B) + n(D \times B)$$

since $(A \times B) \cap (D \times B) = \emptyset$.

Question. Can you prove that $(A \times B) \cap (D \times B) = \emptyset$, whenever $A \cap D = \emptyset$?

Accordingly we shall have

$$(n(A) + n(D)) \times n(B) = n(A) \times n(B) + n(D) \times n(B)$$

In this particular instance this statement will mean

$$(2 + 3) \times 4 = 2 \times 4 + 3 \times 4$$

or

$$5 \times 4 = 20 = 8 + 12$$

Here we have an example of the manner in which our two operations are related.

We would like to establish, in general, that

$$(a + d)b = ab + db$$

where a, d, b are natural numbers. To do this we are going to prove that $(A \cup D) \times B = (A \times B) \cup (D \times B)$ for any sets A, B, D. Thus we shall show first that $(A \cup D) \times B \subseteq (A \times B) \cup (D \times B)$. Suppose $(x, y) \in (A \cup D) \times B$, then $x \in A \cup D$ and $y \in B$. Either (1) $x \in A$ or (2) $x \in D$.

If (1) $x \in A$, then $(x, y) \in A \times B$. Therefore $(x, y) \in (A \times B) \cup (D \times B)$. If (2) $x \in D$, then $(x, y) \in D \times B$. Therefore $(x, y) \in (A \times B) \cup (D \times B)$. Therefore $(A \cup D) \times B \subseteq (A \times B) \cup (D \times B)$.

On the other hand, suppose $(u, v) \in (A \times B) \cup (D \times B)$, then either (1) $(u, v) \in (A \times B)$ or (2) $(u, v) \in D \times B$.

If (1) $(u, v) \in A \times B$

$$\therefore u \in A \text{ and } v \in B$$
$$\therefore u \in A \cup D \text{ and } (u, v) \in (A \cup D) \times B$$

If (2) $(u, v) \in D \times B$

$$\therefore u \in D \text{ and } v \in B$$
$$\therefore u \in A \cup D \text{ and } (u, v) \in (A \cup D) \times B$$

Hence $(A \times B) \cup (D \times B) \subseteq (A \cup D) \times B$

$$\therefore (A \cup D) \times B = (A \times B) \cup (D \times B)$$

Since this result has now been established for any sets A, B, D, we know that

$$n((A \cup D) \times B) = n((A \times B) \cup (D \times B))$$

We are going to assume that $A \cap D = \emptyset$, from which we know (see *Question* on page 13) that $(A \times B) \cap (D \times B) = \emptyset$. Hence

$$n(A \cup D) = n(A) + n(D)$$

and

$$n((A \times B) \cup (D \times B)) = n(A \times B) + n(D \times B)$$

Let us work with each side of the equality

$$n((A \cup D) \times B) = n((A \times B) \cup (D \times B))$$
$$n((A \cup D) \times B) = n(A \cup D) \times n(B)$$
$$= (n(A) + n(D)) \times n(B)$$
$$n((A \times B) \cup (D \times B)) = n(A \times B) + n(D \times B)$$
$$= n(A) \times n(B) + n(D) \times n(B)$$

Hence in general $(n(A) + n(D)) \times n(B) = n(A) \times n(B) + n(D) \times n(B)$. In terms of pronumerals a, b, d, if $a = n(A), b = n(B), d = n(D)$, then

$$(a + d)b = ab + db$$

We refer to this principle as the *distributive property*, and we say that multiplication is distributive with respect to addition. We shall make a number of uses of this property, the first of which follows:

$$a + a = (1 \times a) + (1 \times a)$$
$$= (1 + 1) \times a$$
$$= 2 \times a \text{ or } 2a$$

as we prefer to write the product.

$$a + 2a = (1 \times a) + (2 \times a)$$
$$= (1 + 2) \times a$$
$$= 3a$$

This leads us to think of multiplication, in the special case of natural numbers, as repeated addition. Since multiplication of natural numbers is commutative, we also have

$$a(b + c) = ab + ac$$

EXERCISES

1. The distributive property may be used to advantage as illustrated below:
   (a) $(9 \times 18) + (9 \times 2) = 9(18 + 2) = 9 \times 20 = 180$
   (b) $8 \times 33 = 8(30 + 3) = 8(30) + 8(3) = 240 + 24 = 264$
   Use the distributive property to facilitate the following calculations:
   (c) $7(69) + 7(11)$ (d) 15×23 (e) $27(63) + 27(37)$ (f) 75×42
2. Multiply: (a) $(n + 1)(n + 2)$ (b) $(n + 3)(2n + 4)$
   (c) $(3n + 5)(2n + 7)$ (d) $(n + 3)^2$
   (e) $(2n + 1)^2$ (f) $(2n + 3)^2$
3. Find factors of: (a) $n^2 + 5n + 4$ (b) $n^2 + 4n + 4$ (c) $2n^2 + 7n + 3$

1.09 WHOLE NUMBERS

Since our set N of natural numbers contains the multiplicative identity, 1 (see Section 1.06), it remains unbalanced, so to speak, until we augment it with an identity element for addition. This number, to which we give the name "zero" or "0" has the property that, when added to any other number, it leaves it unchanged; therefore $b + 0 = 0 + b = b$ for any natural number b, and $0 + 0 = 0$. The union of the set consisting of this number, zero, with the set N of natural numbers is the set usually referred to as the *whole numbers*, which we shall designate by W, that is, $W = N \cup \{0\}$. It is important to remember that $0 \notin N$ and that $\{0\} \neq \emptyset \neq 0$ as well as $\{0\} \neq 0$.

The *additive identity*, 0, could well have been introduced earlier in this chapter as $n(\emptyset)$. However zero possesses an extremely important multiplicative property which is best demonstrated after the distributive property has been established. First we wish to note, and leave to the reader to prove, the uniqueness of the additive identity.

Question. Can you show that 0 is a unique number? (*Hint*: Suppose there is another number $0'$ which does the work of zero. Examine $0 + 0'$.)

The proof of the distributive property (Section 1.08) holds in the set W as well as in the set N. Hence it is possible to demonstrate the effect of multiplying by zero, as follows:

$$\begin{aligned} a &= a \times 1 \\ &= a(1 + 0) \\ &= (a \times 1) + (a \times 0) \\ &= a + (a \times 0) \end{aligned}$$

Clearly $a \times 0$ is playing the role of zero and, since zero is a unique number, $a \times 0$ must be zero, that is, $a \times 0 = 0$.

The question arises immediately: Can the product of two numbers be zero if each number is different from zero? That is, if $a \neq 0$ and $b \neq 0$ can $ab = 0$? Our experience with multiplication would lead us to believe that this is not possible, but it is necessary that we incorporate this property formally in an axiom as follows: If a and b are any two whole numbers such that $a \neq 0$ and $b \neq 0$, then $a \cdot b \neq 0$. This statement is sometimes described by saying that the whole numbers contain no "divisors of zero." The axiom has very important consequences which will be discussed in Sections 1.11 and 2.04.

Historically the symbol 0 played the role of placeholder, making it possible for the nonzero digits to maintain their proper significance and value in numerals such as $10, 20, \ldots, 100, 200, \ldots, 1003, 1023, 1302$, etc. This is completely consistent with our standard interpretation of numerals for numbers represented in the decimal system, where, for example, $576 = 5(100) + 7(10) + 6(1)$. Hence

$$2005 = 2(1000) + 0(100) + 0(10) + 5(1)$$
$$= 2000 + 5$$

Question. Do all previously described properties hold for W as well as for N?

1.10 ORDER

It is frequently helpful to picture the whole numbers as labels for points located at unit intervals on a horizontal line, customarily referred

$$\underset{0123456}{\vdash\!\!\vdash\!\!\vdash\!\!\vdash\!\!\vdash\!\!\vdash\!\!\vdash} \cdots$$

to as the "number line." We are accustomed to the idea that 6 is greater than 4 and 12 is greater than 8 and in general we would agree that b is greater than c whenever the point corresponding to b lies to the right of the point corresponding to c on the number line. We want to formalize this statement in the following definition: If b and c are any two whole numbers, $b > c$ (read "b is greater than c") if and only if there exists a natural number q for which $c + q = b$. The phrase "if and only if" will receive considerable attention in Chapter 2. We shall use it consistently throughout this book whenever we wish to make a definition by relating a new symbol with an equivalent existing concept. In order to abbreviate this phrase we shall use the double-headed double arrow (<=>) (also discussed in detail in Chapter 2), as well as the symbol $\exists$ to stand for "there exists" and the symbol $\ni$ to mean "such that." With these helpful symbols available for our use, the previous definition may be written in the following abbreviated form:*

For $b,c \in W$, $\qquad b > c \iff \exists q \in N \ni c + q = b$

Hence

$$6 > 4 \text{ because } \exists q \text{ (namely 2)} \ni 4 + q = 6$$

As a result of our familiarity with the number line, it is natural for us to assume that for any two whole numbers b and c, either (1) $b > c$ or (2) $b = c$ or (3) $c > b$. This is often referred to as the *Law of Trichotomy* for order. We shall also define $c < b$ to mean the same as $b > c$. We write $b \geq c$ when we mean "either $b > c$ or $b = c$." Hence, for $b,c \in W, b \geq c \iff \exists h \in W \ni c + h = b$.

EXERCISES

In the following exercises, $a, b, c, d \in W$.
1. If $a > b$, show that $a + d > b + d$.
2. If $a > b$, show that $ad > bd$, if $d \neq 0$.
3. If $a > b$ and $c > d$, show that $a + c > b + d$.
4. If $a > b$ and $b > c$, show that $a > c$.

1.11 SUBTRACTION

The topic of subtraction could be deferred until negative integers have been introduced, and many persons will argue that this is preferable. However it is our purpose to consider as many as possible of the elementary concepts which may be discussed profitably at the level of whole numbers. We believe therefore that it is a definite advantage to the reader to introduce subtraction at this stage in spite of the limitations which will attend it.

For the whole numbers b and c, we wish to define $b - c = d$, read "*b* minus *c* equals *d*," if and only if there exists a whole number *d* such that $b = c + d$. In terms of the symbols introduced in the previous section, $b - c = d \iff \exists d \in W \ni b = c + d$. It is immediately obvious that our definition of subtraction applies only to numbers b and c for which $b \geq c$. Therefore the set of whole numbers is most certainly not closed under subtraction and in cases where subtraction does not apply at this stage we merely say it is not defined. Thus $8 - 2 = 6$ because $\exists d$ (namely 6) $\in W \ni 8 = 2 + d$ but, as yet, $2 - 8$ is not defined.

---

*An additional reason for introducing this abbreviated notation here is to familiarize the reader with some of the symbols he will encounter frequently.

18   Natural Numbers

Question. What can you say about commutativity and associativity of subtraction?

In Section 1.09 we introduced an axiom for whole numbers as follows:
$$a \neq 0 \text{ and } b \neq 0 \Longrightarrow a \cdot b \neq 0$$
A similar consideration is embodied in the question: If $a \neq 0$ and $b \neq c$, is it true that $ab \neq ac$? These two matters are essentially the same since

$$ab = ac \Longleftrightarrow ab = ac + 0$$
$$\Longleftrightarrow ab - ac = 0$$
$$\Longleftrightarrow a(b - c) = 0 \quad \text{(See Exercise 1 below.)}$$

It is reasonable to expect that if $2 \cdot a = 2 \cdot 3$, we shall have $a = 3$. That this result is true in general will be established formally by indirect proof in Section 2.04.

Question. How would you prove that $ab \neq ac \Longleftrightarrow a(b - c) \neq 0$?

EXERCISES

1. Prove that the distributive property holds for multiplication with respect to subtraction, that is, $(a - b)d = ad - bd$, where $a \geq b$.
2. The distributive property of multiplication with respect to subtraction often facilitates computation, for example
   (a) $7 \times 99 = 7(100 - 1) = 700 - 7 = 693$
   (b) $(8 \times 119) - (8 \times 9) = 8(119 - 9) = 8 \times 110 = 880$
   Use this distributive property in the following examples:
   (c) 6×89 (d) $14(36) - 14(6)$
   (e) 25×39 (f) $87(149) - 87(49)$
3. Given $a \geq c$ and $b \geq c$, show that, if $a - c = b - c$, then $a = b$.
4. (a) (Converse of Exercise 3). Given $a \geq c$ and $b \geq c$, show that if $a = b$, then $a - c = b - c$.
   (b) If $a + c = b + c$, then $a = b$.
5. What is $n - n$, where $n \in W$?
6. Multiply: (a) $3(n - n)$ (b) $n(n - 3)$.

1.12 INVERSE OPERATION

If we remove a book from a shelf and then replace it in the same position from which it was taken, each of these two actions may be thought of as being the inverse of the other. In other words, returning the book to its original position restores the shelf to its original condition. Similarly if we begin with the book in our hands and first place it in the shelf and then remove it, the act of removing the book leaves the shelf as it was originally. Again putting on one's hat and removing one's hat are inverse procedures of each other.

Hence if we begin by being given the whole number b from which we subtract the whole number c (where $b \geq c$), let us examine the expression $(b - c) + c$. We know that $b - c = d <=> \exists d \in W \ni b = c + d$ or $b = d + c$. However $(b - c) + c = d + c$ and, accordingly, $(b - c) + c = b$. (See Exercises 1 and 2, Section 1.05.) Thus the procedure of adding c to $b - c$ restores that expression to b again.

Let us also proceed in the reverse direction by examining $(b + c) - c$. We know as a result of our definition of subtraction that $(b + c) - c = b$ because $b + c = b + c$. In view of these facts we are accustomed to speak of subtraction as the inverse operation of addition.

It would be natural, then, to expect that multiplication would also have an inverse operation. This operation, called division, is defined in the following section. As must be expected, both subtraction and division are considered in more detail in later chapters.

EXERCISES

1. If $a \geq c$ and $b \geq c, a, b, c \in W$, show that $a + (b - c) = (a + b) - c = (a - c) + b$.
2. If $a \geq b + c$, show that $(a - b) - c = a - (b + c)$.
3. If $a \geq b$, and $b \geq c$, show that $(a - b) + c = a - (b - c)$.
4. Show that $(x + y)(x - y) = x^2 - y^2$, for $x, y \in W$ and $x \geq y$.

1.13 DIVISION

We have seen that subtraction is the inverse operation of addition. In a similar fashion multiplication has division as its inverse operation. When we have only the whole numbers at our disposal we caution the reader immediately (as we did in connection with our introduction of subtraction) that the set of whole numbers will *not* be closed under division.

For any whole number b and any natural number c we shall define $\frac{b}{c} = b \div c = d <=> \exists d \in W \ni b = cd$ and we shall read $\frac{b}{c}$ as "b divided by c." For example, $8 \div 2 = \frac{8}{2} = 4$ because $\exists d$ (namely 4) $\in W \ni 8 = 2d$. Thus division is defined for the ordered pair $(8, 2)$ but not for $(2, 8)$, $(3, 8)$, or $(8, 3)$, and so on.

It is most important to note in the definition that the divisor c belongs to N. This means that c cannot be zero. The reason we avoid ever having $c = 0$ as the divisor is that, if we have $b \neq 0$, there simply does not exist any number d for which $b = cd$ since $cd = 0$ for every number d. Hence it is impossible to satisfy the equality $b = cd$, when $b \neq 0$ and $c = 0$. Accordingly the expression $\frac{b}{0}$ has no meaning for us, now nor at any future time. Of great importance is the fact that $\frac{b}{b} = 1$.

Question. What is the status of division from the point of view of commutativity and associativity?

We designate as *even numbers* the set $\{0,2,4,6,8...\}$ of whole numbers, each of which has 2 as a factor. For such a number n we know that $n = 2m, m \in W$ and therefore $\frac{n}{2} = m$. Hence we can describe the even numbers as the set $\{n \in W | n = 2m$ where $m \in W\}$. The set of the remaining whole numbers, that is, the set $\{n \in W | n = 2m + 1$ where $m \in W\} = \{1,3,5,7,...\}$ is called the set of *odd numbers*. These two sets provide useful material for many exercises. For example, we can show that the set of even numbers is closed under addition as follows: Consider any two even numbers p and q. Since they belong to the set $\{2m | m \in W\}$ we may represent $p = 2a$ and $q = 2b$ where $a \in W$ and $b \in W$. Then $p + q = 2a + 2b = 2(a + b)$ by virtue of the distributive property. Since $a + b \in W$, the expression $2(a + b) \in \{2m | m \in W\}$ and hence is an even number, thus demonstrating the desired closure.

Question. Is the set of odd numbers closed under addition?

EXERCISES

1. (a) Is the set of even numbers closed under multiplication?
   (b) Is the set of odd numbers closed under multiplication?
2. Explain why the sum of any two consecutive even numbers cannot be divided by 4, and why the sum of any two consecutive odd numbers is always divisible by 4.
3. Show why the sum of any three consecutive natural numbers must be divisible by 3.

1.14 PRIME NUMBERS

Much of the emphasis up to this point has been in the direction of combining two numbers to give the result of an operation. It is also important to consider the reverse step, particularly in the case of multiplication, that is, factoring of products. When a number different from 1 has only itself and 1 as factors, or, equivalently, when a number has only two factors, we say the number is a *prime number*. The Unique Factorization Theorem, one of the most significant theorems in elementary number theory, establishes the uniqueness (apart from order) of the factorization of any number as a product of powers of prime numbers, for example, $1125 = 3^2 \times 5^3$. In order for this theorem to be true, it is necessary to postulate, as we did, that the number 1 shall not be considered to be a prime number; otherwise a factorization would never be unique since the number 1 could appear as a factor as many times as desired. Hence 2 is not only the smallest prime number, but also the only even prime number. Two numbers, 15 and 16 for example, may be *relatively prime* to each other, that is have no common factor other than 1, without either one being prime. An interesting feature of prime numbers is the fact that there are many conjectures about them which can be described in very simple language but which mathematicians have been unable to prove or disprove, such as:

(1) Is every even number, greater than 2, the sum of two prime numbers?
(2) Are there infinitely many pairs of prime numbers differing by 2, such as 11 and 13, 17 and 19, 29 and 31?

EXERCISE

Express as a product of powers of primes: 3072; 1280; 1944.

1.15 GREATEST COMMON DIVISOR

If the significance of the topic, *Greatest Common Divisor,* were entirely restricted to routine problems in elementary arithmetic, we would devote little space to it in this discussion. It is a fact, however, that this concept plays an important role in more advanced algebra as well as in number theory.

As its name implies, the Greatest Common Divisor or GCD of two natural numbers x and y, commonly written as (x,y), is the largest number which belongs to the set of factors of both x and y. The set of factors of 18 is $\{1,2,3,6,9,18\}$ and the set of factors of 24 is $\{1,2,3,4,6,8,12,24\}$. The set of common factors of x and y (that is, factors of both x and y) is $\{1,2,3,6,9,18\} \cap \{1,2,3,4,6,8,12,24\} = \{1,2,3,6\}$. Hence $(18,24) = 6$ and for two relatively prime numbers x and y, $(x,y) = 1$. When numbers are completely factored and expressed as products of powers of their prime divisors, the GCD is easily obtained by taking the product of the highest powers of these divisors which are factors of both numbers; that is,

$$(2^2 \cdot 3^5 \cdot 5^3, \ 2^4 \cdot 3^3 \cdot 5^2) = 2^2 \cdot 3^3 \cdot 5^2$$

Question. Can you explain why the previous sentence is true?

EXERCISES

1. What is the GCD of 1536 and 486?
2. What is the GCD of 768 and 405?
3. What is the GCD of two consecutive natural numbers?

1.16 LEAST COMMON MULTIPLE

It will often be desirable to obtain the smallest number which has, as factors, each of two given numbers x and y, that is, the *Least Common Multiple* or LCM of x and y. Suppose, for example, that we wish to obtain the LCM of 18 and 24. Clearly the product 18×24 is a common multiple of 18 and 24 but it is not the smallest such multiple. We might proceed to multiply one of the numbers, say 18, successively by the numbers $1, 2, 3, 4, 5, \ldots$ obtaining the set of multiples $\{18, 36, 54, 72, 90, \ldots\}$. We could then select the smallest of these numbers, namely 72, which has 24 as a factor. Alternatively we could form a similar set of multiples of 24, that is, $\{24, 48, 72, 96, \ldots\}$ and select the smallest number occurring in both sets. A more efficient procedure is to express each number as a product of powers of its prime divisors and then select the larger of the two powers of each prime divisor as a factor of the LCM of the two numbers. Hence we write $18 = 2 \cdot 3^2$ and $24 = 3 \cdot 2^3$. Clearly the larger of the two powers of a prime number is the smallest power of that prime number which is divisible by each of the given powers. Therefore we should retain 3^2 and 2^3 as factors of the LCM giving the product 72. In general the product of powers of prime divisors chosen in this manner must give the desired LCM, for example, the LCM of $2^2 \cdot 3^5 \cdot 5^3$ and $2^4 \cdot 3^3 \cdot 5^2$ is $2^4 \cdot 3^5 \cdot 5^3$.

EXERCISES

1. What is the LCM of 162, 144, 30?
2. Can you show that the product of two numbers is equal to the product of their GCD and their LCM?

1.17 SIGNIFICANCE OF NUMBER BASE

So far we have been writing numerals for whole numbers in the notation most familiar to us, namely the decimal (base ten) system. In this system $342 = 300 + 40 + 2 = 3(100) + 4(10) + 2(1)$. Our experience with exponents has established 100 as 10^2 and would lead us to write 10 as 10^1 if we wished. If we recall the fact that $b^n \times b^m = b^{n+m}$ and note that $b^n \times 1 = b^n$, then we may extend our multiplication law in a consistent manner to include $b^n \times b^0 = b^{n+0} = b^n$ by defining $b^0 = 1$. Hence we have $342 = 3(10)^2 + 4(10)^1 + 2(10)^0$, exhibiting an attractive decreasing sequence of exponents. In Section 1.09 we observed that not only does zero maintain the proper significance for nonzero digits in a numeral but also actually plays its proper role as a coefficient, as for example $2043 = 2(10)^3 + 0(10)^2 + 4(10)^1 + 3(10)^0$. In this example we have assumed ten as the base and, in greater detail, we could write

$$2043_{(ten)} = 2[10_{(ten)}]^3 + 0[10_{(ten)}]^2 + 4[10_{(ten)}]^1 + 3[10_{(ten)}]^0$$

It is quite possible that the reader may wonder at this point why we have replaced 10 by $10_{(ten)}$, read "one zero in base ten." The reason is that we are accustomed to interpret 10 as $1(ten) + 0(1) = $ ten. However, if we were using base five instead of base ten, then $10_{(five)} = 1(five) + 0(1) = $ five and, in general, $10_{(b)} = 1(b) + 0(1) = b$. In this section our attention is going to be directed to problems arising from consideration of number base and accordingly we wish to eliminate any ambiguity concerning the base we are using. For example $2043_{(five)} = 2(five)^3 + 0(five)^2 + 4(five)^1 + 3(five)^0$. We have written the word "five" rather than the symbol "5" because, properly speaking, the symbol 5 is not available when working in base five.* If we were counting in base five we would say: "One, two, three, four, one zero, one one, one two, one three, one four, two zero,..." and write 1,2,3, 4,10,11,12,13,14,20,.... Five five's is automatically written as $1(five)^2 = 100_{(five)}$. Hence we may also write

$$2043_{(five)} = 2[10_{(five)}]^3 + 0[10_{(five)}]^2 + 4[10_{(five)}]^1 + 3[10_{(five)}]^0$$

We may compare $2043_{(five)}$ and $2043_{(ten)}$ by expressing the former as a numeral in base ten:

$$2043_{(five)} = 2(125_{(ten)}) + 0(25_{(ten)}) + 4(5_{(ten)}) + 3 = 273_{(ten)}$$

---

*It is difficult to maintain the strictest consistency in this respect. Especially in working with the smaller numbers as bases, when it is desirable to represent higher powers of the base, it is convenient to be able to use decimal numerals as exponents.

24 Natural Numbers

In addition to providing an opportunity for careful thinking, this sort of investigation serves to emphasize for us many properties of the decimal system which familiarity has tended to obscure. In general, if b is our base, we shall write the number $a_n b^n + a_{n-1} b^{n-1} + \cdots + a_1 b + a_0$ or $a_n [10_{(b)}]^n + \cdots + a_1 [10_{(b)}]^1 + a_0 [10_{(b)}]^0$ as $a_n a_{n-1} a_{n-2} \cdots a_1 a_{0_{(b)}}$, provided $a_0, \ldots, a_n$ belong to the set $\{0, 1, 2, \ldots, b-1\}$.

A very interesting base in which to work is base two. When numerals are written in base two, the only digits available are 0 and 1, and we refer to the representation as binary. Hence the number 2 is represented by 10, 3 by 11, 4 by 100, etc.

Question. Can you complete the following sequence of binary numerals for the first sixteen natural numbers: 1, 10, 11, 100, ...?

It is merely a matter of adding powers of two to change a binary numeral to equivalent decimal form. For example:

$$101011_{(two)} = 1(2^5) + 0(2^4) + 1(2^3) + 0(2^2) + 1(2^1) + 1(2^0)$$
$$= 32 + 8 + 2 + 1 = 43_{(ten)}$$

We should like to point out the following quick way to obtain the decimal equivalent of a binary numeral, for example, $101011_{(two)}$: Multiply the left hand 1 by 2; add the next digit 0, giving 2; multiply the result by 2 and add the next digit, 1, giving 5; multiply the result by 2 and add the next digit, 0, giving 10; and so on—obtaining 21 and finally 43. The procedure may be represented in telescoped form as follows:

	1	0	1	0	1	1
		2	4	10	20	42
	1	2	5	10	21	43

Question. Why does the above procedure give the desired result?

The next question is: How shall we change a decimal numeral into binary form? The most obvious approach is to begin by determining the greatest power of 2 which is equal to or is just less than the given number. Let us illustrate with $43_{(ten)}$. In this case the greatest power of $2 (\leq 43)$ is $2^5 = 32$. Since $43 - 32 = 11$ we must skip $2^4 = 16$ and next remove $2^3 = 8$. This leaves $11 - 8 = 3 = 1(2) + 1$. Hence

$$43 = 32 + 8 + 3 = 1(2^5) + 0(2^4) + 1(2^3) + 0(2^2) + 1(2) + 1$$
$$= 101011_{(two)}$$

This procedure becomes quite laborious if the number is large, and we should like to demonstrate a quicker procedure. This method is

Significance of Number Base

not limited to cases involving only binary and decimal numerals but applies generally. It involves the familiar process of long division which is referred to in later sections as the Division Algorithm, for example, $15 = 14 + 1 = 2(7) + 1$, where we call 7 the quotient and 1 the remainder. To obtain the binary equivalent of $43_{(ten)}$ we divide $43_{(ten)}$ by 2. Thus $43 = 2(21) + 1$. Then we divide the quotient, 21, by 2, obtaining $21 = 2(10) + 1$. We proceed in this manner keeping track of all the remainders as shown below, until we obtain a quotient, 0. The resulting sequence of remainders from the last to the first

```
2 | 43
2 | 21    R1  ↑
2 | 10    R1
2 |  5    R0
2 |  2    R1
2 |  1    R0
      0   R1
```

provides the required binary digits from left to right, that is $43_{(ten)} = 101011_{(two)}$.

Questions. 1. Why is the above procedure correct in changing a numeral from decimal to binary form? (*Hint:* Express $43 = 2(21) + 1 = 2[2(10) + 1] + 1 = \cdots$ continuing to the end and then multiplying out as a sum of powers of 2.)
2. How can you change a numeral from octal (base eight) to binary form? How can this be done without changing back to base ten? Can you change a numeral from binary to octal form?

One reason for the importance of the binary system stems from its relationship to the electronic computer. Current either flows or does not flow through a circuit. When holes in a card allow a wire to pass through and complete an electric circuit, the effect can be interpreted as a one, otherwise as a zero. Hence numbers and instructions in numerical symbols can be introduced into the machine, which can operate at a remarkably high speed.

If we take a second look at binary numerals we notice that in the numeral, "1," the meaning of "1" is $2^{1-1} = 2^0 = 1$; in the numeral, "10," the meaning of "1" is $2^{2-1} = 2^1 = 2$; in the numeral, "100," the "1" has the meaning $2^{3-1} = 2^2$.

In general, therefore, in the binary notation the significance of a one in the nth place from the right is 2^{n-1}. A variation of this, known as

Cyclically Permuted Code (CPC) or the Gray Code, has a one in the nth place from the right represent $2^n - 1$ and also attributes to the ones alternately positive and negative signs, beginning with positive for the left-most one. This means that, instead of having the meanings 1, 2, 4, 8, 16, ... from right to left, the individual 1's in CPC stand for 1, 3, 7, 15, 31, ... Hence the number 2 is represented as 11, 3 as 10, 4 as 110, 5 as 111 in this notation.

Questions. 1. Can you complete the following sequence of CPC numerals for the first sixteen natural numbers: 1, 11, 10, 110, 111 ...?

2. Can you devise rules (two are needed) for writing the CPC numeral for the number larger by one than a given number?

3. Can you add such numbers?*

Observe the following advantage in the CPC system, namely, the fact that only one digit of the numeral is ever changed in going from any natural number to the next larger natural number.

A very simple but intriguing application of binary numbers occurs in a standard sorting procedure by which numbers may be arranged in normal order.†

EXERCISES

1. Can you explain why the following procedure, known sometimes as Russian Peasant Multiplication, is correct? For example, the product 35×26 is evaluated by successively dividing 35 and succeeding quotients by 2 (discarding the remainders) and multiplying 26 and succeeding products by 2, striking out numbers opposite even numbers in the set of quotients and adding those that remain, as follows:

35	26
17	52
~~8~~	~~104~~
~~4~~	~~208~~
~~2~~	~~416~~
1	832
	910

*See author's paper, "A Variation on Binary Notation" in the *Mathematics Teacher*, Volume LVI, November, 1963.
†For further information on this topic the reader is referred to page 25 of *The Gentle Art of Mathematics*, by Dan Pedoe, published by The Macmillan Company.

We would not wish to conclude this brief discussion of binary numbers without drawing the reader's attention to the game of Nim, a nice description of which is given on pages 21–24 of the delightful book by Mr. Pedoe.

2. Can you tell how the following game works? Person A asks person B to select a number from 1 to 31 and then to tell him only in which of the following five groups of numbers it appears. A then adds up the upper left-hand corner numbers of the groups designated by B to obtain the chosen number.

1	3	5	7		2	3	6	7		4	5	6	7
9	11	13	15		10	11	14	15		12	13	14	15
17	19	21	23		18	19	22	23		20	21	22	23
25	27	29	31		26	27	30	31		28	29	30	31

8	9	10	11		16	17	18	19
12	13	14	15		20	21	22	23
24	25	26	27		24	25	26	27
28	29	30	31		28	29	30	31

3. When the numeral for a number is written in base ten, how can you tell easily what the remainder will be when the number is divided by ten?
4. When the numeral is written in base b, can you tell easily what the remainder will be when the number is divided by $10_{(b)}$?
5. When the numeral for a number is written in base ten, how can you decide whether the number is exactly divisible by 2? by 5? by 4? by 25?
6. Write $387_{(ten)}$ as a numeral in base two.
7. Write $1101011_{(two)}$ as a numeral in base ten.
8. Change $110011101_{(two)}$ to a numeral in base four; likewise to a numeral in base eight.
9. Change $312_{(four)}$ to a numeral in base two.
10. Change $675_{(eight)}$ to a numeral in base two.
11. When the numeral for a number is written in base eight, how can you decide whether the number is exactly divisible by 2? Can you decide easily whether the number is exactly divisible by 5? by 4?
12. Change $212212_{(three)}$ to a numeral in base nine.
13. Change $867_{(nine)}$ to a numeral in base three.
14. What is the smallest number of integral weights which will weigh every integral weight up to 60 pounds, if the weights and the object to be weighed are always placed on separate pans of the scale? What is this number if the weights may also be put on the pan with the object to be weighed?
15. Perform the following operations in the indicated arithmetic and check your answers by changing all numerals to base ten:

(a) $11011_{(two)}$
   $+10101_{(two)}$

(b) $1011_{(two)}$
   $\times 101_{(two)}$

(c) $10001_{(two)}$
   $- 1010_{(two)}$

28   *Natural Numbers*

(d) $100011_{(two)} \div 101_{(two)}$ (e) $342_{(five)}$
                                              $+413_{(five)}$

(f) $324_{(five)}$ (g) $4312_{(five)}$ (h) $12033_{(five)} \div 34_{(five)}$
    $\times 432_{(five)}$ $-1423_{(five)}$

16. (a) Without changing first to base ten
    (i) Change $342_{(five)}$ to a numeral in base two, and
    (ii) Change $110101_{(two)}$ to a numeral in base five.
    (b) Check your answers in (a) by changing first to base ten.

17. (a) Change 0.7 to a binary fraction. (*Hint:* Multiply by $\frac{2}{2}$ successively.)
    (b) Check by evaluating the quotient $\dfrac{111_{(two)}}{1010_{(two)}}$.

18. In which number base has this multiplication been performed?

$$\begin{array}{r} 123 \\ \times\ 32 \\ \hline 312 \\ 1101 \\ \hline 11322 \end{array}$$

1.18 MATHEMATICAL SYSTEMS

Whenever one or more operations are defined on a set of elements we have what is known as a *mathematical system*. Hence the natural numbers and the whole numbers we have been studying, with the operations of addition and multiplication, form such systems.

An interesting mathematical system may consist of as few as two elements. Consider the set $\{0,1\}$ with the operations $\oplus$ and $\otimes$ given by the tables below. This is an example of a *modular system*, and the

$\oplus$	0	1		$\otimes$	0	1
0	0	1		0	0	0
1	1	0		1	0	1

operations are addition and multiplication *modulo* two (not to be confused with binary arithmetic). We say: $a \equiv b \pmod{2}$ (read "a is congruent to b modulo 2") $\iff a = b + 2\lambda$, where λ is any number or, in other words, when $a - b$ is a multiple of 2. Hence we have $1 + 1 \equiv 0 \pmod{2}$.*

---

*In general $a \equiv b \pmod{m}$ means that $a - b$ is a multiple of m. Thus $17 \equiv 5 \pmod{3}$ since $17 - 5 = 4 \times 3$.

This system has a nice interpretation as the addition and multiplication of even and odd numbers, in which 0 is the representative of the set of all even numbers and 1 is the representative of the set of all odd numbers. Since any two even numbers may be represented by $2m$ and $2n$, their sum is $2(m+n)$, an even number, which is the reason for writing $0 \oplus 0 = 0$ in the table. Similarly the sum of any two odd numbers, $2m+1$ and $2n+1$ is $2(m+n+1)$, again an even number; hence we have $1 \oplus 1 = 0$ in the table. Of course any number of either set could have been used as the representative of that set, but 0 and 1 were chosen since they are the smallest nonnegative members.

Question. Can you show that the remaining items in the two tables given above are correct?

If the addition table were given as shown on the right while the multiplication table remained as before, we would have a different system which possesses the following interpretation. Let 0 represent an open switch and 1 a closed switch in an electric circuit. We shall let $\oplus$ indicate the operation of combining two switches in a parallel hook-up while $\otimes$ will indicate

$\oplus$	0	1
0	0	1
1	1	1

a series hook-up  . When an open and a closed switch are hooked up in parallel, current will flow as if there is only a single closed switch in the circuit—hence $0 \oplus 1 = 1$; it is the same with two closed switches in parallel, that is, $1 \oplus 1 = 1$. However, current will not flow when an open and a closed switch are in series. Hence $0 \otimes 1. = 0$, as in the diagram below.

Questions. 1. Can you verify the correctness of the remaining items in the tables under the latter interpretation?
2. Are the two operations $\oplus$ and $\otimes$ discussed in this section commutative and associative?
   (a) When related to even and odd numbers.
   (b) When related to switches.
3. Is the $\otimes$ operation distributive with respect to the $\oplus$ operation? (a) and (b) as in *Question* 2.
4. Is the $\oplus$ operation distributive with respect to the $\otimes$ operation? (a) and (b) as in *Question* 2.
5. Can you diagram the circuits in the various cases involved in 2(b), 3(b), and 4(b)?

30   Natural Numbers

As we have seen, the elements of a mathematical system need not be numbers, and it might be profitable to consider another non-numerical example. Consider the set $\{A,B,C,D\}$ with operations $*$ and $\#$ defined by the following tables:

*	A	B	C	D		#	A	B	C	D
A	B	C	D	A		A	A	B	C	D
B	C	D	A	B		B	B	D	B	D
C	D	A	B	C		C	C	B	A	D
D	A	B	C	D		D	D	D	D	D

Questions. 1. Do you think the two operations, $*$ and $\#$, are commutative and associative?
2. Do you think each operation is distributive with respect to the other?

Whenever it is possible to set up a 1 : 1 correspondence (indicated by $\leftrightarrow$) between the elements of two systems in such a way that the result of operating on the images of two elements gives the image of the result of operating on the original two elements, we say the correspondence is an *isomorphism* or the systems are *isomorphic*. For this to be true, when $a \leftrightarrow a'$ and $b \leftrightarrow b'$ then we must have $(a \triangle b)' = a' \square b'$, where $\triangle$ and $\square$, respectively, are symbols for the operation in each system.

For example consider the set W of whole numbers and the set V of ordered pairs $(a, 2a)$ where $a \in W$, that is, $V = \{(a, 2a) | a \in W\}$. Let the operation $\triangle$ in W be ordinary addition $(+)$, that is, $a \triangle b = a + b$, and define the operation $\square$ in V by

$$(a, 2a) \square (b, 2b) = (a + b, 2a + 2b)$$

Let the 1 : 1 correspondence between the two sets be given by

$$a \leftrightarrow (a, 2a)$$

Hence

$$b \leftrightarrow (b, 2b)$$

and

$$a \triangle b = a + b \leftrightarrow (a + b, 2(a + b))$$

We recall that $(a, 2a) \square (b, 2b) = (a + b, 2a + 2b)$. Since the two expressions on the right are equal, by virtue of the distributive property; we have $a \triangle b \leftrightarrow (a, 2a) \square (b, 2b)$. Therefore the sets W and V are isomorphic with the operations as defined.

When two mathematical systems are isomorphic, their basic structures are identical—this means that the essential characteristics and behavior of the two systems are alike. If there is more than one operation associated with each system then the above condition must hold for each pair of operations.

Questions. Below you will find partly completed addition and multiplication tables for the number system modulo four.
1. Can you complete these tables?
2. Can you establish an isomorphic correspondence between the set $\{A, B, C, D\}$ (as described above) and the set $\{0, 1, 2, 3\}$ with the operations $+$ and $\times$ defined on it, as completed in the previous *Question*?

+	0	1	2	3
0				3
1	1			
2			0	
3		0		2

×	0	1	2	3
0		0		
1				3
2	0		0	
3				1

1.19 MATHEMATICAL INDUCTION

All the properties of natural numbers which we have discussed so far will continue to hold in the extended sets of numbers which we will need to produce. However there is one property which we have not yet mentioned *which is peculiar to the natural numbers* and is of the greatest importance, viz., *Mathematical Induction*.

This principle states *two* conditions, which when satisfied by any set S of numbers, guarantee that the set S contains *all* the natural numbers. The *first* condition may be described by saying the set S is *inductive*. This means that the number $k + 1$ belongs to S *whenever* k belongs to S. The *second* condition states that the number 1 belongs to S. More briefly the Principle of Mathematical Induction states:

If, for a given set S of numbers, (1) S is inductive, that is, $k + 1 \in S$ whenever $k \in S$ and (2) $1 \in S$, then all the natural numbers belong to S. This property can be made more plausible by citing the following illustrations.

Picture dominoes standing close enough in an endless line so that when any one of them falls backward it knocks down the one immediately behind it. Then if the first domino is pushed over, all will fall. Another example has to do with a ladder having an infinite number of rungs. It is known that one can always advance to the $k + 1$st rung

32   *Natural Numbers*

whenever one has reached the kth rung. Then the assurance of being able to reach the first rung guarantees that one can climb the whole ladder.

While these illustrations may be convincing, they do not in any way form a proof of the Principle of Mathematical Induction. It, or some principle equivalent to it, must be assumed as an axiom.

By way of example let us employ the Principle of Mathematical Induction to show that the product of any two *consecutive* natural numbers is divisible by 2. It will be convenient to represent our two consecutive natural numbers by n and $n+1$ and we might well let $P(n)$ stand for the statement (or proposition) which we wish to prove is true for all natural numbers n, namely, $n(n+1)$ contains the factor 2, that is, $P(n)$ states: $n(n+1) = 2m$, for some $m \in N$.

We begin by letting S be the set of *those* natural numbers n for which $P(n)$ is true. Essentially we need to prove two theorems about S.

(1) We wish to prove S is inductive. To do this we assume that $k \in S$. This means that $P(n)$ is assumed to be true in the case $n = k$ or, in short, that $P(k)$ is true, that is, $k(k+1) = 2m, m \in N$. Hence this is a statement we are free to use. We wish to *show* that $k+1 \in S$ or, that $P(k+1)$ is true, or that $(k+1)(k+2) = 2q$, for some $q \in N$. We proceed by multiplying $(k+1)(k+2)$ as follows (by virtue of the distributive and commutative properties):

$$(k+1)(k+2) = (k+2)(k+1)$$
$$= k(k+1) + 2(k+1)$$

From above:

$$k(k+1) = 2m$$
$$\therefore (k+1)(k+2) = 2m + 2(k+1)$$
$$= 2(m+k+1)$$

Hence $m+k+1$ is the number q which we wished to obtain and $P(k+1)$ is true. Accordingly we have proved that $k+1 \in S$ as a result of knowing (assuming) that $k \in S$ and therefore we have established that S is inductive.

(2) We wish to prove that $1 \in S$ or that $P(1)$ is true. But $P(1)$ is the statement, $1(1+1) = 1 \cdot 2$ contains the factor 2 which is true by inspection. Since we have verified both of the required conditions we may apply the Principle of Mathematical Induction and conclude that $P(n)$ is true for *all* natural numbers n, that is, S contains *all* the natural numbers and hence the product of any two consecutive natural numbers is divisible by 2.

As a second example we will prove that, for every natural number

n, $x^{2n-1} + y^{2n-1}$ has $x + y$ as a factor. Again we will let $P(n)$ stand for the statement to be proved and, as before, let S be the set of those natural numbers n for which $P(n)$ is true.

(1) We assume the truth of $P(k)$, that is, $x^{2k-1} + y^{2k-1}$ contains $x + y$ as a factor. Hence, if $f(x,y)$ represents the other factor involved, we may write $x^{2k-1} + y^{2k-1} = (x + y) f(x,y)$. We wish to prove that $P(k + 1)$ is true, that is, $x^{2k+1} + y^{2k+1}$ also contains $x + y$ as a factor.

Since
$$y^{2k-1} = (x + y) f(x,y) - x^{2k-1}$$
$$\therefore x^{2k+1} + y^{2k+1} = x^2 \cdot x^{2k-1} + y^2 \cdot y^{2k-1}$$
$$= x^2 \cdot x^{2k-1} + y^2 [(x + y) f(x,y) - x^{2k-1}]$$
$$= x^2 \cdot x^{2k-1} - y^2 \cdot x^{2k-1} + y^2(x + y) f(x,y)$$
$$= (x^2 - y^2) x^{2k-1} + y^2(x + y) f(x,y)$$
$$= (x + y)(x - y) x^{2k-1} + (x + y)y^2 f(x,y)$$
[See Exercise 4, Section 1.12]
$$= (x + y) [(x - y) x^{2k-1} + y^2 f(x,y)]$$

Hence $P(k + 1)$ is true and $k + 1 \in S$ whenever $k \in S$.

(2) If $n = 1$, $P(n)$ becomes the statement, $x + y$ has $x + y$ as a factor, which is certainly true.

Hence the Principle of Mathematical Induction may be applied and, therefore, $P(n)$ is true for all natural numbers n, that is, $x^{2n-1} + y^{2n-1}$ is divisible by $x + y$ for all natural numbers n.

A third example will illustrate the use of Mathematical Induction in establishing the truth of an inequality. We wish to prove that $2^n \geq 2n$, where n is any natural number.

Let $P(n)$ be the proposition: $2^n \geq 2n$, where n is a natural number. Let S be the set consisting of those natural numbers for which $P(n)$ is true.

To Prove: S contains *all* the natural numbers.

Proof. For $n = 1$ we have $2^n = 2 = 2n$; $\therefore 1 \in S$.

Assume that $k \in S$, that is, that $2^k \geq 2k$. We wish to establish that $(k + 1) \in S$, that is, that $2^{k+1} \geq 2(k + 1)$.

We know	$2(2^k) \geq 2(2k)$	Why?
	$\therefore 2^{k+1} \geq 2k + 2k$	Why?
Since	$k \geq 1, 2k \geq 2$	Why?
	$\therefore 2^{k+1} \geq 2k + 2$	Why?
	$\therefore 2^{k+1} \geq 2(k + 1)$	Why?
	$\therefore (k + 1) \in S$	

Hence it follows by the Principle of Mathematical Induction that all the natural numbers belong to S. Therefore $2^n \geq 2n$ for every natural number n.

34 Natural Numbers

We shall conclude our illustrations of Mathematical Induction by proving Exercise 10 (a), at the end of this section, that is, that $b^q \cdot b^n = b^{q+n}$, for every natural number n and any given, fixed, natural number q, under the assumptions stated in Exercise 10. This exercise will formally establish the results predicted informally in Section 1.07.

Let $P(n)$ be the proposition: $b^q \cdot b^n = b^{q+n}$, where q and n are natural numbers. Let S be the set of those natural numbers n for which $P(n)$ is true while q remains fixed.

To Prove: Every natural number belongs to S.

Proof. For $n = 1$, $b^q \cdot b^1 = b^q \cdot b = b^{q+1}$. Hence $1 \in S$.
Assume $k \in S$, that is, $b^q \cdot b^k = b^{q+k}$.
We wish to prove that $k + 1 \in S$, that is, $b^q \cdot b^{k+1} = b^{q+k+1}$.

We know that
$$b^q \cdot b^{k+1} = b^q \cdot (b^k \cdot b) \quad \text{Why?}$$
$$= (b^q \cdot b^k) \cdot b \quad \text{Why?}$$
$$= b^{q+k} \cdot b \quad \text{Why?}$$
$$= b^{q+k+1} \quad \text{Why?}$$

Hence $P(k + 1)$ is true, that is, $k + 1 \in S$. Therefore it follows by the Principle of Mathematical Induction that $b^q \cdot b^n = b^{q+n}$ for all natural numbers n and any given natural number q.

In each of the above four examples, it should be evident that *two* facts have been verified, in order to be able to establish the result guaranteed by the Principle of Mathematical Induction, namely, (1) The proposition is true for $n = k + 1$ whenever it is true for $n = k$, and (2) The proposition is true for $n = 1$.

It is instructive to consider what can happen when only one of these two hypotheses is satisfied. A classical example of a proposition, $P(n)$, which is true for $n = 1, 2, 3, \ldots, 39$ and which *fails* for $n = 40$ is the following: The expression $n^2 + n + 41$ represents a prime number for n equal to any natural number.

Question. Can you verify the statement made concerning the above $P(n)$ for $n = 1, 2, 3, 4, 5$, and 40?

In this illustration, although the second hypothesis is satisfied, the first one fails and the proposition does not hold in general. This demonstrates that the first of the two hypotheses is an essential condition of this Principle.

Again, let us assume that $2^k \geq 2k + 15$, for some natural number k.
Then
$$2 \cdot 2^k = 2^{k+1} \geq 2(2k + 15)$$
$$\geq 2k + 2k + 30$$
$$\geq 2k + 2 + 30$$
$$\geq 2(k + 1) + 15$$

Hence we have established that the proposition $2^n \geq 2n + 15$ is true for $n = k + 1$, whenever it is true for $n = k$. However it is not possible to conclude that it is true for all natural numbers n because it is easily seen to be not true for $n = 1$ (and, incidentally, for $n = 2, 3, 4$). Here, although the first hypothesis is satisfied, the second one fails, thus demonstrating that the second hypothesis is also an essential condition of the Principle of Mathematical Induction.

EXERCISES

Employ the Principle of Mathematical Induction to prove the following statements:
1. The product of any three consecutive natural numbers is divisible by 3.
2. The product of any k consecutive natural numbers is divisible by k.
3. For every natural number n,
   (a) $2^{2n-1} + 1$ has 3 as a factor
   (b) $4^{n+1} + 5^{2n-1}$ has 21 as a factor
   (c) $6^{n+1} + 7^{2n-1}$ has 43 as a factor
   (d) $11^{n+1} + 12^{2n-1}$ has 133 as a factor
   (e) $q^{2n-1} + 1$ has $q + 1$ as a factor
   (f) $q^{n+1} + (q+1)^{2n-1}$ has $q^2 + q + 1$ as a factor
4. For every natural number n and $x > y$, $x^{2n} - y^{2n}$ has $(x + y)$ as a factor.
5. If $u_1 = 1$ and $u_k = u_{k-1} + 3$ for $k > 1$, then $u_n = 3n - 2$ for every natural number n.
6. If $u_1 = 2$ and $u_k = 2u_{k-1}$ for $k > 1$, then $u_n = 2^n$ for every natural number n.
7. If $u_1 = 3$ and $u_k = 3u_{k-1}$ for $k > 1$, then $u_n = 3^n$ for every natural number n.
8. $2^n \geq 1 + n$, for every natural number n.
9. $3^n \geq 1 + 2n$, for every natural number n.
10. (a) $b^q \cdot b^n = b^{q+n}$ for every natural number n and any given, fixed, natural number q.
    (b) $(ab)^n = a^n b^n$ for every natural number n.
    (c) $(b^q)^n = b^{q \cdot n}$ for every natural number n and any given, fixed, natural number q.
    (d) $(b^n)^q = b^{n \cdot q}$ for every natural number n and any given, fixed, natural number q.
    (In parts (a),(b),(c),(d), assume that it is known from the definition of b^n that $b^1 = b$ and that $b^k \cdot b = b^{k+1}$ for any natural number k).

2 *Elementary Logic*

Although a great deal of the subject matter of mathematics at this junior high school level is descriptive and informal in character, there are a good many instances where a teacher will wish to supply a proof in order to increase the students' understanding of the topic. It is our conviction that some elementary logic should be presented here to give junior high school teachers the background knowledge needed to understand a few of the extremely basic aspects of proof.

2.01 PROPOSITIONS AND TRUTH TABLES

In the realm of formal logic as well as in much of everyday experience we deal with statements or propositions. The mathematical propositions which we are going to encounter will have one very desirable characteristic: Each is either true or false, never both true and false. For example, the statement, "Seattle is a city in the state of Washington" is true, while the statement, "San Francisco is a city in the state of Washington" is false. In agreement with many writers we shall let small letters, $p, q, r, s, \ldots$ represent propositions.

One of the first concepts which needs to be defined is the *negation* of a proposition p. This new proposition we shall designate as $\bar{p}$, read "not p." If p stands for the statement "$1 + 1 = 2$," then $\bar{p}$ stands for the proposition, "It is not true that $1 + 1 = 2$," or "$1 + 1 \neq 2$." The essential characteristics of $\bar{p}$ relative to p are systematically presented in the *truth table* at the right where T and F represent truth and falsity, respectively, the only possible truth states for p.

p	$\bar{p}$
T	F
F	T

The next step in the development of an "algebra" of logic involves the process of combining two propositions to form a new proposition. We are going to consider four such compound propositions. We wish first to define the *conjunction* of p and q, written $p \wedge q$, and interpreted as "*p and q*"—a proposition that is true only when p and q are both true. Its truth table is on page 37, where, of course, the total number of cases is twice as large as for $\bar{p}$. Hence, if p stands for "salmon is a kind of fish" and q for "a giraffe has four legs," then $p \wedge q$ stands for the proposition "salmon is a kind of fish *and* a giraffe has four legs," which illustrates the first line of the truth table since the propositions *p* and *q* are both true.

p	*q*	*p* ∧ *q*
T	T	T
T	F	F
F	T	F
F	F	F

Another very essential combination of propositions is the *disjunction* of *p* and *q*, written *p* ∨ *q* and interpreted as "*p or q*." This proposition

p	*q*	*p* ∨ *q*
T	T	T
T	F	T
F	T	T
F	F	F

is true when either one or both of *p* and *q* are true. For this reason it is referred to as "inclusive" disjunction in contrast to "exclusive" disjunction (which is not encountered as often) which is false when *p* and *q* are both true, as well as when they are both false. (An example of exclusive disjunction is: "This afternoon he is going to the ball game or he is going to the movies." Clearly he cannot do both.) If *p* stands for "red is a number" and *q* stands for "five is a color," then *p* ∨ *q* stands for the proposition "red is a number *or* five is a color" which illustrates the bottom line of this truth table since the propositions *p* and *q* are both false. On the other hand, "red is a number or red is a color" is true since one of the propositions, "red is a color," is true.

Since a truth table exhibits the essential character of a proposition, two identical truth tables will be said to represent *equivalent* propositions, which may be considered as the same proposition for logical purposes. For example, consider the following truth table:

p	*q*	$\overline{p}$	$\overline{q}$	*p* ∨ *q*	$\overline{(p \vee q)}$	$\overline{p} \wedge \overline{q}$
T	T	F	F	T	F	F
T	F	F	T	T	F	F
F	T	T	F	T	F	F
F	F	T	T	F	T	T

Evidently $\overline{p} \wedge \overline{q}$ and $\overline{(p \vee q)}$ are equivalent propositions. In this connection we remark that it is extremely easy to make a serious error

38   Elementary Logic

in stating the negation of a compound of statements in any language. For example, it is incorrect to interpret the statement, "It is not true that: $2 + 2 = 5$ or Los Angeles is the capital of the United States" as equivalent to "$2 + 2 \neq 5$ or Los Angeles is not the capital of the United States." The ambiguities in communication which result from such misstatements may have dangerous consequences.

Questions. 1. What statement is a correct alternative expression for the illustrative proposition in the second sentence above?
2. Can you obtain, in terms of $\bar{p}$ and $\bar{q}$, a proposition which is equivalent to $\overline{(p \wedge q)}$?

The question of commutativity of conjunction and disjunction is easily answered by referring to their definitions as given by their truth tables. The following truth table demonstrates the associativity of conjunction.

p	q	r	$p \wedge q$	$q \wedge r$	$(p \wedge q) \wedge r$	$p \wedge (q \wedge r)$
T	T	T	T	T	T	T
T	T	F	T	F	F	F
T	F	T	F	F	F	F
T	F	F	F	F	F	F
F	T	T	F	T	F	F
F	T	F	F	F	F	F
F	F	T	F	F	F	F
F	F	F	F	F	F	F

The corresponding property of disjunction may be verified in a similar way.

Question. Are $(p \wedge q) \vee r$ and $p \wedge (q \vee r)$ equivalent propositions?

It is now within our capability to construct more complicated propositions using conjunction, disjunction, and negation and having a given truth table. For example, the table below describes the two sets of circumstances under which the unknown proposition is to be true, that is, when p is true and q is false and when p is false and q is true.

p	q	?
T	T	F
T	F	T
F	T	T
F	F	F

By taking the conjunction, $p \wedge \bar{q}$, of p and $\bar{q}$, we obtain a proposition true only when p and q have the truth values given in the second row, and $\bar{p} \wedge q$ gives us a proposition true only when p and q have the truth values given in the third row. The disjunction of these two propositions, that is, $(p \wedge \bar{q}) \vee (\bar{p} \wedge q)$, is therefore, a proposition satisfying the given truth table.

Question. Can you construct a proposition to fit the truth table given below?

p	q	r	?
T	T	T	F
T	T	F	T
T	F	T	T
T	F	F	F
F	T	T	T
F	T	F	T
F	F	T	T
F	F	F	F

[Note that, in order to be able to compare truth tables with ease, we find it convenient to adopt a consistent procedure for inserting truth and false values for the *basic* propositions, viz., in the right hand column, (that is, for r) T and F alternate; in the second column from the right (for q) they alternate in pairs; in the third column from the right (for p) in groups of four; and so on in powers of two.]

We come now to the combination of propositions known as the *conditional* of p and q, written $p \to q$, and interpreted as "if p then q," for example, if it is cold outside, people wear warm clothing. At first glance you may not believe that $p \to q$ should enjoy the same treatment as the previous propositions. However, logicians agree on the fact that $p \to q$ is a proper compound proposition. This proposition may also be interpreted as "p is sufficient for q," "q is necessary for p," or "p only if q." (Note that we have not included the clause, "p implies q," in the above listing of interpretations. This clause is being held in reserve to be associated later in this chapter with the conditional proposition under special circumstances.)

We may define $p \to q$ either by giving its truth table, which appears below, or by accepting $\overline{(p \wedge \bar{q})}$ as a proposition equivalent to $p \to q$. The proposition $\overline{(p \wedge \bar{q})}$ means "the negation of the conjunction of p and not q," or, less formally, "not both p and not q." The motivation

p	q	$p \to q$
T	T	T
T	F	F
F	T	T
F	F	T

for using $\overline{(\overline{p} \wedge \overline{q})}$ as a definition for $p \to q$ lies in the extent to which the above phrase represents the meaning we wish to associate with the expression, "if p, then q." Clearly, when p is true, we wish the truth or falsity of $p \to q$ to coincide with the truth or falsity, respectively, of q. However, when p is false, we have no reason to consider $p \to q$ as other than true, regardless of the truth or falsity of q. Let us illustrate the somewhat striking properties of this proposition by an example. The following three propositions are true:

"If 2 times 3 equals 6, then coal is black."
"If 2 times 3 equals 7, then coal is black."
"If 2 times 3 equals 7, then coal is white."

while the statement, "If 2 times 3 equals 6, then coal is white" is false.

Questions. 1. Is the proposition $q \to p$ equivalent to $p \to q$?
2. Is the proposition $p \to q$ equivalent to $\bar{p} \vee q$?

The last combination of propositions, which we wish to include is the *biconditional*, $p \leftrightarrow q$, of two propositions p and q. The biconditional of p and q is, by definition, equivalent to $(p \to q) \wedge (q \to p)$ with the resulting truth table given below. Since one interpretation associated

p	q	$p \to q$	$q \to p$	$p \leftrightarrow q$
T	T	T	T	T
T	F	F	T	F
F	T	T	F	F
F	F	T	T	T

with $p \to q$ is "p only if q" and the usual meaning of $q \to p$ is "if q then p" or "p if q" then it is natural to interpret $p \leftrightarrow q$ as "p if and only if q" or, equivalently, "p is necessary and sufficient for q". For example, the two propositions, "$3 + 2 = 5$ if and only if Texas is larger than Delaware," and "$3 + 2 = 6$ if and only if Texas is smaller than Delaware," are both true, while the following two propositions are false: "$3 + 2 = 6$ if and only if Texas is larger than Delaware," "$3 + 2 = 5$ if and only if Texas is smaller than Delaware."

Question. Can you give another combination of propositions to which $p \leftrightarrow q$ is equivalent?

We have indicated that we can construct a proposition to fit any given truth table. As an illustration let us consider the following hypothetical situation.

By the year 2000 our world has become automated to a high degree. In college, for example, a student can find out at any time from a newly developed electronic computer, whether he is passing or failing in any course he is taking. One such machine, which operates in a cubicle the size of a telephone booth, answers "yes" or "no" to such questions and to logical combinations of questions. The machine is in such constant use that each student is allowed to ask only one question, as for example, "Am I passing in History 317?" The students are very secretive regarding the information they receive, and only one student enters the cubicle at a time. The machine has only one defect—it is supersensitive to radiation and occasionally it gives the incorrect answer, at which time a green indicator changes to red, so that students still are properly informed, that is, all except the blind students and the (red-green) color-blind students. These students immediately set about to devise a question whose "yes" or "no" answer would give them the correct course information they desired, regardless of the color of the indicator. What question did they ask?

Let p represent the proposition, "I am passing in History 317" and q represent the proposition, "The indicator is green." Then we want a "yes" answer to correspond to the truth of p and a "no" answer to correspond to falsity for p, regardless of the truth or falsity of q. The table below indicates how we arrive at the truth table for the required proposition. When q is true (green indicator) the truth and falsity of the required proposition must correspond *directly* to the truth and falsity of p respectively, and when q is false (red indicator) the truth values of the required proposition must correspond *oppositely* to the truth values of p. Hence the required proposition could be $p \leftrightarrow q$ (or any proposition equivalent to it) and the blind and color-blind students

p	q	Machine Answer	Required Proposition
T	T	Yes	T
T	F	Yes	F
F	T	No	F
F	F	No	T

might well ask the question, "Am I passing in History 317 if and only if the indicator is green?" Another question which they might ask and which would accomplish the same purpose corresponds to the proposition $(p \land q) \lor (\bar{p} \land \bar{q})$, viz., "Is it true that either I am passing in History 317 and the indicator is green or I am failing in History 317 and the indicator is red?"

EXERCISES

1. Show that $(p \land q) \lor r$ and $(p \lor r) \land (q \lor r)$ are equivalent propositions.
2. Do the same for $(p \lor q) \land r$ and $(p \land r) \lor (q \land r)$. (The two equivalences described in Exercises 1 and 2 are known as the distributive properties of conjunction and disjunction.)
3. If p denotes "Fred is a skier" and q denotes "George is a skier," write the following statements in symbolic form.
   (a) Fred is a skier but George does not ski.
   (b) Both Fred and George do not ski.
   (c) Fred does not ski or George does not ski.
   (d) It is not true that Fred or George skis.
   (e) Neither Fred nor George skis.
   (f) It is not true that Fred does not ski and George does not ski.
4. From the following four statements, pick out the one which is the negation of "If Jones passed the test then Smith failed the test."
   (a) Jones failed the test or Smith failed the test.
   (b) Jones and Smith both passed the test.
   (c) Jones failed the test and Smith passed the test.
   (d) Jones and Smith both failed the test.
5. If p stands for "John got an A in mathematics" and q represents "Mary got an E in English", give a verbal interpretation for each of the following:
   (a) $(q \to p) \land (p \to q)$ (b) $p \land \bar{q}$ (c) $(\bar{p} \land \bar{q}) \to (p \lor q)$
   (d) $p \lor (\bar{q} \to \bar{p})$ (e) $(p \land q)$ (f) $p \to \bar{q}$
   (g) $(p \lor q)$ (h) $\bar{p} \leftrightarrow q$ (i) $(p \lor \bar{p}) \to q$
6. Paul said, "I will drive my dad's car or I will go with Bob." Paul drove his dad's car and took Bob with him. Did he tell the truth? What if he and Bob went together by plane? What if Paul drove his dad's car and Bob stayed home?
7. Give the truth tables for the following propositions:
   (a) $(p \to q) \lor (p \leftrightarrow q)$
   (b) $[p \to (q \lor r)] \land [(p \land r) \to \bar{q}]$
8. Obtain a proposition in terms of p, q, r, and their negations, having the following as its truth table:

p	q	r	?
T	T	T	F
T	T	F	T
T	F	T	T
T	F	F	T
F	T	T	T
F	T	F	T
F	F	T	T
F	F	F	F

9. Using only negation, conditional or biconditional propositions, give a compound statement which states symbolically "*p* or *q* but not both."
10. Prove that the negation of, "*p* is a necessary and sufficient condition for *q*" is equivalent to, "*p* is a necessary and sufficient condition for *q*."
11. A logician is held prisoner by a tribe of logically minded head-hunters. He is guarded alternately by one of two tribesmen who can answer only "yes" or "no" and of whom he knows that one tells the truth always while the other lies consistently. Which one is truthful he does not know. His prison cell contains two doors marked *A* and *B* and he is told that one door leads to freedom while the other door leads to certain death, but again, which is which? He is allowed to ask only one question. What question should he ask in order to be sure of knowing which door leads to freedom?
12. (a) The proposition $q \to p$ is known as the *contrapositive* of $p \to q$. Show that these two propositions are equivalent.
    (b) The proposition $q \to p$ is known as the *converse* of $p \to q$. Show why these two propositions are not equivalent.
    (c) For the statement, "If a plane quadrilateral is a square, then the quadrilateral is a rectangle", give (i) the converse, (ii) the contrapositive.

2.02 TRUTH SETS

It will assist our understanding of elementary logic to see how sets may be employed to advantage in relation to propositions. A proposition such as "$x > 5$" may be represented by *p* and its truth or falsity is determined only when we know what number is to be substituted for x. Hence the set of numbers available to us in this case is of prime importance. We are accustomed to give the name *universal set* or *universe*, as we did in Section 1.03, to the set in question. As we extend our number system in future chapters we will have ever expanding sets available as our universe of numbers. However, we are free at any time to impose an arbitrary restriction on the universe if the particular problem under consideration will have a more suitable solution within the limited set. With respect to the proposition, "$x > 5$", let us adopt the set *W* of whole numbers as the universal set. Then the set $P = \{6,7,8,9,...\}$ is the set of numbers belonging to *W*, for which *p* is true. *P* is called the *truth set* or *solution set* of the proposition *p*, and in symbols we may write, $P = \{x \in W | p \text{ is true}\}$, that is, *P* is the set of those whole numbers for which the proposition *p* is true.

When we are dealing with propositions of a more general nature, the universal set U will be the set of all conditions or circumstances under which the proposition *p* has true or false values. *P* will be the

44   Elementary Logic

subset of U for which p is true. In Section 1.03 we defined the complement of any set. If we denote the complement of P in U by $\bar{P}$, then $\bar{P} \subseteq U$ and $P \cup \bar{P} = U$. Clearly the proposition $\bar{p}$ will have $\bar{P}$ as its truth set. In the previous example $\bar{P} = \{0,1,2,3,4,5\}$.

The proposition $p \wedge q$ is true only when both p and q are true. Hence the circumstances under which $p \wedge q$ is true must belong to both P and Q, if Q denotes the truth set of q. Therefore the truth set of $p \wedge q$ is $P \cap Q$. On the other hand $p \vee q$ is true whenever p or q is true, that is, under circumstances belonging either to P or Q. Hence $P \cup Q$ is the truth set of $p \vee q$. Thus we observe a very attractive duality between the disjunction of propositions and the union of their truth sets. For example, with the same set W, as above, let p be the proposition, "x > 5", as before, and q be the proposition, "9 > x." The truth set Q of the proposition q is $\{0,1,2,3,4,5,6,7,8\}$. The truth set for $p \wedge q$ is clearly $\{6,7,8\} = P \cap Q$ and the truth set for $p \vee q$ is the set $W = P \cup Q$. Note also the duality exhibited between the conjunction of propositions and the intersection of their truth sets.

We will find that Venn diagrams, introduced in Section 1.03, are very helpful in dealing with truth sets. For example, the proposition $p \rightarrow q$ was originally defined as equivalent to $\overline{(p \wedge \bar{q})}$. The proposition $\bar{p} \vee q$ is also equivalent to $\overline{(p \wedge \bar{q})}$ (see Section 2.01) and has as its truth set, $\bar{P} \cup Q$, whose Venn diagram is given below:

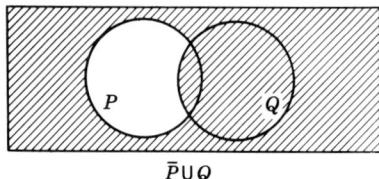

$\bar{P} \cup Q$

Questions. 1. Can you show, by comparing Venn diagrams, that the truth set for $\overline{(p \wedge \bar{q})}$ is the same as $\bar{P} \cup Q$?
2. What is the Venn diagram for the truth set of $\bar{p} \wedge q$?

Similarly the truth set of $p \leftrightarrow q$ is given by $(\bar{P} \cup Q) \cap (P \cup \bar{Q})$ with the following Venn diagram: Why?

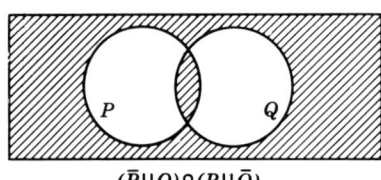

$(\bar{P} \cup Q) \cap (P \cup \bar{Q})$

Questions. 1. Does the above Venn diagram also represent the truth set of the proposition $(p \rightarrow q) \wedge (q \rightarrow p)$? Of the proposition $(\bar{p} \vee q) \wedge (p \vee \bar{q})$? Of $\overline{(p \wedge \bar{q})} \wedge \overline{(\bar{p} \wedge q)}$? Of $\overline{(p \wedge \bar{q}) \vee (\bar{p} \wedge q)}$?
2. Does the above Venn diagram also represent $(P \cap Q) \cup (\bar{P} \cap \bar{Q})$?

EXERCISES

1. It was found that out of 100 students in a small college, 28 were studying Russian, 30 German, and 42 French; it was known further that 8 students were studying Russian and German; 10 were studying Russian and French, and 5 French and German. If 3 people were studying all three languages,
   (a) How many students were studying no language?
   (b) How many students were studying French only?
   (c) How many students studied German if and only if they studied French?
2. (a) Determine which sets are empty by obtaining truth tables for the propositions corresponding to the following truth sets:
    (i) $(A \cup C) \cap (\bar{A} \cup \bar{B})$ (ii) $(A \cap B) - B$
    (iii) $(A \cap B) \cap (\bar{B} \cap C)$ (iv) $(A \cup B) \cap (\bar{A} \cup \bar{B})$
   (b) Verify by drawing Venn diagrams.
3. (a) Determine whether one set is a subset of the other by obtaining truth tables for the propositions corresponding to the following pairs of truth sets:
    (i) $A - B; B \cap \bar{A}$ (ii) $\bar{A} \cap \bar{B}; A \cup B$
    (iii) $A; A \cap B$ (iv) $\bar{A}; B - A$
   (b) Verify by drawing Venn diagrams.

2.03 LOGICAL TRUTH AND LOGICAL FALSITY

Frequently we shall encounter a proposition which is true in all possible situations. A very simple example is $p \vee \bar{p}$, as illustrated by the statement, "$2 + 2 = 5$ or $2 + 2 \neq 5$." Such a proposition is said to be *logically true* and is often referred to as a *tautology*. A proposition which is false in all cases, for example, $p \wedge \bar{p}$, is described as being *logically false* or a *self-contradiction*.

p	$\bar{p}$	$p \vee \bar{p}$	$p \wedge \bar{p}$
T	F	T	F
F	T	T	F

Question. What is the *truth set* of a logically true proposition? Of a logically false proposition?

46   Elementary Logic

The reader will recall that in Section 2.01 we drew attention to the statement, "p implies q," whose introduction we were deferring. It is here that we wish to make use of it. When the conditional proposition, $p \to q$, is logically true, that is, true under all logical circumstances, we shall say "p implies q,"* and we shall indicate this special relationship by use of the double arrow (=>) that is, $p \Rightarrow q$.

In order to compare a conditional proposition and an implication, let us contrast the truth tables of the propositions $(p \vee q) \to (p \wedge q)$ and $(p \wedge q) \to (p \vee q)$, respectively, where p and q are any two propositions.

p	q	$p \wedge q$	$p \vee q$	$(p \vee q) \to (p \wedge q)$	$(p \wedge q) \to (p \vee q)$
T	T	T	T	T	T
T	F	F	T	F	T
F	T	F	T	F	T
F	F	F	F	T	T

Accordingly we interpret $(p \vee q) \to (p \wedge q)$ as "if $(p \vee q)$ then $(p \wedge q)$" and $(p \wedge q) \Rightarrow (p \vee q)$ as "$(p \wedge q)$ implies $(p \vee q)$," since the latter conditional proposition is logically true.

It is a necessary consequence of our definition of logical truth, that there cannot exist any logical circumstance under which the logically true proposition is false. Hence such a proposition must have the universal set as its truth set. If we examine again the Venn diagram for the truth set, $\bar{P} \cup Q$, corresponding to $p \to q$ we shall see that the

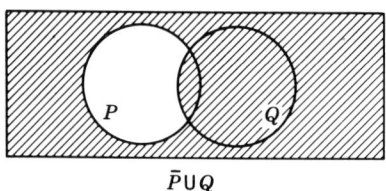

$\bar{P} \cup Q$

unhatched region must represent the empty set if $p \to q$ is to become logically true. Thus we are led to the conclusion that we must have $P \subseteq Q$ if $p \Rightarrow q$.

Similarly, when $p \leftrightarrow q$ is logically true, that is, when $p \Leftrightarrow q$,

---

*Although this interpretation has been adopted by a number of contemporary writers, the reader is cautioned that he will not find this exact usage in most older and many current textbooks. We wish to employ the concept because we are of the opinion that its use is most advantageous from the point of view of clarity and explicitness.

say "p is equivalent to q" or, in more colloquial language, "p means q." For example, the truth table given below demonstrates that $\overline{(p \wedge q)} \Leftrightarrow (\bar{p} \vee \bar{q})$:

p	q	$p \wedge q$	$\overline{(p \wedge q)}$	$\bar{p}$	$\bar{q}$	$\bar{p} \vee \bar{q}$	$\overline{(p \wedge q)} \to (\bar{p} \vee \bar{q})$
T	T	T	F	F	F	F	T
T	F	F	T	F	T	T	T
F	T	F	T	T	F	T	T
F	F	F	T	T	T	T	T

It is in this sense that we have employed and shall continue to employ the double-headed double arrow ($\Leftrightarrow$) in writing definitions in abbreviated form. Again let us examine the Venn diagram for the truth set, $(\bar{P} \cup Q) \cap (P \cup \bar{Q})$, of $p \leftrightarrow q$:

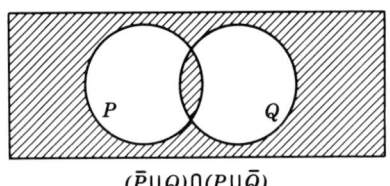

$(\bar{P} \cup Q) \cap (P \cup \bar{Q})$

Evidently the unhatched region must represent the empty set as a result of which we must conclude that $P = Q$ if $p \Leftrightarrow q$. This can also be seen in another way. When $p \Leftrightarrow q$ we know that the truth tables for p and q must be identical and hence we must have both $p \Rightarrow q$ and $q \Rightarrow p$. Therefore, as developed earlier in this section, we know that both $P \subseteq Q$ and $Q \subseteq P$, from which it follows that $P = Q$.

Questions. 1. Can you demonstrate that $\overline{(P \cup Q)} = \bar{P} \cap \bar{Q}$?
2. What are the two definitions which have been given for "p is equivalent to q?"
3. Can you show that these two definitions are completely consistent, that is, can each one be derived from the other?

EXERCISES

1. If p is logically true, prove that:
   (a) $p \vee q$ is logically true
   (b) $\bar{p} \wedge q$ is logically false
   (c) $p \wedge q$ is equivalent to q
   (d) $\bar{p} \vee q$ is equivalent to q

2. If p and q are logically true and r is logically false, what is the status of $(\bar{p} \vee \bar{q}) \wedge r$?
3. Determine which of the following propositions are logically true.
   (a) $(p \rightarrow q) \leftrightarrow (\bar{q} \rightarrow \bar{p})$ (b) $(p \rightarrow q) \leftrightarrow (q \rightarrow p)$
   (c) $(p \leftrightarrow q) \rightarrow (p \vee q)$ (d) $(p \wedge q) \rightarrow (p \leftrightarrow q)$
   (e) $(p \leftrightarrow q) \rightarrow (p \rightarrow q)$ (f) $(p \vee q) \rightarrow (p \rightarrow q)$
   (g) $(p \rightarrow q) \rightarrow (p \vee q)$.
4. Same as Exercise 3 for the following:
   (a) $(p \vee \bar{p}) \rightarrow p$ (b) $p \rightarrow (p \vee \bar{p})$
   (c) $(p \wedge \bar{p}) \rightarrow p$ (d) $((p \vee \bar{p}) \wedge q) \leftrightarrow q$
   (e) $(p \wedge q) \vee (\bar{p} \wedge \bar{q}) \leftrightarrow (\bar{p} \vee q) \wedge (p \vee \bar{q})$
5. (a) Show that $(p \wedge q) \vee (\bar{p} \wedge \bar{q}) \Longleftrightarrow (\bar{p} \vee q) \wedge (p \vee \bar{q})$ by use of the distributive properties of conjunction and disjunction (See Exercises 1 and 2, Section 2.01, and Exercise 4(d) above.)
   (b) How does the result in 5(a) relate to the final *Question* in Section 2.02?

2.04 VALID ARGUMENTS

Our purpose in developing this minimum amount of elementary logic has been to enable us to describe concisely some of the more fundamental aspects of proof, including indirect proof. An *argument* can be defined as the assertion that a certain conclusion or theorem is a logical consequence of a given hypothesis or set of premises. It is a valid argument if and only if the conjunction of the premises implies the conclusion; or, in other words, whenever all the premises are true, the conclusion is also true.

Perhaps the simplest situation which appears in an argument occurs when the logical truth of p and the logical truth of $p \rightarrow q$ are given as premises. If we examine the truth table of $p \rightarrow q$, we see that the last three lines are not admissible as a result of this hypothesis, the second line being eliminated because $p \Longrightarrow q$ and the third and fourth lines being eliminated since p is logically true. Therefore we are obliged

p	q	$p \rightarrow q$
T	T	T
~~T~~	~~F~~	~~F~~
~~F~~	~~T~~	~~T~~
~~F~~	~~F~~	~~T~~

to conclude that q is true. Another way of illustrating this argument is to verify that the conjunction of p and $p \to q$ implies our conclusion. This is demonstrated in the truth table below:

p	q	$p \to q$	$p \wedge (p \to q)$	$(p \wedge (p \to q)) \to q$
T	T	T	T	T
T	F	F	F	T
F	T	T	F	T
F	F	T	F	T

We abbreviate the preceding valid argument by setting up the schematic form exhibited at the right. This very basic type of argument bears the classical name, *modus ponens*, or *rule of detachment*. The following is an example of this type of argument, where p stands for "this person is a college student" and q stands for "this person is clever:"

p
$p \Rightarrow q$
$\therefore q$

Bob is a college student.
All college students are clever people.
$\therefore$ Bob is a clever person.

We may find it helpful here to employ the idea of set in a very elemental way by thinking of the set of college students and the set of clever people as subsets of the universal set of all people. Then, clearly, the hypothesis of the argument tells us that the set of college students is a subset of the set of clever people. Since Bob belongs to the smaller set, he must also belong to the larger set which contains it. The diagram which illustrates this situation is known as an Euler diagram.

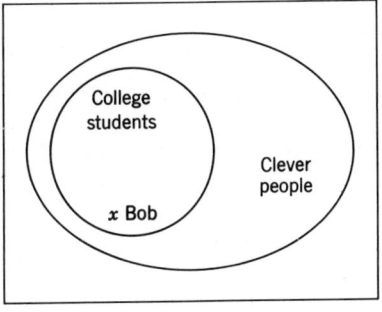

Question. Can you demonstrate that the argument (often referred to as *modus tollens*) exhibited at the right is valid?

$\bar{q}$
$p \Rightarrow q$
$\therefore \bar{p}$

There is no mystery involved in this argument if we recall (See Exercise 12, Section 2.01) that $p \to q$ is equivalent to the contrapositive, viz., $\bar{q} \to \bar{p}$. On the other hand the argument at the right (although employed too frequently) is an illustration of a *fallacy*, that is, an invalid argument. Consider for example the following argument:

$$\begin{array}{c} q \\ p \Rightarrow q \\ \hline \therefore p \end{array}$$

> John got passing grades in mathematics.
> All intelligent students get passing grades in mathematics.
> ∴ John is an intelligent student.

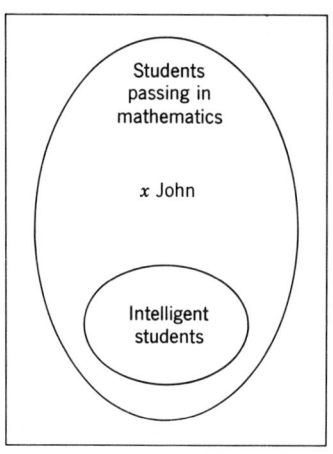

This is an invalid or fallacious argument since the set consisting of John and the set consisting of all intelligent students *may* be disjoint subsets of the set of those students getting passing grades in mathematics. The fundamental fallacy observed here stems from the fact that $p \to q$ is not equivalent to its converse, $q \to p$.

Question. Can you demonstrate that the argument at the right also represents a fallacy?

$$\begin{array}{c} p \Rightarrow q \\ \bar{p} \\ \hline \therefore \bar{q} \end{array}$$

It has probably occurred to the reader before now that more than one premise in an argument may be an implication.

Question. Can you show that the proposition $(p \to q) \land (q \to r)$ implies $p \to r$?

The tautology $((p \to q) \land (q \to r)) \Rightarrow (p \to r)$ is often called the *Law of Syllogism* and is a most useful step in establishing a valid argument. For example,

> If a polygon is a square, then the polygon is a rectangle.
> If a polygon is a rectangle, then the polygon is a parallelogram.
> ∴ If a polygon is a square, then the polygon is a parallelogram.

Hence if we represent p: This polygon is a square
                       q: This polygon is a rectangle
                       r: This polygon is a parallelogram

then

$$p => q$$
$$q => r$$
$$\therefore p => r$$

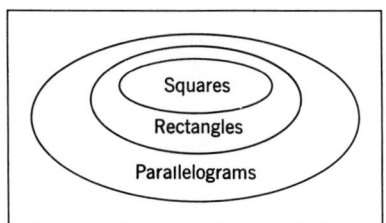

Attention should be drawn to the fact that the validity or fallacy of an argument depends only on whether or not the conjunction of the premises implies the conclusion and not on the inherent truth or falsity of the conclusion. This will be evident in the following two examples:

All cats are two-legged.
All two-legged animals can fly.
∴ All cats can fly.

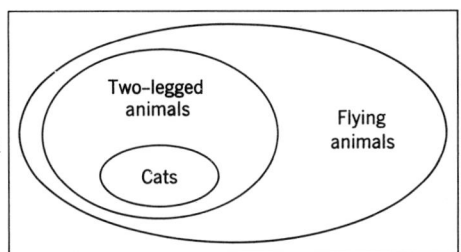

If we let p stand for: This animal is a cat.
q: This animal is two-legged.
r: This animal can fly.

then

$$p => q$$
$$q => r$$
$$\therefore p => r$$

This argument is valid in spite of the fact that both premises, as well as the conclusion, are false.

On the other hand, let us consider:

The diagonals of a square meet at right angles.
A square is a rhombus.
∴The diagonals of a rhombus meet at right angles.

52   Elementary Logic

If we let *p* stand for: This quadrilateral is a square.
   q: The diagonals of this quadrilateral meet at right angles.
   r: This quadrilateral is a rhombus.

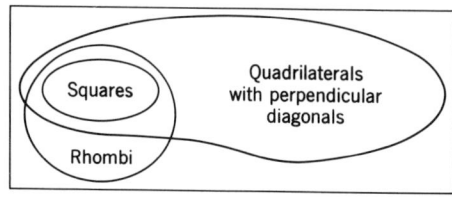

$p \Rightarrow q$
$p \Rightarrow r$
$\therefore r \Rightarrow q$

Here the argument is clearly invalid while both premises and conclusion are true. Note that the Euler diagram reflects strictly the premises of the argument in complete disregard of the fact that *all* rhombi have their diagonals meeting at right angles.

One particular type of proof, known as *indirect proof*, requires our special attention. In an indirect proof we assume that the desired conclusion is false, that is, that its negation is true. We then proceed by means of a valid argument to arrive at a contradiction, that is, a conclusion which is the negation of a premise or the negation of an implication of the premises. Since the conjunction of that premise and its negation is logically false, we conclude that our original assumption was inadmissible and that the theorem must therefore be true. (If we had been led to a result in agreement with a premise, it would have told us nothing with respect to the original assumption.) In short, we want to show that $p \rightarrow q$ is logically true. If, given the truth of p and assuming the truth of $\bar{q}$, we are able to demonstrate the truth of $\bar{p}$, then we know $\bar{q}$ is untenable and q must be true.

Another way of looking at this situation is the following. If we are able to derive the truth of $\bar{p}$ from the truth of $\bar{q}$, then we have established the logical truth of the contrapositive, $\bar{q} \rightarrow \bar{p}$, which is equivalent to $p \rightarrow q$.

An example of indirect reasoning would be the following:

Hypothesis: $6 + 5 = (2 + 4) + 5$
To prove: $6 = 2 + 4$

Proof. Suppose $6 \neq 2 + 4$. Then "6" and "2 + 4" are names for two different numbers. Hence if $6 = n(A)$ and $2 + 4 = n(B)$, it is impossible to establish a 1 : 1 correspondence between the elements of A and the elements of B. If $5 = n(C)$ where $C \cap A = \emptyset$ and $C \cap B = \emptyset$, then it will be impossible to establish a 1 : 1 correspondence between the elements of $A \cup C$ and those of $B \cup C$. Hence $n(A \cup C) \neq n(B \cup C)$ and $6 + 5 \neq (2 + 4) + 5$. This latter statement contradicts our hypothesis and, therefore, we know that $6 = 2 + 4$.

In Section 1.09 the following axiom for whole numbers was introduced: $a \neq 0$ and $b \neq 0 \Rightarrow ab \neq 0$. In Section 1.11 it was demonstrated further that

$$ab = ac <=> a(b - c) = 0$$

As a second illustration of indirect proof we would like to prove the following:

Theorem. $ab = 0 \Rightarrow$ either $a = 0$ or $b = 0$ or both

Proof. Suppose $a \neq 0$ and $b \neq 0$. Then by the above axiom, introduced in Section 1.09, $ab \neq 0$. But our hypothesis states that $ab = 0$. Since these two statements are direct contradictions of each other we must conclude that it cannot be true that $a \neq 0$ and $b \neq 0$. Hence we have shown that either $a = 0$ or $b = 0$ or both.

As a result of this theorem we have the corollary:

$$ab = ac \text{ and } a \neq 0 \Rightarrow b = c$$

Proof. Since $ab = ac <=> a(b - c) = 0$, then, since $a \neq 0$, we have $b - c = 0$ and $b - c = 0 <=> b = c$. This corollary is often referred to as the *Cancellation Law of Multiplication*. Hence if we know that $5b = 5 \cdot 2$ then we may conclude immediately that $b = 2$.

Another very elegant example of an indirect proof is given by Euclid's proof that the number of prime numbers is infinite. The argument proceeds by assuming that the number of prime numbers is finite, let us say n. Let these n prime numbers be represented by $p_1, p_2, \ldots, p_n$. Then consider the number $P = p_1 p_2 \cdots p_n + 1$. P is either a prime number or a product of prime numbers. It is clear that P is not divisible by $p_i, i = 1, 2, \ldots, n$, while P is certainly greater than any $p_i, i = 1, 2, \ldots, n$. Hence, if P is prime it is not one of the p_i and if P is composite it must be the product of primes greater than any $p_i, i = 1, 2, \ldots, n$. Therefore in either case, a prime number different from $p_i, i = 1, 2, \ldots, n$, has been shown to exist. This contradicts our assumption that the number of prime numbers is exactly n; hence their number cannot be finite.

EXERCISES

1. State whether each of the following arguments is valid or invalid:
   (a) All basketball players are over six feet tall.
   Jim is a basketball player.
   ∴ Jim is over six feet tall.
   (b) All students who study hard get A grades.
   Bill got an A grade.
   ∴ Bill studied hard.
   (c) All students who study hard get A grades.
   Bill did not get an A grade.
   ∴ Bill did not study hard.
   (d) All basketball players are over six feet tall.
   Jim is not a basketball player.
   ∴ Jim is not over six feet tall.
2. Test the validity of the following arguments:

   (a) $p => \bar{q}$
   $\bar{p} => r$
   q
   ∴ r

   (b) $p => q$
   $q \lor r$
   $\bar{r}$
   ∴ p

3. Determine the valid conclusion involving t and s which is a consequence of the following set of premises:

   $p \lor \bar{q}$
   $r => \bar{s}$
   $\bar{r} => q$
   $\bar{t} \lor \bar{p}$
   ∴ ?

4. Write the following argument in symbolic form and test its validity:
   If the Rangers beat the Hawks then the Wings will beat the Leafs.
   The Canadiens beat the Maroons or the Rangers beat the Wings.
   If the Hawks beat the Rangers then the Maroons will beat the Canadiens.
   The Leafs beat the Wings.
   ∴ The Rangers beat the Wings.
5. Establish indirect proofs for the following theorems:

   (a) $p \lor q$
   $\bar{q}$
   ∴ p

   (b) $p <=> q$
   $q => \bar{r}$
   r
   ∴ $\bar{p}$

6. If c and d are natural numbers and cd is an odd number, establish by indirect proof that c and d are both odd numbers.
7. If m is a natural number and $m + 5 = 3 + 5$, prove by indirect method that $m = 3$.
8. Three men are told that a hat will be placed on each of their heads. One of the men, called N, has normal vision, another, called H, sees with only one eye, while the third, called B, is blind. The men are told that there are altogether 3 white and 2 red hats from which those placed on their heads will be chosen. N was asked if he knew what the color of his hat was, and he replied "No." Then H was asked the same question and he answered "No." At this moment B announced that he knew the color of his hat. What color was it and how did he know?
9. A true-false exam consists of five questions. The instructor has stated that there are more true than false questions and that no three consecutive questions have the same answer. The student knows the correct answer to question two and deduces that questions one and five must have opposite answers to each other. Under these conditions he can determine all the correct answers. What are the answers to the five questions?
10. Prove or disprove that 31 rectangles each of a size just sufficient to cover two squares of a standard checker board can be placed on the board so as to cover all squares except two diagonally opposite ones.
11. A census-taker came to a house and asked the person who answered the door how many occupants there were in the house and what their ages were. The person said there were three occupants altogether, that the product of their ages was 225, and the sum of their ages equaled the house number. The census-taker looked at the house number and replied that the information was insufficient. The person then said, "I am the oldest," after which the census-taker wrote down the correct ages and left. What were the ages?
12. A certain community is known to consist exclusively of young married couples and their children. If it is known that the following facts are true:
    (1) There are more parents than children,
    (2) There are more boys than girls,
    (3) Every boy has a sister,
    show that there is at least one childless couple.

3 Extension of Whole Numbers

3.01 SENTENCES, OR WHY IS EXTENSION NECESSARY?

Although we dealt only with the set of whole numbers, in Chapter 1, we found that this set exhibited a wide variety of properties and opened up a good many avenues of exploration. One such avenue which we have not investigated is the mathematical sentence.

The following are statements (or propositions in terms of Chapter 2) which we refer to as *numerical* (sometimes called closed) sentences because they involve numbers and they make a specific assertion (which may or may not be true):

$$3 + 5 = 7$$
$$10 - 4 = 6$$
$$4 + 9 = 13$$
$$14 - 6 = 9$$

We are able to verify the truth or falsity of each sentence by reference to previously established procedures. However, if we are given a sentence like

$$? + 5 = 7$$
$$\text{or } \square + 5 = 7$$
$$\text{or } x + 5 = 7$$

we cannot describe it as true or false until we replace ? or □ or x by some number. We call such sentences *open sentences* since their truth or falsity is an "open question." For convenience we generally prefer to use a literal symbol, like x, to indicate the place where a number is to be substituted. The set of numbers from which the replacement is to be selected is called the *universe* or *universal set*. Our present universe is, therefore, the set of whole numbers. If we choose the number 3 to replace x in the sentence, $x + 5 = 7$, we obtain the false numerical sentence, $3 + 5 = 7$, and this will be the case for any replacement except 2. We say that the set consisting of 2, that is, $\{2\}$, is the *solution set* of the open sentence $x + 5 = 7$. Similarly the solution set of $8 + x = 8$ is $\{0\}$. (Note that $\{0\}$ is quite different from the empty set $\emptyset$ as well as from the number 0.)

What is the solution set for the open sentence $7 + x = 6$? Here the answer must be $\emptyset$ since no whole number produces a true numerical sentence when used as a replacement in the open sentence, $7 + x = 6$. We have defined $b - c = d <=> b = c + d$, only in the case where $b \geq c$. In our example we see that we have $b < c$ and our lack of a non-empty solution set is equivalent to the fact that $6 - 7$ is not yet defined in our number system.

3.02 THE CONCEPT OF NEGATIVE NUMBER – THE INTEGERS

We have seen in Section 3.01 that our set of whole numbers is insufficient to provide solution sets for simple sentences like $7 + x = 6$. We wish to remedy this deficiency.

In this first extension of our number system we face a choice of procedures which, once made, will determine the manner in which the whole system is to be developed, if we are to be consistent. We may assume the appropriate postulates for two undefined operations in the enlarged system, make the necessary definitions, and develop the body of available theorems. On the other hand, we may approach the extension in a more exploratory and less mathematically sophisticated fashion, keeping in mind what we already know about the earlier system in order to guide us in extending our operations to the enlarged system. In so doing we develop the rules for our operations in what we consider the most effective form and then verify the standard properties for our operations. Although it is not necessarily the easier of the two approaches, we have chosen the latter because we believe it lends itself more suitably to presentation at the level of junior high school students. And we believe that junior high school teachers will find it valuable to think through these steps which lead to the final stage where the system that has been constructed may be examined from the point of view of asking the question: What is a good set of postulates which will serve to establish this elegant system adequately and concisely? Our purpose is to develop the familiar body of knowledge associated with the real number system in such a way that it will be crystal clear exactly why each standard procedure is valid.

So far we have developed the addition of whole numbers in a very fundamental manner based on the union of disjoint sets. It will be

58 Extension of Whole Numbers

helpful to recall that in Section 1.10 we have pictured the whole numbers as labels for a set of evenly spaced points on a horizontal straight line where, as a matter of convention, the numbers increase to the right. In a more formal statement, "to each whole number there corresponds a point on the number line." It is equally possible to think of the number, 3, for example, as corresponding to the *right displacement* (pictured as

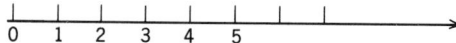

an arrow of proper length) which carries a point 3 units to the right, for example, from 0 to 3 or from 2 to 5 or from 104 to 107. It will be very

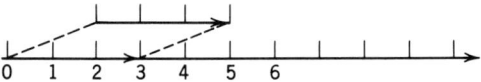

convenient, then, to think of the addition of two whole numbers, for example, $2 + 3 = 5$, as the combination of two right displacements of 2 units and 3 units, respectively, which carries a point from 0 to 5 and therefore represents the single right displacement corresponding to 5

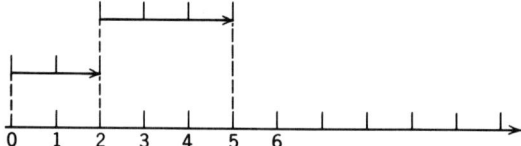

The subtraction operation $5 - 3$ is the procedure of asking ourselves what number added to 3 gives 5 or what right displacement combined with a right displacement of 3 units gives a right displacement of 5 units. An alternative way of arriving at the answer would be to proceed in the reverse direction, as follows: Begin with the final right displacement of 5 units and combine with it a *left displacement* of 3 units, producing a right displacement of 2 units.

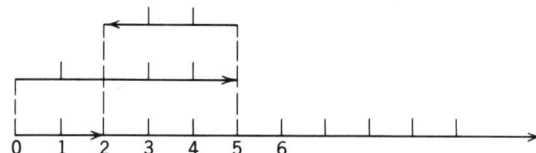

If we return to our original problem of giving a meaning to $6 - 7$, we might ask ourselves what sort of displacement combined with a right displacement of 7 units would give a right displacement of 6 units. Apparently a left displacement of 1 unit would accomplish this result. Let us decide to accept this left displacement of 1 unit as a useful device. What happens when we apply it to the point corresponding to 0? Evidently the point is displaced one unit to the left of 0. It is clear, therefore, that we need to extend the number line to the left of 0 and to label points at unit intervals to the left of 0. In order to have names for these labels, let us invent the numbers $-1, -2, -3, \ldots,$* called "negative one," "negative two," "negative three," etc. This new set, N', of numbers we call the *negative integers* and designate as the set, I, of *integers*, the union of this set, N', and the set, W, of whole numbers, that is, $I = N' \cup W$. The set, N, of natural numbers is often referred to as the set of *positive integers* and if $a \in N, a > 0$.

We have seen that a right displacement of 7 units combined with a left displacement of 1 unit results in a right displacement of 6 units. In other words, a left displacement of 1 unit carries a point from 7 to 6 or from 0 to -1 on the number line. A left displacement of 2 units will carry a point from 0 to -2. Evidently a left displacement of 1 unit combined with a left displacement of 2 units will produce a left displacement of 3 units. By analogy with our interpretation of right displacements we will consider this statement as corresponding to the numerical sentence $(-1) + (-2) = -3$. Similarly $(-3) + (-5) = -8$. Corresponding to 0 is the zero displacement which, when applied to any point, leaves it unchanged. Hence we have

$$8 + 0 = 8$$
$$(-5) + 0 = -5$$
$$(-1) + 1 = 0$$
$$5 + (-5) = 0$$

If we combine a right displacement of 5 units with a left displacement of 8 units we may think of this as a right displacement of 5 units combined with a left displacement of 5 units and a left displacement of 3 units; hence there is produced a left displacement of 3 units and this is written as

$$\begin{aligned} 5 + (-8) &= 5 + [(-5) + (-3)] \\ &= [5 + (-5)] + (-3) \\ &= 0 + (-3) \\ &= -3 \end{aligned}$$

*Sometimes the symbols used to represent negative integers make use of the elevated dash, for example, $^-1, ^-2, ^-3, \ldots,$ in order to avoid any possibility of confusion with the operation of subtraction. It is our belief that the proper interpretation of the dash as a sign of operation or as a part of the symbol for a negative number will be evident from the context.

Similarly
$$(-5) + 8 = (-5) + [5 + 3]$$
$$= [(-5) + 5] + 3$$
$$= 3$$

It will be convenient to think of -1 as the "the negative of 1" (in the sense of "the opposite of 1") as well as "negative 1" and it is clear that to each positive integer there corresponds, as its negative, a negative integer. In fact, the negative integers may be considered as a reflection of the positive integers, when both sets of numbers correspond to points on the number line and the mirror is located at 0 perpendicular to the number line. As a result of this 1:1 correspondence we can say that, to each negative integer there corresponds, as its negative, the positive integer which labels the point displaced an equal distance from zero in the positive direction. For this reason we shall expect to have $-(-1) = 1$ and $-(-b) = b$ for any $b \in I$. In order to avoid confusion we shall read "the negative of b" for the integer $(-b)$, rather than "negative b," since, unless otherwise informed, we would not know whether $(-b)$ belongs to N, N', or $\{0\}$. For example, if $b = 2$, then $b \in N$ and $-b = -2 \in N'$, but if $b = -2$, then $b \in N'$ and $-b = 2 \in N$. Thus $b \in N \iff -b \in N'$ and $-b \in N \iff b \in N'$. The negative of 0 is 0.

Since $8 + (-5) = 3$, the existence of -5 has made it possible to answer the question, $3 - 8 = ?$ In fact the introduction of the negative integers has made subtraction possible, not only for any two whole numbers but also for any two integers. Let us, therefore, extend our previous definition of subtraction (see Section 1.11) as follows, making the set of integers closed under subtraction: If b and c are any integers, $b - c = d \iff \exists d \in I \ni b = c + d$. Hence $5 - (-8) = 13$ since $13 + (-8) = 5$. Note, also, that $5 + 8 = 13$, as a result of which the reader will not be surprised at the general result $b - (-c) = b + c$ which we shall now prove.

By the definition of subtraction, if $b, c \in I$, we know $b - (-c) = d \iff b = d + (-c)$, where $d \in I$.

Hence
$$b + c = [d + (-c)] + c$$
$$= d + [(-c) + c]$$
$$= d + 0$$
$$= d$$
$$= b - (-c)$$

We have seen in this section that to every integer b there corresponds the negative of b, that is, $-b$. Clearly $b + (-b) = 0$. Any number which, when added to a given number, gives 0, is called an *additive inverse* of the given number. Hence $-b$ is an additive inverse of b.

Questions. 1. Can you show that the additive inverse of b is unique? (*Hint:* Assume that an integer b' behaves similarly to $-b$.)
2. What is the additive inverse of $(-b)$?

Finally let us extend our definition of order to the set of integers as follows:

If $a, b \in I, a > b \iff \exists c \in N \ni a = b + c$. For example, $-3 > -5$ because $\exists c$ (namely 2) $\in N \ni -3 = -5 + c$; $2 > -6$ because $2 = -6 + 8$. Then, for $b \in I$, $b \in N' \iff 0 > b$. Evidently for any integer b, either (1) $b > 0$, (2) $b = 0$, or (3) $b < 0$.

Question. In the above definition of order for integers, why have we specified that $c \in N$?

EXERCISES

1. Find the value of
   (a) $9 + (-3)$ (b) $9 - 3$ (c) $(-9) + (-3)$ (d) $(-9) + 3$
2. Arrange the following in order of increasing magnitude:
   $$-1, -8, -2, 10, -5, 0, -15, 3, -3$$
3. If $b = -5$, evaluate
   (a) $b + 3$ (b) $b + 8$ (c) $(-b) + (-3)$ (d) $(-b) + (-8)$
4. Prove that $b - c = b + (-c)$
5. Prove that $a > b \iff a + c > b + c$ for $a, b, c \in I$

3.03 ABSOLUTE VALUE

Whenever we add integers, positive or negative, we shall *think* of right and left displacements on the number line. However this would not be a satisfactory basis for determining properties of our addition procedure.

Since right displacements correspond to positive integers and left displacements correspond to negative integers, we find it very useful to be able to describe in terms of the given integer the distance involved in the displacement, that is, the length of the displacement. We define $|b|$, read "the absolute value of b," to be the number of units in the displacement or, more generally, the length of the displacement corresponding to b, that is, the length of the displacement of a point from 0 to b. The number of units in this displacement will be either 0 or a positive integer. Hence $|5| = 5$, $|0| = 0$ and $|-3| = 3$. We may say that $|b|$ is the larger of b and $-b$ and a more formal definition is:

$$|b| = b \text{ if } b \in W, \text{ that is, if } b \geq 0$$
$$= -b \text{ if } b \in N', \text{ that is, if } b < 0$$

Let us consider the following six examples in the light of the definition of absolute value given above:

$$3 + 5 = 8 = |3| + |5|$$
$$5 + (-3) = 2 = |5| - |-3|$$
$$3 + (-5) = -2 = -(|-5| - |3|)$$
$$(-3) + 5 = 2 = |5| - |-3|$$
$$(-5) + 3 = -2 = -(|-5| - |3|)$$
$$(-3) + (-5) = -8 = -(|-3| + |-5|)$$

We have now discovered how we wish to proceed in adding integers and we are in a position to formulate a rule for addition, as contrasted with being given one, which will incorporate our discovery. We shall have to consider four cases and it should be emphasized again that our purpose in formalizing the addition of integers is to enable us to discover its properties more efficiently and *not* to devise a procedure for computation.

When $a \geq 0$ and $b \geq 0$ we want $a + b = |a| + |b|$ (1)
When $a \geq 0$ and $b < 0$ we want $a + b = |a| - |b|$ if $|a| \geq |b|$ (2)
$= -(|b| - |a|)$ if $|b| > |a|$ (3)
When $a < 0$ and $b \geq 0$ we want $a + b = |b| - |a|$ if $|b| \geq |a|$ (4)
$= -(|a| - |b|)$ if $|a| > |b|$ (5)
When $a < 0$ and $b < 0$ we want $a + b = -(|a| + |b|)$ (6)

It should be clear that this definition has been set up in terms of operations on whole numbers which we know how to carry through and with whose properties we are familiar.

Questions. 1. Do you believe the addition of integers is commutative? If we were to attempt to demonstrate this fact completely, we would need to consider four cases, one of which will be illustrated below:

To show: $c + d = d + c$, where $c \geq 0$, $d < 0$, and $|d| > |c|$
By definition, $c + d = -(|d| - |c|)$, (by line 3)
$d + c = -(|d| - |c|)$, (by line 5)
$c + d = d + c$,
where $c \geq 0$, $d < 0$ and $|d| > |c|$

The other three cases are handled similarly.

2. Do you believe the addition of integers is associative? *(See Question 1.)*
3. Does 0 continue to act as the additive identity? and uniquely?

As was the case with addition of integers, we do not want to merely hand down the rule for multiplying integers. On the contrary we prefer to motivate the discovery of the desired procedure. In order to find out how we would like to have multiplication behave we are going to assume that several properties which held for whole numbers, continue to hold for integers. These are in particular, the associative law of addition, the distributive law of multiplication with respect to addition, and the additive and multiplicative properties of zero. Hence, as a result of these assumptions, we have

$$\begin{aligned} 0 &= (-1)(0) \\ &= (-1)[(-1) + 1] \\ &= (-1)(-1) + (-1)(1) \\ \therefore 1(1) &= [(-1)(-1) + (-1)(1)] + 1(1) \\ \therefore \quad 1 &= (-1)(-1) + [(-1) + 1]1 \\ &= (-1)(-1) + 0 \\ &= (-1)(-1) \end{aligned}$$

Similarly, we have

$$\begin{aligned} (-3)[(-2) + 2] &= 0 \\ \therefore (-3)(-2) + (-3)(2) &= 0 \\ \therefore [(-3)(-2) + (-3)2] + 3(2) &= 3(2) \\ \therefore (-3)(-2) + [(-3) + 3]2 &= 3(2) \\ \therefore (-3)(-2) &= 3(2) \end{aligned}$$

and

$$\begin{aligned} 3(-5) &= 3(-5) + [3(5) + (-(3)(5))] \\ &= 3[-5 + 5] + [-(3)(5)] \\ &= -(3)(5) \end{aligned}$$

and, in general,

$$\begin{aligned} (-a)(-b) &= (-a)(-b) + a[(-b) + b] \\ &= [(-a)(-b) + a(-b)] + ab \\ &= [(-a) + a](-b) + ab \\ &= 0 + ab \\ &= ab \end{aligned}$$

It appears from the above that we are going to want the product of two negative numbers to be positive and the product of a positive

64 Extension of Whole Numbers

number and a negative number to be negative. If these ideas seem surprising to the reader it may be helpful for him to examine the patterns exhibited in the following sequences of statements:

(a) $3 \times 4 = 12$
 $2 \times 4 = 8$
 $1 \times 4 = 4$
 $0 \times 4 = 0$
 $(-1) \times 4 = ?$
 $(-2) \times 4 = ?$
 $(-3) \times 4 = ?$
 $(-4) \times 4 = ?$

(b) $(-4) \times 4 = -16$
 $(-4) \times 3 = -12$
 $(-4) \times 2 = -8$
 $(-4) \times 1 = -4$
 $(-4) \times 0 = 0$
 $(-4) \times (-1) = ?$
 $(-4) \times (-2) = ?$
 $(-4) \times (-3) = ?$

On the basis of the above experience it would seem reasonable for us to adopt the following as a satisfactory rule for multiplying integers: If b and c are integers, we define

$$b \times c = |b| \times |c| \text{ if } b \geq 0 \text{ and } c \geq 0$$
$$\text{or if } b < 0 \text{ and } c < 0$$
$$= -(|b| \times |c|) \text{ if } b \geq 0 \text{ and } c < 0$$
$$\text{or if } b < 0 \text{ and } c \geq 0$$

For example,

$$2 \times 3 = 6 = |2| \times |3|$$
$$(-2) \times (-3) = 6 = |-2| \times |-3|$$
$$2 \times (-3) = -6 = -(|2| \times |-3|)$$
$$(-2) \times (3) = -6 = -(|-2| \times |3|)$$

We also have $\qquad |bc| = |b||c|$

Questions.
1. Do you believe the multiplication of integers is commutative?
2. Do you believe the multiplication of integers is associative?
3. Do you believe the multiplication of integers is distributive with respect to addition?
4. Does 1 continue to act as a multiplicative identity? and uniquely?
5. Does 0 continue to multiply in the usual way?

The statement $(-a) = (-1)a$ is a most important operating rule and one from which many others are immediately derivable, provided we are free to use theorems referred to in the above *Questions*. It may be established as follows (with reasons given for each step):

$(-a) = (-a) + 0$ [additive identity]
$= (-a) + [1 + (-1)]a$ [property of additive inverse and multiplication by 0]
$= (-a) + [1a + (-1)a]$ [distributive property of multiplication over addition]
$= [-a + a] + (-1)a$ [associative property of addition and property of multiplicative identity]
$= 0 + (-1)a$ [additive inverse]
$= (-1)a$ [additive identity]

EXERCISES

1. Evaluate the following:
   (a) $(-9) + 7$
   (b) $(-99) + (-101)$
   (c) $47 + (-39)$
   (d) $(-1329) + (1329)$
   (e) $29 - 37$
   (f) $(-43) - 37$
2. Evaluate the following:
   (a) $29 - (-37)$
   (b) $(-43) - (-37)$
   (c) $(-5) \times 7$
   (d) $6 \times (-8)$
   (e) $(-9) \times (-13)$
3. We wish to compare the three expressions, $|a + b|$, $|a| + |b|$, and $|a| - |b|$.
   (a) Are two of these expressions ever equal? Are all three ever equal? Give examples.
   (b) Is one of these expressions ever larger than the other two? Is one of these expressions ever smaller than the other two?
   (c) By making use of your results in (a) and (b), can you insert the proper symbol ($=, <, \leq, >,$ or $\geq$) between pairs of the above expressions?
4. (a) If a and b are integers, prove that $(-a)b = -(ab) = a(-b)$.
   (b) Prove that the distributive property for multiplication with respect to subtraction continues to hold for integers, that is, $(b - c)d = bd - cd$.
5. For what integers a, b, c, is it true that $a \cdot b \cdot c = a + b + c$?

3.04 RELATIONS AND EQUIVALENCE CLASSES

In Section 1.06 we defined the Cartesian product of sets A and B as $A \times B = \{(a,b) | a \in A \text{ and } b \in B\}$. We now wish to define a *relation* as any subset of the Cartesian product of two sets. For example, the set $\{(1,3), (1,4), (1,5), (2,5)\}$ constitutes a relation; likewise the set $\{(x, x^2) | x \in N\}$. We sometimes indicate a relation by R and if $(a, b) \in$ R we may also write $a \text{ R } b$. Hence, in the first of the above examples, 1 R 3, 1 R 4, 1 R 5, 2 R 5.

Frequently we do not actually specify the ordered pairs but simply indicate how they may be obtained. For example, we may say that $a \text{ R } b$ if and only if $b = a^2$ or that $a \text{ R } b$ if and only if $|a - b|$ is an even number (a and b natural numbers). In this context we may say that, in our first example, R is the relation of being the square, and in the second example R is the relation of being congruent modulo 2 (see Section 1.18).

An equivalence relation is a relation which possesses the following three properties:

(1) Reflexivity: $a \text{ R } a$
(2) Symmetry: If $a \text{ R } b$ then $b \text{ R } a$
(3) Transitivity: If $a \text{ R } b$ and $b \text{ R } c$, then $a \text{ R } c$

For example, if the relation, R, means "is congruent to modulo 2" or "lives in the same city as," R is easily seen to be an equivalence relation in each case. On the other hand, if R should mean "is five times as large as" or "is an uncle of," then R is not an equivalence relation in either of these cases. In fact both of the latter examples fail to satisfy even one of the requirements of an equivalence relation.

Question. In which of the following examples of a relation, R, is R an equivalence relation?

(a) $R \equiv$ is the square of
(b) $R \equiv$ is the same age as
(c) $R \equiv$ is a friend of

We see from the above condition (1) that an equivalence relation is necessarily a subset of the Cartesian product of two equal sets. For this reason we often refer to an equivalence relation "on a set." Such a relation has the effect of separating the set on which it operates, into distinct subsets known as *equivalence classes*, of related elements. For example, if the set in question is the set N of natural numbers and $a \text{ R } b \iff a - b = 3K$, K an integer, or $a \equiv b \pmod 3$ (see Section 1.18), then the set N is separated into the three equivalence classes: $\{1,4,7,10,\ldots\}, \{2,5,8,11,\ldots\}$, and $\{3,6,9,12,\ldots\}$.

Question. Consider the set of all the cities in the United States. If $a \text{ R } b \iff a$ and b are cities in the same state, what are the equivalence classes with respect to this relation?

EXERCISES

1. Is R an equivalence relation if R stands for
   (a) is an aunt of
   (b) is the same sex as
   (c) is 5 more than 3 times as large as
   (d) lives within a mile of
2. Obtain the equivalence classes in the set of natural numbers, with respect to the relation R: "is congruent to (mod 5)."

3.05 RATIONAL NUMBERS

In Section 3.02 we enlarged the system of whole numbers by inventing the negative integers, in order to provide solutions for sentences like $x + g = h$ where $g > h$.

In Section 1.13, where b was any whole number and c any natural number such that c is a factor of b, we defined $b \div c = \frac{b}{c} = d \iff b = cd$ for some whole number d. Hence in this case d is a solution of the sentence $cx = b$. We would like to have a solution of the sentence $cx = b$ when b and c are *any* integers such that $c \neq 0$. Therefore we wish to invent new numbers to provide solutions for sentences like $cx = b$, with $c \neq 0$, in the case where c is not necessarily a factor of b.

The common notation, of course, for the solution of such an equation, for example, $3x = 2$ is $\frac{2}{3}$ or 2/3. However we would like to make clear that we are starting without any preconceived ideas concerning the properties of these numbers and for this reason we shall use the notation $\left[\frac{2}{3}\right]$ instead of $\frac{2}{3}$. In general, then, we shall denote the invented solution of the equation $cx = b$, $c \neq 0$, by $\left[\frac{b}{c}\right]$. These numbers $\left[\frac{b}{c}\right]$, which could be thought of equally well as ordered pairs (b, c) of integers, form a new class of numbers called *fractions*.

If the two equations $a = bx$ and $c = dy$, with $b \neq 0$ and $d \neq 0$, should have the same solution m, we would have $a = bm$ and $c = dm$. If we assume that the associative and commutative properties of multiplication continue to hold with the new numbers, then we have $ad = bdm$ and $bc = bdm$ from which we conclude that $ad = bc$. With this as motivation we are led to make the following definition:

$\left[\frac{a}{b}\right] \approx \left[\frac{c}{d}\right]$ (read "fraction a divided by b is equivalent to fraction c divided by d") $\iff ad = bc$

Let us note the following facts concerning this relation between fractions:

(1) $\left[\dfrac{a}{b}\right] \approx \left[\dfrac{a}{b}\right]$ since $ab = ba$

(2) $\left[\dfrac{a}{b}\right] \approx \left[\dfrac{c}{d}\right] \Longrightarrow \left[\dfrac{c}{d}\right] \approx \left[\dfrac{a}{b}\right]$ since $ad = bc \Longrightarrow cb = da$

(3) $\left[\dfrac{a}{b}\right] \approx \left[\dfrac{c}{d}\right]$ and $\left[\dfrac{c}{d}\right] \approx \left[\dfrac{f}{g}\right] \Longrightarrow \left[\dfrac{a}{b}\right] \approx \left[\dfrac{f}{g}\right]$

That (3) is true may be seen as follows: We are given $ad = bc$ and $cg = df$ with $b, d, g \neq 0$ and we wish to prove that $ag = bf$.
(a) Suppose $a = 0$; then $bc = ad = 0$. Since $b \neq 0$, it follows that $c = 0$ (see Section 2.04). Hence $df = cg = 0$. And since $d \neq 0$, it follows that $f = 0$. Since $a = f = 0$, it follows that $ag = bf (= 0)$ as required. (b) Suppose $a \neq 0$; then $ad = bc \neq 0$ (see Section 1.09) and hence $c \neq 0$ (see Section 2.04).
Therefore $ad = bc$ and $cg = df \Longrightarrow (ad)(cg) = (bc)(df)$
$\Longrightarrow (ag)(cd) = (bf)(cd)$
$\Longrightarrow ag = bf$ since $cd \neq 0$ (see Sections 1.09 and 2.04).

Therefore the "equivalence" of fractions is actually an equivalence relation as defined in Section 3.04 and provides us with the means of forming equivalence classes of equivalent fractions. To such an equivalence class we give the name *rational number*. For example, the set $\left\{\ldots, \left[\dfrac{-4}{-6}\right], \left[\dfrac{-2}{-3}\right], \left[\dfrac{2}{3}\right], \left[\dfrac{4}{6}\right], \left[\dfrac{6}{9}\right], \ldots\right\}$ is such a set of equivalent fractions since $(-2)(3) = (-3)(2), (-4)(9) = (-6)(6)$, etc.

From a set theoretical point of view there is a vast difference between an equivalence class and any one of its elements. Hence we would like to use the symbol $\left\langle\dfrac{r}{s}\right\rangle$ where r and s are integers with $s \neq 0$, to represent an equivalence class of the type described above, that is a rational number $\left\langle\dfrac{r}{s}\right\rangle$. How shall we choose r and s in $\left\langle\dfrac{r}{s}\right\rangle$ to represent the rational number? It would be most surprising and not at all reasonable if we should have $\left\langle\dfrac{2}{3}\right\rangle \neq \left\langle\dfrac{-4}{-6}\right\rangle$. Actually *any* element $\left[\dfrac{r}{s}\right]$ of a particular equivalence class can be used to supply the symbol $\left\langle\dfrac{r}{s}\right\rangle$ for the set. For example, since $\left\langle\dfrac{2}{3}\right\rangle = \left\{\left[\dfrac{x}{y}\right] \mid \left[\dfrac{x}{y}\right] \approx \left[\dfrac{2}{3}\right]\right\}$ and $\left\langle\dfrac{-4}{-6}\right\rangle = \left\{\left[\dfrac{x}{y}\right] \mid \left[\dfrac{x}{y}\right] \approx \left[\dfrac{-4}{-6}\right]\right\}$, we have $\langle\frac{2}{3}\rangle = \langle\frac{4}{6}\rangle = \{\ldots, [\frac{-4}{-6}], [\frac{-2}{-3}], [\frac{2}{3}], [\frac{4}{6}], [\frac{6}{9}], \ldots\}$. The general result is embodied in the following

Theorem. If a, b, c, d are integers and $b, d \neq 0$,

$$[\frac{a}{b}] \approx [\frac{c}{d}] \iff \langle\frac{a}{b}\rangle = \langle\frac{c}{d}\rangle$$

Proof. (1) First, let us prove the implication ($\Rightarrow$). Since $[\frac{a}{b}] \approx [\frac{c}{d}]$, we know that $[\frac{a}{b}] \in \langle\frac{c}{d}\rangle$, and, by transitivity, every element of $\langle\frac{a}{b}\rangle$ is equivalent to $[\frac{c}{d}]$. Therefore $\langle\frac{a}{b}\rangle \subseteq \langle\frac{c}{d}\rangle$.

Similarly $[\frac{c}{d}] \in \langle\frac{a}{b}\rangle$, and by an identical argument we see that $\langle\frac{c}{d}\rangle \subseteq \langle\frac{a}{b}\rangle$. Therefore $\langle\frac{a}{b}\rangle = \langle\frac{c}{d}\rangle$.

(2) Now let us prove the other implication ($\Leftarrow$). Since $\langle\frac{a}{b}\rangle = \{[\frac{x}{y}] \mid [\frac{x}{y}] \approx [\frac{a}{b}]\}$ and $\langle\frac{c}{d}\rangle = \{[\frac{x}{y}] \mid [\frac{x}{y}] \approx [\frac{c}{d}]\}$, if we are given that $\langle\frac{a}{b}\rangle = \langle\frac{c}{d}\rangle$, then we know that $[\frac{a}{b}] \in \langle\frac{c}{d}\rangle$ and $[\frac{c}{d}] \in \langle\frac{a}{b}\rangle$. Therefore $[\frac{a}{b}] \approx [\frac{c}{d}]$. Thus the result is established that $[\frac{a}{b}] \approx [\frac{c}{d}] \iff \langle\frac{a}{b}\rangle = \langle\frac{c}{d}\rangle$. Since $[\frac{a}{b}] \approx [\frac{c}{d}] \iff ad = bc$. We can say, further, that $\langle\frac{a}{b}\rangle = \langle\frac{c}{d}\rangle \iff ad = bc$.

We have, then, two concepts, the fraction $[\frac{a}{b}]$ and the rational number $\langle\frac{a}{b}\rangle$, which share the following relationship: $[\frac{a}{b}] \approx [\frac{c}{d}] \iff \langle\frac{a}{b}\rangle = \langle\frac{c}{d}\rangle$. Although we have chosen to point out the basic differences in the two concepts, in practice we are accustomed to do away with the brackets and to use the symbol "$\frac{a}{b}$" to represent either the fraction or the rational number. For example, we shall think of $\frac{2}{3}$ as one member of the set of equivalent fractions, each of which is a solution of the equation $3x = 2$, as well as the rational number which represents the equivalence class.

70   Extension of Whole Numbers

We recognize that there is a certain amount of controversy concerned with the proper use of the terms "fraction" and "rational number." It is our point of view that we may be somewhat informal with regard to our use of these terms without losing sight of the fundamental importance of each.

When we say that $\frac{2}{3} = \frac{4}{6}$ we are saying that $\frac{2}{3}$ and $\frac{4}{6}$ name the same rational number, namely the solution of the sentence $3x = 2$. With respect to the fractional numeral $\frac{b}{c}$, we shall refer to b as the *numerator* and to c as the *denominator* and this is what we shall mean when we speak of the numerator and denominator of a fraction.

Of particular importance will be the fact that $\frac{d}{d} = 1$ for $d \neq 0$ and also that $\frac{b}{1} = b$ where $b, d \in I$. As a result of this latter equality we can say that the integers form a subset of the set R' of rational numbers. Alternatively it is sometimes stated that the set $\{b|b \text{ is an integer}\}$ is isomorphic to the set $\left\{\frac{b}{1} | b \text{ is an integer}\right\}$.

As yet we do not know where on the number line to place the rational numbers we have just brought into existence. Let us defer this problem until we have decided how we wish to add rational numbers. One fact should be apparent by now—since integers are essentially the same as rational numbers with 1 as denominator we would want the rational numbers, which include the integers, to behave in addition and in multiplication in a manner consistent with the behavior of the integers. Hence in our search for a suitable addition rule we might proceed as follows. Recall that

$$\frac{a}{b} = x \iff a = bx$$

$$\frac{c}{d} = y \iff c = dy$$

Here x and y stand for the rational numbers for which we would like to define the sum, $x + y$. Let us assume that we can multiply a and bx by d, obtaining $ad = (bd)x$. In arriving at the right side of the equation, we have also assumed that the commutative and associative properties hold for multiplication of numbers in our enlarged universe (the set of rational numbers).

Question. Can you show that $(bx)d = (bd)x$?

Similarly, $bc = (bd)y$ and, if we also assume distributivity, $ad + bc = bd(x + y)$. This latter equation is equivalent to

$$\frac{ad + bc}{bd} = x + y$$

With this motivation let us decide to adopt the addition rule, $\frac{a}{b} + \frac{c}{d} = \frac{ad + bc}{bd}$, where a and c are any integers and b and d are any nonzero integers. (If anyone is tempted to imagine that we have "proved" rather than defined the addition rule, he should note again the many assumptions made in arriving at the motivating equation.)

Questions. 1. Can you show that the addition of rational numbers is commutative and associative?

2. Can you verify that $0 + \frac{a}{b} = \frac{a}{b}$?

We are now in a position to note that, for example,

$$\frac{1}{2} + \frac{1}{2} = \frac{2 + 2}{4}$$
$$= \frac{4}{4}$$
$$= 1$$

Hence it would be most natural to locate the point on the number line corresponding to $\frac{1}{2}$ at the center of the interval from 0 to 1, so that a displacement of $\frac{1}{2}$ combined with a second displacement of $\frac{1}{2}$ would be equivalent to a single displacement of 1. Similarly

$$\frac{3}{2} + \frac{1}{2} = \frac{6 + 2}{4} \quad \text{and} \quad \left(\frac{1}{3} + \frac{1}{3}\right) + \frac{1}{3} = \frac{6}{9} + \frac{1}{3}$$
$$= \frac{8}{4} \qquad\qquad\qquad\qquad = \frac{18 + 9}{27}$$
$$= 2 \qquad\qquad\qquad\qquad\quad = \frac{27}{27}$$
$$\qquad\qquad\qquad\qquad\qquad\quad = 1$$

It would be laborious to attempt to be exhaustive in this motivation, but it is hoped that these considerations would lead one to begin to fill in the unit intervals between integers with points corresponding to rational numbers such as $\frac{1}{2}, \frac{1}{3}, \frac{1}{4}, \frac{2}{3}, \frac{3}{4}, \frac{3}{2}$, etc. It should be pointed out that although the intervals may appear to be "filled up" with points corresponding to rational numbers, this is far from being true as we

72   Extension of Whole Numbers

shall show later—a great many points are not yet labeled, even if we could put in all the rational numbers.

Let us proceed in an exactly analogous fashion to motivate the definition of multiplication of rational numbers.

Again

$$\frac{a}{b} = x \iff a = bx$$

$$\frac{c}{d} = y \iff c = dy$$

Then

$$ac = (bx)dy$$
$$= (bd)xy \iff \frac{ac}{bd} = xy$$

Hence this illustration suggests to us the following multiplication rule for rational numbers:

$\frac{a}{b} \times \frac{c}{d} = \frac{a \times c}{b \times d}$, where a and c are integers and b and d are any non-zero integers.

Questions. 1. Can you prove that the multiplication of rational numbers is commutative, associative, and distributive with respect to addition?
2. Can you show that $1 \times \frac{a}{b} = \frac{a}{b}$?
3. Can you show that $0 \times \frac{a}{b} = 0$?

We may look at the number $\frac{8}{4}$ from the point of view either of the definition of division in which

$$\frac{8}{4} = 2 \iff 8 = 4 \times 2$$

or of the multiplication of rational numbers in which

$$\frac{8}{4} = \frac{2 \times 4}{1 \times 4}$$
$$= \frac{2}{1} \times \frac{4}{4}$$
$$= 2 \times 1$$
$$= 2$$

Here we see that what has long been known, colloquially, as "cancellation" is, in reality, the separation of a factor of 1 from the remaining part of the product. The fact that, for example, $\frac{4}{4}$ is a multiplying factor in the above example is of the greatest significance. If this point is clearly understood, a student should never be tempted to "cancel" a's in a rational expression like $\dfrac{2a+bc}{3a}$.

It is important to note that when we are adding or multiplying fractions, any fraction may be replaced by one equivalent to it. For example,

$$\frac{2}{3}+\frac{5}{7}=\frac{14}{21}+\frac{15}{21}; \qquad \frac{4}{6}\times\frac{15}{21}=\frac{2}{3}\times\frac{5}{7}$$

In general we have

$$\frac{a}{b}=\frac{a'}{b'} \iff ab'=a'b$$

and

$$\frac{c}{d}=\frac{c'}{d'} \iff cd'=c'd$$

Therefore

(1) $\dfrac{a}{b}+\dfrac{c}{d}=\dfrac{ad+bc}{bd}\times\dfrac{b'd'}{b'd'}$ and (2) $\dfrac{a}{b}\times\dfrac{c}{d}=\dfrac{ac}{bd}\times\dfrac{b'd'}{b'd'}$

$\qquad\qquad\qquad =\dfrac{ab'dd'+cd'bb'}{bdb'd'} \qquad\qquad\qquad =\dfrac{ab'cd'}{bdb'd'}$

$\qquad\qquad\qquad =\dfrac{a'bdd'+c'dbb'}{b'd'bd} \qquad\qquad\qquad =\dfrac{a'bc'd}{bdb'd'}$

$\qquad\qquad\qquad =\dfrac{a'd'+b'c'}{b'd'}\times\dfrac{bd}{bd} \qquad\qquad =\dfrac{a'c'}{b'd'}\times\dfrac{bd}{bd}$

$\qquad\qquad\qquad =\dfrac{a'}{b'}+\dfrac{c'}{d'} \qquad\qquad\qquad\qquad =\dfrac{a'}{b'}\times\dfrac{c'}{d'}$

Incidentally the above property is not one which would be shared by every definition which might have been given for addition of fractions. Let us suppose, for a moment, that the following definition had been given:

$$\frac{a}{b}\oplus\frac{c}{d}=\frac{a+c}{b+d}$$

Then $\dfrac{2}{3}\oplus\dfrac{1}{2}=\dfrac{3}{5}$ whereas $\dfrac{4}{6}\oplus\dfrac{3}{6}=\dfrac{7}{12}$. Since $\dfrac{3}{5}\neq\dfrac{7}{12}$ this counterexample demonstrates that the property fails to hold in this "pseudoaddition."

74 Extension of Whole Numbers

Question. Can you show why $\dfrac{b}{c} + \dfrac{d}{c} = \dfrac{b+d}{c}$?

It should be noted that the additional rule

$$\frac{a}{b} + \frac{c}{d} = \frac{ad+bc}{bd}$$

may be interpreted as

$$\frac{a}{b} + \frac{c}{d} = \frac{a}{b} \times \frac{d}{d} + \frac{b}{b} \times \frac{c}{d}$$
$$= \frac{ad}{bd} + \frac{bc}{bd}$$
$$= \frac{ad+bc}{bd}$$

by reference to the above *Question*.

Question. When b and d have a common factor f, specifically $b = b_1 f$ and $d = d_1 f$, how would you establish the result

$$\frac{a}{b} + \frac{c}{d} = \frac{ad_1 + cb_1}{b_1 d_1 f}?$$

We have seen in the previous two paragraphs two very important ways in which the fraction $\dfrac{d}{d}$ may be used to advantage: (1) in reducing a fraction and (2) in obtaining a fraction equal to the original but having a larger denominator. We should note that

$$a\left(\frac{1}{b}\right) = \frac{a}{1} \times \frac{1}{b}$$
$$= \frac{a \times 1}{1 \times b}$$
$$= \frac{a}{b}$$

Hence

$$b\left(\frac{1}{b}\right) = \frac{b}{b} = 1$$

Any number which gives 1 as the product when multiplied with a given number is called a *multiplicative inverse* of the given number. Hence $\dfrac{1}{b}$ is a multiplicative inverse of b, provided, of course, that $b \neq 0$. We also call $\dfrac{1}{b}$ the *reciprocal* of b. The multiplicative inverse of b is often written b^{-1} and read "b inverse."

Questions. 1. Can you show that the multiplicative inverse of b is unique?

2. Can you show that b is the reciprocal of $\frac{1}{b}$?

3. What is the reciprocal of $\frac{a}{b}$ when $a \neq 0$ (and, of course, $b \neq 0$)?

4. How can it best be demonstrated that $\dfrac{\frac{a}{b}}{\frac{c}{d}} = \dfrac{ad}{bc}$?

Just as a negative integer corresponds to each positive integer, similarly a negative rational number will correspond to each positive rational number. Each will be said to be the negative of the other, and each is the additive inverse of the other. Thus $\left(-\frac{a}{b}\right) + \frac{a}{b} = 0$.

Questions. 1. Can you show that the additive inverse of $\frac{a}{b}$ is unique?

2. Can you use the information in *Question* 1 to show that $-\left(\frac{a}{b}\right) = (-1)\left(\frac{a}{b}\right)$?

3. Can you show that $\dfrac{-a}{b} = \dfrac{a}{-b} = (-a)\dfrac{1}{b} = a\left(\dfrac{1}{-b}\right) = -\left(\dfrac{a}{b}\right)$?

4. (a) Can you define subtraction of rational numbers in keeping with the definitions given in Sections 1.11 and 3.02? (b) Can you show that $\dfrac{a}{b} - \dfrac{c}{d} = \dfrac{a}{b} + \left(-\dfrac{c}{d}\right)$, where a, b, c, d are integers, $b, d \neq 0$? (c) Is multiplication of rational numbers distributive with respect to subtraction?

We are now in a position to give the solution set of any open sentence of the type $ax + b = cx + d$, where a, b, c, d, are integers and $a \neq c$.

Question. Would we be justified in making the above statement where a, b, c, d are any rational numbers, with $a \neq c$?

In fact, not only does the necessary rational number exist as a

76   Extension of Whole Numbers

replacement for x but also we are able to construct it. We proceed as follows: If there exists an x such that $6x + 7 = 2 + 3x$, then

$$(6x + 7) + (-7) = (2 + 3x) + (-7)$$
∴ $$6x + [7 + (-7)] = 2 + [3x + (-7)]$$
$$6x + 0 = 2 + [(-7) + 3x]$$
$$6x = [2 + (-7)] + 3x$$
$$6x = -5 + 3x$$
∴ $$6x + (-3x) = (-5 + 3x) + (-3x)$$
∴ $$[6 + (-3)]x = -5 + [3x + (-3x)]$$
∴ $$3x = -5 + 0$$
$$3x = -5$$
∴ $$\tfrac{1}{3}(3x) = \tfrac{1}{3}(-5)$$
∴ $$x = -\tfrac{5}{3}$$

Hence we have discovered that if there is an x satisfying the open sentence $6x + 7 = 2 + 3x$, then that x is $-\tfrac{5}{3}$. By so doing we have also established the uniqueness of $x = -\tfrac{5}{3}$ since, if x' were any other x satisfying the given sentence, a repetition of the above algebraic steps would yield $x' = -\tfrac{5}{3} = x$. It must now be verified that $x = -\tfrac{5}{3}$ is actually the solution. We see that, if $x = -\tfrac{5}{3}$,

$$6x + 7 = 6\left(-\tfrac{5}{3}\right) + 7$$
$$= -10 + 7$$
$$= -3$$

and

$$2 + 3x = 2 + 3\left(-\tfrac{5}{3}\right)$$
$$= 2 - 5$$
$$= -3$$

Therefore the solution set of the open sentence $6x + 7 = 2 + 3x$ is $\left\{-\tfrac{5}{3}\right\}$.

Suppose we are given that $ab = 0$, where a and b represent rational numbers. If $a \neq 0$, then $\tfrac{1}{a}$ exists and

$$\tfrac{1}{a}(ab) = \tfrac{1}{a}(0)$$
∴ $$(\tfrac{1}{a} \times a)b = 0$$
∴ $$1 \times b = b = 0$$

Similarly, if $b \neq 0$, we would obtain $a = 0$. We know that if $a = 0$ or $b = 0$, then $ab = 0$. Hence we verify again, as we did in Section 2.04, that the following is a true theorem: $ab = 0 \iff a = 0$ or $b = 0$. (See Sections 1.09, 1.11, and 2.04).

Since $\frac{5}{3} = \frac{2}{3} + \frac{3}{3}$, we would expect to find the point corresponding to $\frac{5}{3}$ lying on the number line to the right of the point corresponding to $\frac{2}{3}$ and we would state that $\frac{5}{3} > \frac{2}{3}$. As a second example, in order to compare $\frac{4}{3}$ with $\frac{3}{2}$ we may write $\frac{4}{3} = \frac{4}{3} \times \frac{2}{2} = \frac{8}{6}$ and $\frac{3}{2} = \frac{3}{2} \times \frac{3}{3} = \frac{9}{6}$. Since $\frac{9}{6} = \frac{8}{6} + \frac{1}{6}$, we would conclude that $\frac{3}{2} > \frac{4}{3}$.

Therefore we would like to extend our definition of order to rational numbers. In order to do so we want to define the *positive rational numbers* as the rational numbers corresponding to points lying to the right of 0 on the number line. It is true then that for *any* rational number $\frac{a}{b}$,

(1) either $\frac{a}{b}$ is positive or $\frac{a}{b} = 0$ or $-\frac{a}{b}$ is positive (one and only one condition).

(2) if $\frac{a}{b}$ and $\frac{c}{d}$ are positive, *then both their sum and their product are positive rational numbers.* If $\frac{a}{b}$ is positive, we write $\frac{a}{b} > 0$.

Then, in general, we shall define $\frac{a}{b} > \frac{c}{d} \iff \exists$ a positive rational number $\frac{g}{h} \ni \frac{a}{b} = \frac{c}{d} + \frac{g}{h}$. For example $\frac{3}{2} > \frac{4}{3}$ since $\frac{3}{2} = \frac{4}{3} + \frac{1}{6}$ and $\frac{-4}{3} > \frac{-3}{2}$ since $\frac{-4}{3} = \frac{-3}{2} + \frac{1}{6}$.

Questions. 1. If $b > 0$, can you show that $\frac{1}{b} > 0$? Similarly, if $b < 0$, can you show that $\frac{1}{b} < 0$?

2. If $a > b$, can you show that $ac > bc$, if $c > 0$, and $ac < bc$ if $c < 0$, where $a, b, c \in I$? where $a, b, c \in R'$, the set of rational numbers?

3. If $x \neq 0$ can you show that $x^2 > 0$?

4. If a, b, c, d are all positive integers, is it true that $\frac{a}{b} > \frac{c}{d} \iff ad > bc$?

We shall have some additional remarks to make in Chapter 7 concerning rational numbers, including an answer to the question, "How many rational numbers are there"?

78   Extension of Whole Numbers

EXERCISES

1. Simplify

   (a) $\dfrac{a}{b} - \dfrac{a}{a+b}$

   (b) $\dfrac{a}{a-b} - \dfrac{b}{b-a}$

   (c) $\dfrac{a}{1 - \dfrac{b}{a+b}}$

   (d) $\dfrac{a^2}{1-b} - \dfrac{b^2}{1-a}$

2. Find the solution set for the sentence $8x - 5 = 3x - 9$.

3. Prove that

   (a) $\dfrac{a}{b} = \dfrac{c}{d} \iff \dfrac{a}{c} = \dfrac{b}{d}$, where none of b, c, d, is zero.

   (b) $\dfrac{a}{b} = \dfrac{c}{d} \iff \dfrac{a}{b} = \dfrac{a+c}{b+d}$ where none of b, d, and $b + d$ is zero.

   (c) $\dfrac{a}{b} = \dfrac{c}{d} \iff \dfrac{a-b}{a+b} = \dfrac{c-d}{c+d}$, where none of $b, d, a + b$, or $c + d$ is zero.

4. Prove or disprove: The reciprocal of the sum of any two fractions is equal to the sum of the reciprocals of the fractions.

5. If a particular variety of bulbs is planted, fewer than $\tfrac{5}{8}$ of them will grow into plants. If, however, they are given proper care, it is known that more than $\tfrac{3}{8}$ of them will survive satisfactorily. If a careful gardener has 15 growing plants, what can be said regarding the number of bulbs which must have been planted originally?

6. Show that there is always a rational number lying between any two rational numbers.

3.06 DECIMAL FRACTIONS

With very good motivation we reserve the name *decimal fraction* for a sum of terms like the following

$$a_0 + \frac{a_1}{10} + \frac{a_2}{10^2} + \frac{a_3}{10^3} + \cdots$$

which we represent by $a_0 \cdot a_1 a_2 a_3 \ldots$ where the a_i are whole numbers ≤ 9. Any decimal fraction involving a finite number of digits may be converted into a fraction whose numerator is a whole number and whose denominator is a positive integral power of ten, for example

$$0.235 = \frac{2}{10} + \frac{3}{10^2} + \frac{5}{10^3} = \frac{200}{1000} + \frac{30}{1000} + \frac{5}{1000} = \frac{235}{1000}.$$ The following

Decimal Fractions

examples will illustrate the fact that the four standard operations of arithmetic, that is, addition, subtraction, multiplication, and division, when carried out on decimal fractions with a finite number of digits reduce essentially to those operations carried out on natural numbers.

(a)
$$0.235 + 0.897 = \frac{235}{1000} + \frac{897}{1000}$$
$$= \frac{235 + 897}{1000}$$
$$= \frac{1132}{1000}$$
$$= \frac{1000}{1000} + \frac{132}{1000}$$
$$= 1 + 0.132$$
$$= 1.132$$

(b)
$$0.235 - 0.897 = \frac{235 - 897}{1000}$$
$$= \frac{-662}{1000}$$
$$= -.662$$

(c)
$$1.354 \times 0.28 = \frac{1354}{1000} \times \frac{28}{100}$$
$$= \frac{1354 \times 28}{1000 \times 100}$$
$$= \frac{37912}{100,000}$$
$$= 0.37912$$

(d) $1.354 \div 0.28$
$$= \frac{1.354}{0.28} \times \frac{100}{100}$$
$$= \frac{135.4}{28}$$

$$= \frac{1}{10}\left(\frac{1354}{28}\right) = \frac{1}{10}\left(48 + \frac{10}{28}\right) = 4.8 + \frac{10}{280}$$

or $$= \frac{1}{100}\left(\frac{13540}{28}\right) = \frac{1}{100}\left(483 + \frac{16}{28}\right) = 4.83 + \frac{16}{2800}$$

or $$= \frac{1}{1000}\left(\frac{135400}{28}\right) = \frac{1}{1000}\left(4835 + \frac{20}{28}\right)$$

$$= 4.835 + \frac{20}{28000}$$

```
           4.835
      ┌─────────
   28 │ 135.4
        112
        ─────
         23.4
         22.4
        ─────
          1.00
          0.84
         ─────
          0.160
          0.140
         ─────
          0.020
```

80 Extension of Whole Numbers

Example (d) demonstrates the fact that an indicated quotient of two decimal fractions can always be converted to an equal fraction with a natural number as denominator and the division might have been carried out as shown above. The finite sequence of digits of any decimal fraction may be extended indefinitely by affixing as many zeros as desired to the right of the nonzero digit which is furthest to the right in the numeral; for example, $0.235 = 0.2350 = 0.235000\ldots$.

3.07 IRRATIONAL NUMBERS

We are progressing in our efforts to obtain the solution set for more complicated open sentences and are now able to solve any linear equation, that is, an equation of the type $ax + c = 0$, with $a \neq 0$, where a and c are rational numbers.

Question. If $a \neq 0$, what is the solution set for the open sentence $ax + b = 0$? Is it unique?

Hence the next type of algebraic equation to challenge us would be one like $ax^2 + b = 0$, where a and b are integers, with $a \neq 0$. This is an example of a quadratic equation, that is, an equation in which the highest power of x occurs as x^2.

It is not difficult to verify that $\frac{2}{3}$ and $-\frac{2}{3}$ belong to the solution set of the open sentence $9x^2 - 4 = 0$ but, if our universe is R', can we find a nonempty solution set for the open sentence $x^2 - 3 = 0$?

Let us suppose that there exists a rational number $\frac{b}{c}$, *in its lowest terms*, that is, b relatively prime to c, such that $\left(\frac{b}{c}\right)^2 - 3 = 0$. (If there exists $\frac{b'}{c'}$ such that $\left(\frac{b'}{c'}\right)^2 = 3$ and $(b', c') \neq 1$ (see Section 1.15), then $b' = k \cdot b$ and $c' = k \cdot c$, where $(b, c) = 1$, and $\frac{b'}{c'} = \frac{b}{c}$; hence $\left(\frac{b}{c}\right)^2 = 3$.)

This condition may be rewritten as $b^2 = 3c^2$. We see that 3 must be a factor of b^2, and we wish to determine whether or not 3 is thereby compelled to be a factor of b. If we look at the complete set of integers we see that they may be separated into three sets (equivalence classes (Section 3.04)): (1) those integers that are divisible by 3 and hence have the form $3n$, for some integer n; (2) those that have a remainder of 1 when divided by 3 and hence have the form $3n + 1$, for some integer n; (3) those that have a remainder of 2 after division by 3 and are, therefore, of the form $3n + 2$, for some integer n.

Let us suppose, first, that b is an integer of the form $3n + 2$. Then, making use of the distributive property, we obtain

$$b^2 = (3n + 2)^2$$
$$= 9n^2 + 12n + 4$$
$$= 3(3n^2 + 4n + 1) + 1$$

This contradicts our knowledge that b^2 is divisible by 3 and hence b cannot be of the form $3n + 2$. Next, let us suppose that b is of the form $3n + 1$. This time we find that

$$b^2 = (3n + 1)^2$$
$$= 9n^2 + 6n + 1$$
$$= 3(3n^2 + 2n) + 1$$

and again division of b^2 by 3 results in a remainder of 1. Since we encounter a contradiction by supposing that b has either of the forms $3n + 1$ or $3n + 2$, we have no alternative but to conclude that b is of the form $3n$. If we replace b by $3n$ in the equation $b^2 = 3c^2$ we obtain $9n^2 = 3c^2$ or $3n^2 = c^2$.

Notice how similar this equation is to the equation $b^2 = 3c^2$, which resulted in b having the form $3n$. Clearly, an exactly similar argument will result in c having the form $3m$, where m is some integer. But if $b = 3n$ and $c = 3m$, for some integers m and n, then b and c have a common factor 3 and are not relatively prime which contradicts our original assumption. This is another example of an indirect proof and establishes for us the fact that no rational number exists whose square is equal to 3. We see then the need to invent many more numbers if we are to be able to solve even relatively simple equations such as $x^2 - 3 = 0$. If b is a positive integer, we call the positive number whose square is b "the square root of b" and write it as $\sqrt{b}$. Then $(\sqrt{b})^2 = b$ and also $(-\sqrt{b})^2 = b$. In general, if k is odd, we define $\sqrt[k]{b}$ (read "the k'th root of b") to be that number such that $(\sqrt[k]{b})^k = b$ and if k is even, and $b > 0$, $\sqrt[k]{b}$ is the positive number such that $(\sqrt[k]{b})^k = b$ and, of course, in this case $(-\sqrt[k]{b})^k = b$.

Questions. 1. Can you show in a similar or alternative manner to that used above that there is no rational number equal to $\sqrt{2}$?
2. Where does the argument similar to the above argument fail when applied to $\sqrt{4}$?

We might also proceed to convince ourselves that there are points on the number line which correspond to irrational numbers by making use

82   Extension of Whole Numbers

of the Pythagorean Theorem which we prove later in Chapter 8. Thus, if we consider a right triangle with legs one unit long, the length of the hypotenuse will have to be $\sqrt{2}$ units, since $1^2 + 1^2 = (\sqrt{2})^2 = 2$. If we use the length of this hypotenuse as a displacement from 0, we arrive at a definite point, P, on the number line. However, if the answer to *Question* 1, above, is "yes," the point P is not one to which it is possible to give a rational num-

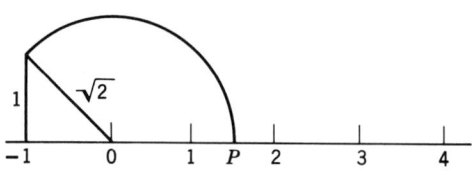

ber as a label. If we use 1 and $\sqrt{2}$ units as lengths of the legs of a second right triangle we obtain an hypotenuse whose length is $\sqrt{3}$ units. Continuing in this manner we can produce a segment whose length is $\sqrt{m}$ units for any positive integer m. These include only a few of the infinitely many irrational numbers.

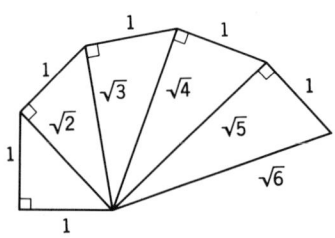

It is impossible in a presentation such as this to attempt to give any logical development of the irrational numbers. However we do wish to leave with the reader some important facts regarding them. It is possible (but not in an easy, elementary way) to employ the concept of sets of rational numbers in constructing the irrational numbers. This approach bears the name of the method of *Dedekind Cuts* and addition and multiplication of irrational numbers can be defined and their properties studied. In a somewhat easier approach we can also describe irrational numbers by equivalence classes of infinite sequences of rational numbers, making use of the sophisticated but very practical notion of *limit*. Without being specific regarding the meaning of limit of a sequence we will note, for example, that the number $\sqrt{2}$ can be approximated as closely as we wish by a never-ending sequence of decimal fractions, 1, 1.4, 1.41, 1.414, 1.4142, 1.41421,....

Question. Is the previous statement reasonable? Check by squaring 1.4, 1.41, 1.414, 1.4142, 1.41421,....

The same is true of π with the sequence 3, 3.1, 3.14, 3.142, 3.1416, 3.14159,....

If it is not practical to attempt to give all the details of the development of the irrational numbers, it is at least worth noting that many of the proofs of theorems relating to irrational numbers proceed along lines similar to the corresponding theorem in the case of rational numbers.

There are two principal types of irrationals: (1) algebraic and (2) transcendental. The *algebraic* irrational numbers are those like $\sqrt[3]{5}$ or $\sqrt[4]{3 + 2\sqrt[5]{7}}$, or $\sqrt{2} + 3$ which are solutions of polynomial equations with rational coefficients, that is, equations of the type $a_n x^n + a_{n-1} x^{n-1} + \cdots + a_1 x + a_0 = 0$, where the coefficients $a_i, i = 0, 1, 2, \ldots, n$ are rational numbers.

Question. Can you determine a polynomial equation with rational coefficients satisfied by $\sqrt[4]{3 + 2\sqrt[5]{7}}$? (*Hint:* set x equal to the given expression and raise both sides of this equation to the fourth power.)

Those irrational numbers which, like π, are not algebraic are called *transcendental*. They include, for example, expressions like $a\pi^n + b$, with a and b rational, as well as the values of most logarithmic and trigonometric functions. We give the name *real numbers* (referred to in the future as the set R), to the union of the set of rational numbers and the set of all irrational numbers.

In Chapter 7 we shall take a closer look at decimal expansions, in particular at nonterminating decimals of the repeating and nonrepeating varieties and at the relation existing between decimal numerals and rational and irrational numbers. We shall accept as a fundamental premise the fact that the set of all numbers represented by terminating and nonterminating decimals is the set of real numbers.

By way of concluding this section we are going to assume that the real numbers obey the same general rules and possess roughly the same properties as the rational numbers. These include commutativity and associativity as well as an identity and inverse (for all numbers $\neq 0$ in the case of multiplication) for the two operations, along with distributivity of multiplication with respect to addition. They are described in more detail in the following section.

EXERCISES

1. Obtain a polynomial equation with rational coefficients satisfied by $\sqrt[3]{a + \sqrt[4]{b + 2c}}$, where $a, b,$ and c are rational numbers.
2. For a and b real numbers show that
$$a < b \iff a < \frac{1}{2}(a + b) < b.$$
3. Is it true for all real numbers $a, b,$ and c that if $a = b + c$, then $a > b$?

84 Extension of Whole Numbers

4. Prove by mathematical induction that if $a_1, a_2, \ldots, a_n$ are positive real numbers, then the sum $a_1 + a_2 + \cdots + a_n$ and the product $a_1 \cdot a_2 \cdots a_n$ are positive, for any natural number n.
5. Assume the truth of the Unique Factorization Theorem (see Section 1.14) and use it to prove that any prime number divides any perfect square an even number of times.
6. Use Exercise 5 to prove that $\sqrt{p}$ is irrational, where p is any prime number.

3.08 THE ALGEBRAIC FIELD

It was our original intention to extend our number system by stages and to verify the standard properties for the operations we defined on the new numbers. Having done this, particularly in the case of the rational numbers, we are now able to consider a more elegant and more mathematically sophisticated way of looking at the number system. The fact is that we can describe the set R' of rational numbers as the smallest infinite set of numbers satisfying the following eleven conditions, or postulates in the sense that if any infinite set A of numbers satisfies these conditions, then R' $\subseteq A$:

(1) The set is closed under a binary operation called addition (+).
(2) The addition operation is commutative.
(3) The addition operation is associative.
(4) The set contains an additive identity, 0, such that $0 + a = a + 0 = a$ for any a in the set.
(5) The set contains an additive inverse, $-a$, for any a in the set, such that $a + (-a) = (-a) + a = 0$.
(6) The set is closed under a binary operation called multiplication ($\times$).
(7) The multiplication operation is commutative.
(8) The multiplication operation is associative.
(9) The set contains a multiplicative identity, $1 \neq 0$, such that $a \times 1 = 1 \times a = a$, for any a in the set.
(10) The set contains a multiplicative inverse, a^{-1}, for any $a \neq 0$ in the set, such that $a \times a^{-1} = a^{-1} \times a = 1$.
(11) The multiplication operation is distributive with respect to the addition operation.

Any set of elements which satisfy the above eleven properties is said to be a *field*. Hence the rational numbers form a field and likewise the real numbers.

We have an intuitive understanding of a positive real number ($x > 0$), and we accept the following as plausible assumptions:

(12) Either $x > 0$ or $x = 0$ or $-x > 0$ (one and only one condition).

(13) If $x > 0$ and $y > 0$, then $x + y > 0$
(14) If $x > 0$ and $y > 0$, then $xy > 0$
and, further, we make the definition
(15) $x > y \iff x - y > 0$

Of tremendous significance is the fact that any result which can be proved as a consequence of the above eleven postulates will hold in any field. Hence, when we have proved, for example, that the identities 0 and 1 are unique in a field, we are then assured that they are unique not only in the set of rational numbers but in the set of real numbers as well and also in any other set whose elements satisfy the axioms of a field.

EXERCISES

1. Show that the set of numbers of the form $a + b\sqrt{5}$, where a and b are rational numbers, form a field.
2. Show that the whole numbers modulo five (See *Question* at end of Section 1.18) form a field whereas the whole numbers modulo four and the whole numbers modulo six do not do so.

3.09 REAL NUMBERS ARE NOT SUFFICIENT

We improved immensely our ability to solve algebraic equations by extending our number system to include all the irrational numbers. However, even with such a large universe as the real numbers to use as a replacement set, we are still forced to give the empty set as the solution set for the open sentence $x^2 + 1 = 0$, since the square of any real number is nonnegative. At this point "common sense" might have dictated that we accept the status quo. However mathematicians were unsatisfied with such an example of "unfinished business" and the procedure which they followed is another excellent illustration* of the way in which new mathematics is created. They literally invented a new number, often called the *imaginary unit* to play the role of $\sqrt{-1}$, which does not exist in the set of real numbers. To represent this new number, the letter "i" was assigned together with the necessary relation, $i^2 + 1 = 0$. By so doing they were striking out on an uncharted course, the consequences of which action were to be immensely fruitful for the whole science of mathematics. Clearly i must combine with the real numbers in some acceptable fashion, as will be discussed

---

*Compare the construction of the negative integers, the rational numbers, and the irrational numbers.

86 Extension of Whole Numbers

below, and in this sense i has been adjoined to the real numbers thereby producing the set of numbers of the form $a + bi$, where a and b are real numbers. We call this new set $\{a + bi | a, b \in \mathbf{R}\}$ of numbers the set of *complex numbers*. With respect to the complex number $a + bi$, the real number a is known as its *real part* and the real number b as its *imaginary part*.* By setting $b = 0$, we see that the real numbers form a subset of the complex numbers. When $a = 0$, we call the subset of numbers, bi, *pure imaginary* numbers.

In defining addition and multiplication of the complex numbers we are motivated, as in previous instances, by our desire to have the operations consistent with already existing operations in the subset. Hence we define

(1) $a + bi = c + di \iff a = c$ and $b = d$
(2) $(a + bi) + (c + di) = (a + c) + (b + d)i$
(3) $(a + bi)(c + di) = (ac - bd) + (ad + bc)i$

Questions.
1. Can you devise some motivation for definition (1) above? (*Hint:* Obtain $a - c = (d - b)i$ and square both sides of the equation.)
2. Can you determine real numbers, p and q, such that $(a + bi) - (c + di) = p + qi$? (*Hint:* Extend the fundamental definition of subtraction to complex numbers.)
3. Can you determine real numbers, r and s, such that $(a + bi) \div (c + di) = r + si$, where c and d are not both 0? (*Hint:* Extend the fundamental definition of division to complex numbers.)
4. (a) Is addition of complex numbers
      (1) Associative? (2) Commutative?
   (b) Is multiplication of complex numbers
      (1) Associative? (2) Commutative?
5. Is multiplication of complex numbers distributive with respect to addition?
6. What complex number plays the role of the additive identity in this number system? of the additive inverse? of the multiplicative identity? of the multiplicative inverse?
7. Are the eleven properties of a field (see Section 3.08) satisfied by the complex number system?

With the given definitions we see (*Question 7*) that the complex numbers do form a field. In fact they behave in a manner consistent

---
*Cf. John L. Kelley, *Introduction to Modern Algebra*, published by Van Nostrand, p. 200.

(although not, of course, isomorphic) with the real numbers except for one detail—we cannot define a "useful" order relation for the complex numbers.

We would be leaving the reader unprepared to understand the treatment of complex numbers given in a great many modern texts, if we failed to present a parallel treatment of them in terms of ordered pairs of real numbers.

Let us, therefore, decide, as before, to invent a new number, represented by the ordered pair* (a, b), where a and b are any real numbers. For such number pairs we shall make the following definitions.

(1) Equality: $(a,b) = (c,d) \Longleftrightarrow a = c$ and $b = d$
(2) Addition: $(a,b) + (c,d) = (a+c, b+d)$
(3) Multiplication: $(a,b) \times (c,d) = (ac - bd, ad + bc)$

Questions. 1. Can you prove that both addition and multiplication of such number pairs are commutative and associative?
2. What is the sum $(a,b) + (0,0)$?
3. What is the sum $(a,b) + (-a,-b)$?
4. What is the product $(a,b) \times (1,0)$?
5. What is the product $(a,b) \times \left(\dfrac{a}{a^2+b^2}, \dfrac{-b}{a^2+b^2}\right)$, where not both a and b are zero?
6. Is multiplication distributive with respect to addition?

The reader will have noticed by now the similarity between the behavior of (a, b) and that of the complex number $a + bi$, described above. The completion of the answers to the above six *Questions* establishes the fact that these number pairs form a field under the given definitions. The 1:1 correspondence obtained by setting $(a,b) \leftrightarrow a + bi$ may thus be seen to satisfy all the conditions of an isomorphism (see Section 1.18).

Let us now explore the consequences of this isomorphism a little further.

Questions. Can you verify the following statements and describe the significance of each?
1. $(a,0) + (b,0) = (a+b, 0)$
2. $(a,0) \times (b,0) = (ab, 0)$
3. $(a,0) + (0,0) = (a,0)$

---

*It should be noted that the "ordered pair" approach could have been employed equally well in the construction of the integers and also of the rational numbers. It has been our conviction that the more informal approach was more desirable in each of these cases but that a sufficient degree of sophistication has now been attained to make the use of ordered pairs here of general benefit.

4. $(a,0) \times (1,0) = (a,0)$
5. $(a,0) + (-a,0) = (0,0)$
6. $(a,0) \times \left(\frac{1}{a},0\right) = (1,0)$ where $a \neq 0$
7. $(a,0) \times (0,0) = (0,0)$

The results of these seven *Questions* should be sufficient to convince us that $(a,0)$ is behaving just like the real number a. In fact, the previously established isomorphism has, as a special case, the correspondence $(a,0) \leftrightarrow a$. Thus we have a 1:1 correspondence which is again an isomorphism. We are accustomed to say that the subset, $\{(a,0) | a$ a real number$\}$, of the set of complex numbers, is isomorphic to the set of real numbers.

Note that $(a,b) \times (a,-b) = (a^2 + b^2, 0)$ or, in the alternate notation $(a + bi)(a - bi) = a^2 + b^2$. We call the complex number, $a - bi$, the *conjugate* of $a + bi$ and represent it as $\overline{a + bi}$. Since the product of any complex number and its conjugate is a real number, the conjugate may be used to advantage when we are dividing two complex numbers. For example,

$$\frac{2 + 5i}{3 - 4i} = \frac{2 + 5i}{3 - 4i} \times \frac{3 + 4i}{3 + 4i}$$

$$= \frac{(2 \times 3 - 5 \times 4) + (2 \times 4 + 5 \times 3)i}{3^2 + 4^2}$$

$$= \frac{-14}{25} + \frac{23}{25}i$$

Question. Can you transform $\frac{a + bi}{c + di}$ into the form $r + si$, where a, b, c, d, r, s, are real numbers, with c and d not both 0?

EXERCISES

1. Transform each of the following expressions into the form $a + bi$, where a and b are rational numbers:
    (a) $(3 + 6i) + (2 - 3i)$ (b) $(7 + 5i) - (1 + 2i)$ (c) $(5 + 7i)(3 + 4i)$
    (d) $(2 - 3i)(-1 + 4i)$ (e) $\frac{4 - 3i}{2 + 5i}$ (f) $\frac{3i}{4 + 7i}$
    (g) $\frac{3 - 6i}{2i}$ (h) $5i^{125} + 4i^{307} + 3i^{574}$ (i) $\sqrt{3 + 4i}$

2. Show that
    (a) $\overline{(a + bi) + (c + di)} = \overline{(a + bi)} + \overline{(c + di)}$
    (b) $\overline{(a + bi) - (c + di)} = \overline{(a + bi)} - \overline{(c + di)}$
    (c) $\overline{(a + bi) \times (c + di)} = \overline{(a + bi)} \times \overline{(c + di)}$
    (d) $\overline{\left[\frac{a + bi}{c + di}\right]} = \frac{\overline{a + bi}}{\overline{c + di}}$, where c and d are not both 0.

3. Verify the following statements and indicate the significance of each:
    (a) $(0,a) + (0,b) = (0, a+b)$
    (b) $(0,a) \times (0,b) = (-ab, 0)$
    (c) $(0,b) \times (0,1) = (-b, 0)$
    (d) $(0,1) \times (0,1) = (-1, 0)$
    (e) $(b,0) \times (0,1) = (0,b)$
    (f) $(a,b) \times (0,1) = (-b, a)$
    (g) $(a,b) = (a,0) + (0,b)$
    $ = (a,0) \times (1,0) + (b,0) \times (0,1)$
    (h) $(a,b) \times (0,1) = [(a,0) + (0,b)] \times (0,1)$
    $ = (a,0) \times (0,1) + (0,b) \times (0,1)$
    $ = (0,a) + (-b, 0)$

4. With reference to Exercise 3, show why there does *not* exist an isomorphism of the form $(0,b) \leftrightarrow bi$ between the subset $\{(0,b) | b$ a real number$\}$ and the set consisting of all multiples of i, that is, products of i and a real number.

5. The array in parentheses $\begin{pmatrix} p & q \\ r & s \end{pmatrix}$, is known as a "two by two matrix," that is, a matrix with two "rows" and two "columns." We define addition and multiplication of such matrices as follows:

$$\begin{pmatrix} p & q \\ r & s \end{pmatrix} + \begin{pmatrix} t & u \\ v & w \end{pmatrix} = \begin{pmatrix} p+t & q+u \\ r+v & s+w \end{pmatrix}$$

$$\begin{pmatrix} p & q \\ r & s \end{pmatrix} \times \begin{pmatrix} t & u \\ v & w \end{pmatrix} = \begin{pmatrix} pt+qv & pu+qw \\ rt+sv & ru+sw \end{pmatrix}$$

If a and b are real numbers, show that the 1:1 correspondence $(a,b) \leftrightarrow \begin{pmatrix} a & b \\ -b & a \end{pmatrix}$ is an isomorphism.

6. Can you provide any justification for interpreting multiplication of a complex number $a + bi$ by i [or (a,b) by $(0,1)$] as a rotation through a right angle? [*Hint:* Think of the complex number (a,b), as an arrow (or directed segment) from the origin $(0,0)$, to the point (a,b), in the coordinate plane.]

4 *Basic Geometrical Concepts*

4.01 GEOMETRY IS ALL AROUND US

Even if geometry were not the well-established discipline that it is, we could not fail to be intrigued by the varied, but nevertheless related, configurations by which we are surrounded. City streets, to some extent, present a pattern of parallel straight lines, creating approximately square and rectangular blocks. The walls of most rooms, as well as skyscrapers, factories, and airplane hangars, conjure up the idea of planes intersecting in straight lines. Clock faces and dials are generally in the form of circles, as well as are ash trays, man-hole covers, targets, and many decorative pools. The ellipse is a favorite design for the boundary of a flower bed and in the construction of gears where a "quick return" is desired. Any object thrown in a direction not "straight down" follows roughly a parabolic path. Any point on the circumference of a wheel, as it rolls without slipping along a straight line, traces out a curve called a cycloid. The hanging wires of telephone and power lines illustrate the catenary curve. These last two curves are illustrated below. The path of a missile in space requires the most

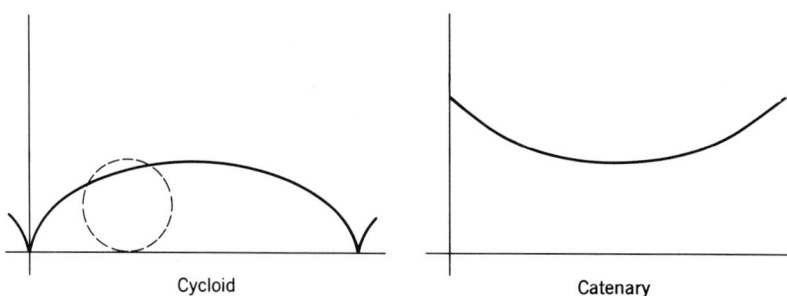

Cycloid   Catenary

careful study by mathematicians in order that the large number of conditions affecting it may be taken into account.

The rectangular box, or parallelepiped, is used as a container in almost every conceivable size. Many water towers, silos, and gas storage tanks are examples of cylinders. Some object in the form of a sphere is an indispensable accompaniment of a multitude of games. While the dirigible and standard "football" may not be the best approximations to an ellipsoid, the ceiling of the Mormon Tabernacle in Salt Lake City is an amazingly good example of a surface forming a portion of an ellipsoid. Ellipsoidal mirrors are used where it is desired to focus a point of light whereas paraboloidal mirrors produce parallel light rays. The creation of the Egyptian pyramids and the conical paper cup span centuries of man's concern with geometry.

The point does not require further elaboration that we are literally surrounded by examples of curves and surfaces, all of which possess definite geometric characteristics. It is not surprising then that for so many years men have considered the study of geometry to be a worthwhile use of their time and that work on problems of geometry should occupy the attention of many mathematicians today.

4.02 EUCLID'S STRENGTHS AND WEAKNESSES

Perhaps the greatest name in geometry and in any case one that will be associated forever with this subject is that of Euclid, who lived in the third century, B.C. His accomplishment in organizing the geometry of his time in the form of a body of postulates, definitions, and theorems will rank always among the great mathematical achievements.

For more than two thousand years the work of Euclid has received universal respect. That mathematicians are now able to suggest improved ways of thinking about geometry, should be considered not as any reflection on but rather as a tribute to his farsightedness in establishing such a powerful foundation for this subject. For one thing, we realize now that it is impossible to define everything with which we wish to deal in geometry, as Euclid attempted to do. When we try to do this we are confronted with the necessity of defining many of the words we are employing. The result is an endless chain of definitions. An example of this is Euclid's first definition, "A point is that which has position but no magnitude." The words "position" and "magnitude," with which Euclid assumed everyone was familiar, lack definition and the situation is compounded in subsequent definitions. For this reason modern geometers have found it desirable to accept point, line, and plane as undefined terms, that is, essentially as mental constructs. Each of us may have his own conception of these three geometric ideas, but their interpretation is not limited to entities which

92   *Basic Geometrical Concepts*

resemble closely any of our own picturizations. The only limitations in interpretation are those which are incurred as a result of the conditions which we impose on our undefined elements. Since we have considerable freedom in choosing the conditions which we wish our geometric elements to obey, we accept the fact that the geometry we create is entirely relative to our basic assumptions.

4.03 WHY POSTULATES?

Geometry is not the only area of mathematics which exhibits this feature of "relativity." We have already seen (Chapter 3) the important role postulates play in establishing the number systems of algebra. Technically an area, like geometry, may be thought of as consisting of the basic postulates together with all the logical consequences which may be derived from these postulates. In the practical sense we tend to think of a somewhat limited body of related facts. In establishing these facts we have the choice of assuming many statements as true and proving a relatively small number of theorems or of assuming fewer postulates and proving a larger number of theorems. Mathematicians prefer, as a matter of principle, to assume as few postulates as possible, since each additional assumption may have a restricting effect on what can be proved. However the study of geometry in high school is based on a reasonable choice of assumptions on the basis of which an adequate number of theorems is proved. The creation of a postulational basis for so much of mathematics has resulted in a tremendous amount of research in mathematics; by adding or eliminating a postulate or by setting up an entirely new set of postulates, the mathematician is faced with new conjectures to be proved or disproved. Hence the scope of mathematical research is virtually unlimited. In this connection it should be noted that it is often much easier to disprove a false statement than to prove a true statement, since in the former case a single counterexample can serve to demonstrate that the statement cannot be true in general. For example, we are all aware that $\frac{23}{37} \neq \frac{2}{7}, \frac{15}{21} \neq \frac{5}{2}, \frac{69}{59} \neq \frac{6}{5}$, and so on. We might therefore be tempted to put complete faith in a statement to the effect that such a procedure of eliminating identical digits in the numerator and denominator of any fractional numeral always produces a fraction unequal to the original fraction. However any one of the fractions $\frac{16}{64}, \frac{26}{65}, \frac{19}{95}, \frac{49}{98}, \frac{98}{196}$, and $\frac{196}{392}$ serves as a counterexample which is sufficient to disprove the conjecture.

Since our discussion of geometry in this material is mostly intuitive, we shall not attempt in any way to be exhaustive in our treatment of postulates.

4.04 WHAT SHOULD WE LOOK FOR IN POSTULATES?

Since postulates serve to establish the foundation of a subject it is natural and desirable that they should be simple in character in order that they may be easily understood. As was mentioned in the previous section, the number of postulates is generally kept reasonably small in order that a satisfactory number of theorems may be proved. Of greater importance in a postulate system are the characteristics of *consistency* and *independence*. We wish to illustrate these two characteristics by describing next a so-called "miniature" geometry consisting only of *four* points, one of many finite geometries which exist.

In establishing this Four Point Geometry we shall accept as undefined terms, "point," "line," and "on" (in the sense of "point A is on line m" or "line m is on point A"). We assume the following postulates:

P1. There exist four and only four distinct points.

P2. On two distinct points there is one and only one line.

P3. Every line contains two and only two points.

A postulate system is said to be *consistent* if it contains no contradictory statements. This is generally verified by constructing, if possible, a *model* or representation of the system in which an interpretation is made for each undefined term in a recognizable structure. If all the postulates are satisfied in the structure, we assume the system to be consistent. For the above Four Point Geometry a possible model is shown at the right, where $A, B, C, D,$ are the four points and the six point pairs $(A,B), (A,C), (A,D), (B,C), (B,D), (C,D)$ represent the six lines. Note that the lines are merely the pairs of points and the points have been joined in the diagram only to assist us in recognizing the lines. If we examine the three postulates one by one we see 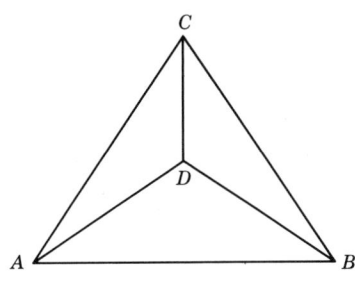 that each is satisfied in the diagram. Hence our postulate system is consistent.

The matter of independence is concerned with the question of whether any particular postulate can be derived as a consequence of the other postulates. If this were so in a given case we would surely obtain a contradiction (or inconsistent set of postulates) if we considered the negation of the postulate in question together with all the other postulates. Hence we shall show that our postulate system is independent by demonstrating, in turn, a model which satisfies each of the postulate systems obtained by negating one, only, of P_1, P_2, or P_3.

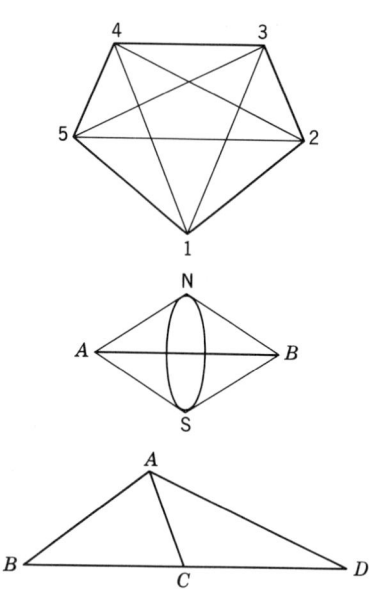

Let us call the negated postulates P'_1, P'_2, and P'_3. Then the reader should verify that the three models shown at the left satisfy the systems, P'_1, P_2, P_3; P_1, P'_2, P_3; P_1, P_2, P'_3, in that order. In the first and second models it should be noted that there are no intersections of lines except at the given points since each line contains only two points. In the first model the existence of five points indicates that postulate P_1 is not satisfied, whereas P_2 and P_3 are true. In the second model the points N and S may be thought of as poles on a sphere and the two curved lines as curves on the sphere. Clearly the existence of the two curved lines demonstrates that postulate P_2 fails to hold, whereas P_1 and P_3 are both satisfied. In the third model, where again we have only four points and only one line through any two points, the line $(B, C.D)$ has three points, thus contradicting postulate P_3. Therefore we have verified that no two of the three postulates imply the truth of the remaining one, and for this reason we say our postulate system is independent.

To return to the Four Point Geometry for a moment we should like to note three theorems which are consequences of the postulates:

Theorem 1. There exist six and only six lines.

Proof. With each of the four given points there may be associated any one of three points making twelve ordered pairs of points. Since order is immaterial as far as lines are concerned, there are exactly six lines. By Postulate P_3, the lines are necessarily distinct.

Theorem 2. Each of the four points lies on three and only three lines.

Proof. With each point three other points may be associated giving three lines on the given point. The three lines are distinct by Postulate P_3.

Definition. Two lines are parallel if they have no point in common. Since each of our lines contains only two points, the definition of parallelism has special significance here.

Theorem 3. Through a point not on a given line there is one and only one line parallel to the given line.

Question. Can you give the proof for Theorem 3?

4.05 IS GEOMETRY TRUE?

In setting up his postulates, Euclid attempted to describe what he thought were self-evident truths, that is, statements which one would feel were obviously true as a result of observation. Consequently for many years people believed that Euclidean geometry was necessarily an accurate picture of the three-dimensional space in which we live. There was one postulate about which we shall have more to say in Chapter 8, to which many mathematicians devoted years of effort in the belief that it could be established as a result of the other postulates and therefore was not a postulate at all but rather a theorem. Much useful mathematical knowledge resulted from the investigation of this postulate, known as the *Parallel Postulate*. The most startling result was the discovery that, by introducing slight changes in the Parallel Postulate, different, legitimate, and quite reasonable geometries were created. An amazing fact about these other geometries, which are known as non-Euclidean geometries, is that we are unable to determine whether one of them or Euclidean geometry is actually a more suitable description of our own three-space. For relatively short distances Euclidean geometry serves us very well. In the outer reaches of space it may prove to be quite inadequate.

4.06 GEOMETRIC FIGURES

If points, lines, and planes are undefined, are we justified in "drawing" geometric figures? Fundamentally, the answer is "no" since such a picture would represent at best merely one interpretation of the

96   Basic Geometrical Concepts

idealization we are considering. It is a fact that geometry can be studied satisfactorily without the use of any diagrams, and we can and should accomplish all our geometric investigation without *depending* on the information derived from any drawing. Nevertheless we generally consider it advisable to draw a representation of the particular geometric entity we are studying, not to provide factual information but rather to suggest lines of attack on the problem. However, whether or not a diagram is present, we need to have a definite geometric concept behind our idealization, whether it be a segment, angle, triangle or something else, and in each of these cases we accept the fact that the entity is some set of points. For example, while we do not attempt to define a line, it is quite consistent for us to think of it as a set of points. Similarly a plane is also a set of points. In the following section we shall be able to be more specific in describing some particular sets of points.

4.07 BETWEENNESS AND DEFINITIONS

Some geometric facts seemed so "obvious" to Euclid that he evidently did not consider it necessary even to mention them as postulates. One of these seemingly innocent concepts has to do with one point being "between" two other points on a line. The modern approach to Euclidean geometry handles this matter in one of two ways. If distance between two points has already been established then betweenness may be defined in terms of distance. Otherwise, betweenness is accepted as an undefined concept and is assigned certain properties. In either case this concept of betweenness becomes a highly important consideration in many problems where we need to be certain concerning the

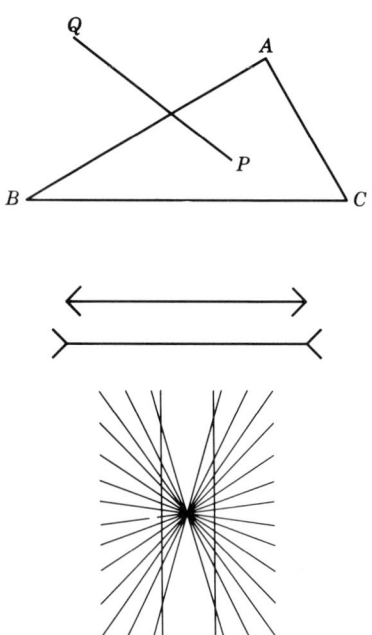

intersection of lines. For example, if P is a point inside a triangle whose vertices are A, B, C and Q is a point outside the triangle, must the line segment, $\overline{PQ}$, have a point in common with the triangle?

This may seem to be a certainty when we look at a picture. One weakness of Euclid was to assume that the picture in this case was sufficient evidence. However there are nice examples,* one of which we describe in the Appendix, which illustrate the errors that can result from conclusions based on a diagram. It is not too different from the examples of optical illusions pictured above. In the first example the two segments are the same length and in the second example they are actually portions of parallel lines.

Equally important is the help which the concept of betweenness affords us in making precise definitions. For example, the idea of segment is not easy to describe in any sentence which avoids the word "between." Let us represent the line through the points A and B by the notation "$\overleftrightarrow{AB}$," which emphasizes the indefinite extent of the line in both directions. We can then define the segment $\overline{AB}$ as the union of the set consisting of the points A and B, and the set containing all points of $\overleftrightarrow{AB}$ which lie between A and B. If we let the symbol "ACB" stand for "C is between A and B," then, in abbreviated notation, we have

$$\overline{AB} = \{A,B\} \cup \{C | C \in \overleftrightarrow{AB} \text{ and } ACB\}$$

Clearly, this definition agrees with the popular conception but is not limited to that conception.

Let us now list a few other definitions in order to sense the flavor of this approach to geometry. A ray can be denoted nicely by the symbol "$\overrightarrow{AB}$" and defined as the union of the segment $\overline{AB}$ and the set of all points C on $\overleftrightarrow{AB}$ such that B is between A and C. A little thought will make clear that the ray $\overrightarrow{AB}$ is, in words, (which admittedly provide a poor substitute for our precise definition) the indefinite extension of the segment $\overline{AB}$ in the direction of B from A along the line $\overleftrightarrow{AB}$.

Questions. 1. Can you give the definition of ray $\overrightarrow{AB}$ in set notation?
2. How does the ray $\overrightarrow{AB}$ differ from the ray $\overrightarrow{BA}$?
3. How would you describe $\overrightarrow{AB} \cap \overrightarrow{BA}$? $\overrightarrow{AB} \cup \overrightarrow{BA}$?

If pictures are helpful then one interpretation of segment, ray, and line, respectively, might be illustrated below:

*Felix Klein, *Elementary Mathematics from an Advanced Standpoint*, published by Dover Publications, Volume 2, pages 200–202.

98 Basic Geometrical Concepts

We now have all the tools needed to define triangle and angle as follows: The triangle with the vertices A, B, C is the union of the segments $\overline{AB}$, $\overline{BC}$, and $\overline{CA}$, that is, $\triangle ABC = \overline{AB} \cup \overline{BC} \cup \overline{CA}$.

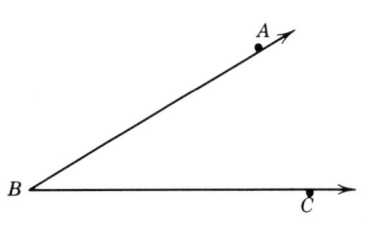

Similarly, the angle ABC, having vertex at the point B, as illustrated at the left, is the union of the two rays $\overrightarrow{BA}$ and $\overrightarrow{BC}$, where $\overrightarrow{BA}$ and $\overrightarrow{BC}$ do not lie in the same line; that is, $\angle ABC = \overrightarrow{BA} \cup \overrightarrow{BC}$. We see exemplified here another powerful use of the idea of set, which can present the above abstract notions with clarity and precision.

Question. Is $\angle ABC$ contained in $\triangle ABC$, or in other words is $\angle ABC$ a subset of $\triangle ABC$?

EXERCISES

1. Are the following statements true or false?
   (a) $\overline{AB} \subseteq \overrightarrow{AB}$ (b) $\overrightarrow{BA} \subseteq \overrightarrow{AB} \cap \overleftrightarrow{AB}$
   (c) $\overrightarrow{AB} \subseteq \overleftrightarrow{AB}$ (d) $\overleftrightarrow{AB} \subseteq \overrightarrow{AB} \cup \overrightarrow{BA}$
2. If P, Q, R, S are four points on a line and we know that RPS and PSQ, what are the other betweenness relations?
3. If P, Q, R, S are four points on a line and we know that RPS and RPQ, what are the other betweenness relations?
4. If we are given that ABC and BDC hold for four points A, B, C, D, on a line, what other betweenness relations must hold?
5. Any point C, of a line $\overleftrightarrow{AB}$ is said to separate the line into two half-lines, neither of which contains the point C. Similarly, any line m in a plane S separates the plane into two half-planes (or sides of m) and, again, neither half-plane contains the line m. The angle ABC also separates the plane containing it into three disjoint sets, the interior and the exterior of the angle and the angle itself.
   (a) Can you think of a way of defining the interior of $\angle ABC$?
   (b) How could you define the interior of $\triangle ABC$?
6. Describe the intersection of $\angle A$ and $\angle B$ of $\triangle ABC$.
7. Is the union of two angles of a triangle the same as the triangle itself? Why or why not?
8. Describe the intersection of $\angle A$ and $\triangle ABC$.
9. Show that $\triangle ABC \subseteq (\angle A \cup \angle B)$.

4.08 MEASURE

In order to measure a segment we must adopt an arbitrary unit of length. Once this is done we can describe the length of a segment $\overline{AB}$ (we may conveniently use the notation "AB" for this length) with respect to that unit as a certain number, K. In other words the number, K, is the length or the measure of the segment. If we think of the real numbers as capable of a 1 : 1 correspondence with the points on a line, then some particular point on the line may be thought of as corresponding to the number 0. We may use any arbitrary distance to represent a unit length, thereby enabling us to locate the point corresponding to the number 1 on one of the rays with end-point corresponding to 0. We shall refer to the number associated with a point P as its coordinate C_p. Once points with coordinates 0 and 1 are located the coordinates of other points may then be determined. We define the length of the segment $\overline{AB}$ as $|C_A - C_B|$, that is, $AB = |C_A - C_B|$.

In two dimensions we find a corresponding situation with regard to the *region* within a closed curve as boundary. Experience has shown that it is a satisfactory procedure to accept the statement that to every closed polygonal region there corresponds a unique positive number, A, called the area of the region. In the case of a rectangular region we motivate the definition of area by thinking of a square, each of whose sides is one unit long. We say the area of the unit square is 1. A rectangle the lengths of whose sides are l and w will clearly contain lw unit squares, if l and w are integers. Similarly, if l and w 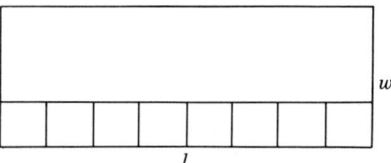 are rational numbers, it can be argued again that the number of unit squares contained in the rectangle is lw. Hence we define the area of this rectangle in general to be lw; that is, the area or measure of the rectangle with respect to the proper unit is the product of the measures or lengths of its sides. This idea of measure as a number as opposed to the actual *measurement* itself (for example, 6 inches, 10 miles, etc.) is one of great significance, avoiding, as it does, the traumatic argument of whether or not "inches times inches are square inches" (regardless of the fact that in physics and engineering such ideas may be expedient for computational purposes).

The concept extends to three dimensions; for example, the measure or volume of a rectangular parallelepiped (or box) is lwh, the product of the measures of its three edges with respect to a proper unit. Perhaps the most valuable aspect of measure is the fact that its use in the

100   Basic Geometrical Concepts

elementary context is consistent with the extremely significant role which it plays in more advanced mathematics.

4.09 COORDINATES

So far in this chapter we have been discussing some informal aspects of Euclidean synthetic geometry treated from a modern point of view. We shall return to this topic in Chapter 8, but we would like to conclude the present chapter with some remarks on coordinate geometry.

It was a French mathematician, René Descartes, who is credited with introducing the techniques of algebra into the study of geometry in the seventeenth century. The essential ingredient in this powerful method of attack is the ability to describe precisely the location of a point. We have assumed that there is a 1:1 correspondence between the real numbers and points on the number line. In this sense each number is the coordinate for the point to which it corresponds and serves to describe its location relative to the point corresponding to zero on the line. It is equally possible to give the exact location of a point in the plane by setting up two intersecting number lines.

It is convenient to have these intersect at right angles, to locate zero at the point of intersection on each line, to have the unit intervals of equal length in the two cases, and to have the numbers increase to the right and up, but none of these conditions is essential. The horizontal number line is the x-axis and the other line is the y-axis. We locate a point by associating with it an ordered pair of two numbers. The first number, called the *abscissa* of the point, is the signed measure of the directed displacement of the point from the y-axis in a direction parallel to the x-axis and the second number, called the *ordinate,* is the signed measure of the directed displacement of the point from the x-axis in a direction parallel to the y-axis. There is a 1:1 correspondence between the points of the plane and these ordered pairs of real numbers.

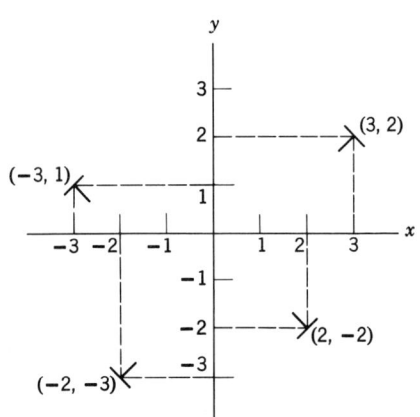

The real power of this "analytical" approach begins to be seen when we notice, for example, the pattern which emerges for all points on the x-axis. A glance at a few of these points, such as those with coordinates* (1,0), (2,0), (3,0),... leads us to the conclusion that the second coordinate will be zero for all points on the x-axis, and the first coordinate will be zero for all points on the y-axis.

Question. What pattern is exhibited by all points which lie two units to the right of the y-axis? Similarly three units below the x-axis?

We may think of a completely general point in the plane as described by the ordered pair, (x, y), of numbers x and y. Clearly, if such a point is to be compelled to be on the x-axis, then we must have $y = 0$, as stated above. And if the point is to be on the y-axis, then, of necessity, $x = 0$. For this reason we say that the equations of the x-axis and the y-axis are, respectively, $y = 0$ and $x = 0$, since each of these is exactly the condition imposed on the coordinates x and y of the point (x, y), which will force the point to be on one or other of those lines. In other words not only does every point (x, y), on the x-axis have its y-coordinate zero but also every point $(x, 0)$ (or (x, y) with $y = 0$) is a point on the x-axis.

Question. What are the equations of the two lines in the previous Question?

We shall see in succeeding chapters how very effective algebraic procedures can be in dealing with analytic geometry.

EXERCISES

1. What is an equation of the line, each of whose points is 8 units to the left of the y-axis?
2. (a) What is an equation of the line, each of whose points has its ordinate equal to its abscissa?
   (b) How should the equation in (a) be altered if the ordinate of each point equals the negative of the abscissa?
3. What is an equation of the line 15 units to the left of the line whose equation is $x = 12$?
4. What is an equation of the line 10 units above the line with equation $y = -3$?
5. What is an equation of the line, each of whose points has its ordinate equal to two-thirds of its abscissa?
6. The slope of the line through the points (x_1, y_1) and (x_2, y_2) is defined to be $\frac{y_2 - y_1}{x_2 - x_1}$, if $x_2 \neq x_1$.

---

*From now on we shall omit the phrase "with coordinates" and simply refer to the point, (1,0), and so on.

(a) Find the coordinates of three points on the line with an equation*
$2x + 3y = 5$ and calculate the slope of this line in three ways.
(b) Repeat the procedure of 6(a) to obtain the slope of the line $bx + ay = 6ab$.
(c) What is the slope of the line (i) $y = mx + b$ (ii) $y - y_1 = m(x - x_1)$?

7. (a) If $P(x,y)$ is a "moving point" on the line through the points $P_1(x_1,y_1)$ and $P_2(x_2, y_2)$, what is the slope of the line through P and P_1, if $x \neq x_1$?
(b) The line through P and P_1 is the same as the line through P_1 and P_2; hence the two slopes are equal. Give the equation which is produced by setting the two slopes equal to each other.
(c) Compare the equation obtained in 7(b) with the equation given in 6(c)(ii).

8. The answer to 7(b) is an equation of the line through the points $P_1(x_1,y_1)$ and $P_2(x_2,y_2)$. Use this information to obtain an equation of the line through the points $(a,0)$ and $(0,b)$. The numbers a and b are called, respectively, the *x intercept* and *y intercept* of the latter line.

9. (a) If a line has slope 3 and passes through the point (2,1), give the coordinates of another point on the line.
(b) If a line has slope m and passes through the point (x_1,y_1) give the coordinates of another point on the line.
(c) Obtain an equation of the line in 9(a).
(d) Obtain an equation of the line in 9(b).
(e) Obtain an equation of the line with slope m and y intercept b.
(f) Obtain an equation of the line with slope m and x intercept a.

10. An answer to exercise 8, that is, an equation of the line with x intercept a and y intercept b is

$$\frac{x}{a} + \frac{y}{b} = 1, \text{ if } a \neq 0 \text{ and } b \neq 0$$

(a) Find the x and y intercepts of the line $2x + 3y = 6$.
(b) At what points does the line, $2x - 5y = 30$, cross the x and y axes, respectively?

11. If we consider the set of lines obtained by letting m be any real number in $y = mx + 5$, we obtain what is called a *family* of lines. In this case the lines of the family share the common property that each line has y intercept 5 (that is, passes through the point (0,5)). What individual property is possessed by the members of each of the following families of lines (for a, b and m, the universe is the set of real numbers)?
(a) $x = a$
(b) $y = 3x + b$
(c) $y - 4 = m(x - 2)$
(d) $y = mx + 3m$

---

*For the sake of brevity, from now on we shall generally omit the phrase "with an equation" and simply refer to the line followed by its equation.

12. The lines
$$x + 2y - 3 = 0$$
and
$$2x - y + 4 = 0$$
intersect in a point. Let us call this point (x', y'), without finding out what x' and y' are as rational numbers.
   (a) What is the characterizing feature of the family of lines represented by the equation $K(x + 2y - 3) + M(2x - y + 4) = 0$, where K and M are any real numbers? (*Hint:* Does the point (x', y') lie on every line of the family in (a)?)
   (b) Compare the family of lines $(x + 2y - 3) + L(2x - y + 4) = 0$, where L is any real number, with the family of lines in (a).
   (c) Does each of the original lines belong to both families of lines in (a) and (b)?
   (d) Find an equation of the line of the family of lines in (a) or (b) which passes through $(3, 5)$.
   (e) Find an equation of the line of the family in (a) or (b) which has slope -2.

5 *Measurement and Approximation*

5.01 EXACT VALUES AND MEASURED VALUES

It may not be too much of an oversimplification to analyze our use of numbers from two points of view. In all our previous considerations we have thought of a number as an abstraction or as an idealized concept; for example, we think of the number 3 as the only characteristic common to all sets of objects which can be put in 1:1 correspondence with the set $\{a,b,c\}$. We carry out operations on numbers and use them in every aspect of our lives. We buy 3 loaves of bread, 10 gallons of gasoline, or a table and 6 chairs. A contractor makes a bid of \$35,000 for a particular construction project. We pay a bill by writing a check for \$35.72 or the bank adds \$2.47 interest to a savings account. History books record that World War II ended in 1945. Perhaps we instruct an architect to draw up plans for a house, to include a living room 30 feet long and 12 feet wide. The diagram of this room is a rectangle whose sides are labeled 30 and 12. We say the measure or area of the room (considered as a rectangle) is the product of the measures of its sides, that is, $30 \times 12 = 360$. It should be evident that we make considerable use of numbers in describing exact, numerical aspects of the matters with which we deal.

It is quite a different matter when we make a measurement,* whether it be of a line segment, angle, time or temperature. For example, suppose that we wish to measure the length and width of the physical room which the contractor constructed. No matter how carefully our ruler is calibrated or how painstaking we are in applying the ruler to the side of the room, we cannot state the exact length (nor was it possible except by accident for the contractor to create a room of the exact dimensions specified by the architect). In other words the actual room is always an approximation of the idealized room, and the measured values are always approximations of the existing dimensions.

---

*See Section 4.08. We shall endeavor to be consistent in distinguishing between *measurement*, for example, 3 inches, 5 miles, 6 hours, 70 degrees, and *measure* which is a number associated with a measurement, for example, 3, 5, 6, 70.

It might be well to point out that this approximation is not to be thought of in the same sense in which we approximate $\sqrt{2}$, for example. The number $\sqrt{2}$ is the ideal abstraction just as is the number 3. It is only when we attempt to represent $\sqrt{2}$ in the arithmetic of rational numbers rather than in the arithmetic of real numbers that we encounter the need to approximate it. Similarly when we think of the length of the circumference of a circle of unit radius, this number, 2π, is an exact description of the idealized concept. It is only when we wish to give to 2π an alternate representation in terms of rational numbers that we again face the matter of approximation. However these are not considerations arising from measurement and hence are not our immediate concern.

Whenever we make a measurement and describe the result, we are giving an approximation of the actual quantity involved, since our ability to distinguish differences of small magnitude in similar measurements is extremely limited. Nothing can be measured exactly and great care should be exercised in describing the measurement in order to avoid the giving of false information.

This inability to measure exactly need not be interpreted as a major failure nor even as a basic weakness of our system of real numbers. The truth is that we simply do not need the luxury of exact values in most of the situations in which we use numbers. In driving from Seattle to Tacoma it may be sufficient for us to know that the distance is between 30 and 40 miles. If one is paying a trucker by the mile, and if he makes the trip twice a day, one might wish to know that the distance is, say, 34 miles. On the other hand, if one is calculating the cost of paving the highway from Seattle to Tacoma one might very likely require that the distance be known still more exactly. The point that we are anxious to make clear is that almost any measurement may be valuable depending on the purpose of the measurement; that is, the value of a measurement is relative to the use we intend to make of it. By way of illustration let us suppose that someone reported that he had made a measurement "to the nearest inch." Would we be in a position to say whether the measurement was or was not the result of careful work, that is, valuable or of little worth? If the measurement were the height of a skyscraper we would probably say that the job was well done, but if it should represent the length of a desk-top it would be considered a very rough approximation. How are we then to make useful measurements and to represent the results intelligently?

5.02 PRECISION AND ACCURACY

When we make any measurement it is very likely that some difference will exist between the true value and the measured value. In

106   *Measurement and Approximation*

dealing with such differences or errors we come in contact with two concepts, namely, precision and accuracy.

The *precision* of a measurement is concerned with the magnitude of error which is inherently associated with the measurement as a result of the way in which it is made. For example, if we are measuring the dimensions of the foundation of a house, the error of the measurement should be smaller if our scale is marked off in inches rather than only in feet; similarly smaller if marked off in quarter-inches rather than in half-inches. Therefore precision depends on the smallest unit of measure employed in obtaining the measurement. Much as we might be led to do so, we do not define precision to be this smallest unit of measure, since reducing the size of the unit would then reduce rather than increase precision. Intuitively we want precision to increase when both the length of the smallest unit employed and correspondingly the error decreases. Hence we shall say that precision is indicated by the size of the smallest unit used in making the measurement.

What do we mean when we give a measurement as $8\frac{2}{4}$ inches? We are saying that the second quarter-inch marking on the scale is closer to the end-point of the line segment being measured than is either of the adjacent quarter-inch markings; that is, we believe $8\frac{2}{4}$ to be closer to the actual length than $8\frac{1}{4}$ or $8\frac{3}{4}$. In other words we are saying that the end-point of the object cannot be more than $\frac{1}{8}$ of a unit away, in either direction, from the $8\frac{2}{4}$ marking. Hence the actual measurement, which we shall call x inches, falls in the range $(8\frac{2}{4} \pm \frac{1}{8})$ inches; that is, $8\frac{3}{8} \leq x \leq 8\frac{5}{8}$. From this discussion we see why some authors, quite properly, choose to define a measurement as a closed interval. On the other hand, if we described the result as $8\frac{1}{2}$ inches, we would mean that the true measurement falls in the range $(8\frac{1}{2} \pm \frac{1}{4})$ inches, and, therefore, $8\frac{1}{4} \leq x \leq 8\frac{3}{4}$. Hence a measurement of $8\frac{1}{2}$ inches is less precise than a measurement of $8\frac{2}{4}$ inches because the first implies the use of a ruler marked off only in half-inches while the second indicates that the ruler was marked off in quarter-inches. If we wish to indicate precision of the order of a quarter-inch we must not reduce $\frac{2}{4}$ to $\frac{1}{2}$ in representing the measurement.

A measurement of $8\frac{2}{4}$ inches indicates that the measurement was made to the nearest quarter-inch while $8\frac{1}{2}$ inches means measurement to the nearest half-inch. The absolute (greatest possible) error is considered to be half the length of the complete range, that is $\frac{1}{8}$ inch when measured to the nearest quarter-inch and $\frac{1}{4}$ inch when measured to the nearest half-inch. In the figure, let C represent the end of a segment being measured by three scales, marked off in inches, half-inches, and quarter-inches, respectively. When measured to the nearest inch the measurement is 8 inches and the error is indicated by the distance BC. If measured to the nearest half-inch the measurement is

Precision and Accuracy 107

$8\frac{1}{2}$ inches and the length CD represents the error. But if the scale can be read to the nearest quarter-inch then the reading is $8\frac{1}{4}$ inches and the error is represented by the distance EC. Precision of a measurement is indicated, then, by the absolute error of the measurement and depends on the smallest distinguishable unit on the scale used in making the measurement.

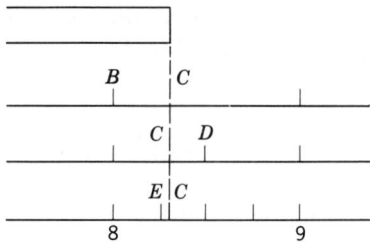

If we wish to indicate that a measurement of 8 inches is precise to a quarter-inch, we might state it as $8\frac{0}{4}$ inches or $(8 \pm \frac{1}{8})$ inches. It is somewhat easier to convey similar information by the use of decimal fractions where a measurement of 8 inches to the nearest $\frac{1}{10}$ inch would be described as 8.0 inches; a measurement to the nearest $\frac{1}{100}$ inch would be described as 8.00 inches, etc. This matter will receive further consideration in Section 5.03.

The two measurements $18\frac{1}{2}$ inches and $1018\frac{1}{2}$ inches have the same absolute error and hence the same precision. Is this error as important in the one measurement as in the other? How shall we evaluate the significance of an error? For example, if we are buying a replacement window shade of width approximately $18\frac{1}{2}$ inches, it would be necessary to be able to measure the distance between the brackets at least to the nearest quarter-inch and possibly even to the nearest eighth-inch, rather than the nearest half-inch, in order to assure a satisfactory fitting. On the other hand, if one is buying approximately $1018\frac{1}{2}$ inches of water-pipe for an intake line, probably precision to the nearest inch rather than the nearest half-inch would be sufficient. In other words, precision ceases to be the most important guide, and the magnitude of the absolute error relative to the measurement itself becomes the important consideration.

This ratio of the absolute error to the measurement itself is known as the *relative error,* and it describes the *accuracy* of a measurement. The accuracy of a measure is said to increase as the relative error decreases. The relative error of the $18\frac{1}{2}$-inch measurement is $\frac{\frac{1}{4}}{18\frac{1}{2}} = \frac{0.25}{18.5}$ or approximately 0.014, whereas the $1018\frac{1}{2}$-inch measurement has a relative error of $\frac{\frac{1}{4}}{1018\frac{1}{2}} = \frac{0.25}{1018.5}$ or approximately 0.00025. Therefore the latter measure has the greater accuracy (since the relative error is smaller) but the precision is the same. Both precision and accuracy are important in different ways. The club treasurer may be just as concerned with an inaccuracy of $2.00 in his books whether he has handled $200 or $20. On the other hand, the small boy buying candy may well be more upset over the loss of a dime than the financier who is overcharged ten cents on his charge account.

EXERCISES

1. Tell which measurement in each pair has (1) the greater precision, (2) the greater accuracy
   (a) 5.2 yds. $2\frac{1}{4}$ yds.
   (b) 0.68 ft.   23.5 ft.
   (c) 0.235 in.   0.146 in.
2. Arrange the following measurements in the order of increasing precision:
   (a) $36\frac{1}{2}$ in., $27\frac{9}{16}$ in., $32\frac{3}{8}$ in., $46\frac{2}{7}$ in., $22\frac{1}{4}$ in.
   (b) 4.62 in., 3.041 in., 3 in., 82.4 in., 0.3762 in.
   (c) $(6 \pm \frac{1}{2})$ ft., (32 ± 0.005) in., (7.2 ± 0.05) miles, $(3\frac{1}{2} \pm \frac{1}{8})$ in.
3. A meter stick is divided into centimeters and tenths of a centimeter. A line segment was measured with such a scale and stated to be $3\frac{7}{10}$ centimeters long.
   (a) What is the closed interval associated with the measurement?
   (b) What is the greatest possible error?
4. The measurement of a line segment was stated to be $7\frac{3}{4}$ inches.
   (a) To what nearest unit or fraction of a unit must this segment have been measured?
   (b) What is the closed interval associated with the measurement?
   (c) What is the greatest possible error in the measurement?
5. The measurement of a line segment was stated as $(2\frac{5}{16} \pm \frac{1}{32})$ inches.
   (a) Between what marks on the scale must the end of the segment lie?
   (b) What is the greatest possible error?
6. The greatest possible error in a measurement of length is what fractional part of the smallest division (interval) used on the measuring instrument?
7. A square has sides measured as $3\frac{2}{7}$ inches long. Find the largest possible area and the smallest possible area of the square.
8. The dimensions of a rectangular box are measured as $10\frac{1}{2}$, $5\frac{9}{2}$, $3\frac{1}{2}$ inches. Find the calculated volume; then determine the greatest possible error by finding the minimum volume possible and then the maximum volume possible.

9. A master machinist measures a $3\frac{1}{2}$ inch piston head to the nearest 0.0001 inch while an astronomer measures the distance, by the parallax, to the star Sirius. The distance to Sirius is 8.6 light years (1 light year is approximately 6×10^{12} miles = distance light travels in a year at 186,000 miles per second). Which measurement is more accurate?
10. Which of the following measurements has the greatest accuracy? Which is least accurate?
   (a) 23.6 in.   (b) 0.043 in.   (c) 7812 in.   (d) 0.2 in.
11. If a measurement, x, has greater precision than a measurement y, does x also have greater accuracy than y? Illustrate.

5.03 SIGNIFICANT DIGITS

In Section 5.01 we discussed the way in which numbers are used when referring to exactly describable properties of objects and in describing idealized conditions, as for example a 30 foot by 12 foot living room. Incidentally we are free to imagine a room with idealized (exact) dimensions of, say, 30.001379 feet and 12.500248 feet, if we wish. The measurement of the area of such an imagined room is then exactly 375.024677841992 square feet. Although this latter number is exact, it does not interest us from any practical point of view for obvious reasons. Consequently we are going to devote our attention to numbers which represent measured values.

When we measure the length of a room and state it as 32* we are saying that the length, x, is between 31.5 and 32.5 that is, $31.5 \leq x < 32.5$.† Here we have measured to the nearest unit and the absolute error is one-half unit. If we stated the length as 32.0, we would be saying that the length, x is between 31.95 and 32.05, that is, $31.95 \leq x < 32.05$ and we would have measured to the nearest tenth of a unit. In the first case we say the number is given to two *significant digits* (or, if we wish to be more correct, that the numeral representing the number is given to two significant digits), and in the second case to three significant digits. Let us consider the measures 28000 and 0.028. They both have the same number (two) of significant digits, but the precisions of the two measures are quite different. However the relative errors in the two cases are $\frac{500}{28000}$ and $\frac{0.0005}{0.028}$, respectively.

---
*From here on we shall generally omit the unit of length, it being understood, and employ the concept of measure (see Section 5.01) rather than measurement.
†We employ half-open intervals here in order to avoid ambiguity concerning the interval to which the end-point measures belong.

110 Measurement and Approximation

Since these two ratios are equal we say the two measures have the same accuracy. Consequently accuracy of a measure is closely related to the number of significant digits. Accuracy, but not precision, is unaffected by the position of the decimal point provided the significant digits remain unchanged. Just as we do not want to indicate greater precision in a measure than actually exists, so also we do not wish to indicate greater than the true accuracy by including more significant digits than are justified. For instance, it is highly unreasonable to say that we measured a room in feet and found the measure of one side to be 32.001379. For such data would mean that we were claiming to have measured to the nearest one-millionth of a unit, an accomplishment only possible in a laboratory with very specialized equipment. A more logical statement would be 32.0 or, possibly, 32.00, if a carefully calibrated steel tape were used. In this example both the precision and the accuracy were indicated as being unreasonably high.

We shall expect, therefore, to interpret any nonzero digit in a numeral as a significant digit; also any zero occurring between nonzero digits; similarly, any zero occurring to the right of a nonzero digit, provided the zero in question lies to the right of the decimal point, will be considered significant. By way of illustration, zeros are significant in the following numerals: 3005, 4.06, 100.0, .18500, 709.0180. For example, a measurement of 3005 millimeters is equal to 3.005 meters and we see that the zeros are significant, and there are four significant digits. However, a measurement of 0.00012 meters is equal to 0.12 millimeters and the zeros are evidently not significant (or else they would survive in terms of the new unit). We may indicate the desired precision by writing a number in what is generally referred to as "scientific notation," for example, as 3.0×10^2. Of course $3 \times 10^2 = 300$ with one significant digit and indicates $250 \leq x < 350$; $3.0 \times 10^2 = 300$ with two significant digits, and indicates $295 \leq x < 305$ and $3.00 \times 10^2 = 300$ with three significant digits and indicates $299.5 \leq x < 300.5$.

Questions. 1. How many significant digits are indicated in each of the following measures: 583, 50083, 583.0, 2.18, 2.0018, 0.0015, 0.001500, 0.001005, 0.0010050, 200.00?

2. How would you express the measure 39000 with the proper precision if it is known to have
   (a) 5 significant digits?   (b) 4 significant digits?
   (c) 3 significant digits?   (d) 2 significant digits?

Sometimes a bar is placed above or below a zero digit to indicate that the zero is a significant digit. For example, 25$\bar{0}$00 has the same number (three) of significant digits as 2.50×10^4. Unless specified to the contrary, a measure of 25000 is considered to have two significant digits.

Significant Digits

Question. Can you write x to the correct number of significant digits, given the following information?
  (a) $197.5 \leq x < 198.5$
  (b) $2.395 \leq x < 2.405$
  (c) $2.305 \leq x < 2.315$
  (d) $2.35 \leq x < 2.45$
  (e) $499.5 \leq x < 500.5$
  (f) $495 \leq x < 505$
  (g) $450 \leq x < 550$

EXERCISES

1. Give the range in which the measure falls and then tell the greatest possible error of the measure:
   (a) 527000 (b) 5270 (c) 52700
   (d) 52.7 (e) 0.5270 (f) 527

2. For the following measures do the same as in Exercise 1:
   (a) 0.3800 (b) 3.800×10^5
   (c) 3.80×10^3 (d) 0.00038000

3. With reference to Exercise 2,
   (a) which of the measures is most precise? most accurate?
   (b) which is least precise? least accurate?
   (c) do any two measures have the same precision? same accuracy?

4. State the number of significant digits in each measure.
   (a) 520 (b) 0.002 (c) 38.90
   (d) 0.0603 (e) 4.700×10^5 (f) 2.8×10^9
   (g) 2.80×10^9 (h) 0.0500

5. (a) Suppose you measured a segment to the nearest tenth of a unit. Which of the following states the measure best: 3.2? 3.20? 3.200?
   (b) Same as (a) if measured to the nearest hundredth of a unit.

6. Express the following in scientific notation:
   (a) 463,000,000 (b) 327,000 (c) 0.000462
   (d) 32.004 (e) 2 (f) 0.0000400
   (g) 36.8×10^5 (h) 0.8×10^{-7} (i) 72 billion
   (j) 58$\bar{0}$00 (k) 58$\bar{0}\bar{0}$0 (l) 58$\bar{0}\bar{0}\bar{0}$

7. Show by use of a bar over a zero, the precision of the following measurements:
   (a) 4200 feet, measured to the nearest foot
   (b) 23,000 miles, measured to the nearest hundred miles
   (c) 48,000,000 people, reported to the nearest ten-thousand people

8. (a) State the greatest possible error for each measure:
   (1) 52 (2) 4.1 (3) 2580 (4) 36$\bar{0}$
   (5) 7.03 (6) 0.006 (7) 54,000 (8) 54,$\bar{0}$00
   (b) Find the relative error of each measure in (a).

112   *Measurement and Approximation*

5.04 ADDITION AND THE ROUNDING OF NUMBERS

Let us suppose that we are adding the following numbers that represent measures:

$$423.8$$
$$1.356$$
$$12.85$$

Since 423.8 may be in error by as much as 0.05 it is useless to carry any digit beyond the tenths place in this addition problem, in spite of the fact that each of the three numerals has four significant digits. In other words where the operation is addition there is no advantage in retaining any number in a form more precise than the least precise number being added. Consequently it is desirable to round the second and third numbers to one decimal place. There are two procedures in common usage to accomplish this purpose. Most people are probably in the habit of increasing the preceding digit by one whenever the digit to be discarded is five or larger.

Questions. 1. How do you round the following to 3 significant digits: 103499, 2.3042, .0097952?

2. How do you round the following to the nearest tenth: 10.35, 2.3499, 979.99?

This rounding rule is satisfactory for many purposes. In an addition problem, however, in which a relatively large number of five's have been discarded in the "rounding off" process, we may find that too large a sum has been obtained. We can illustrate this effect in the following example consisting only of three numbers

$$423.81$$
$$1.35$$
$$\underline{12.85}$$
$$438.01$$

If we round to tenths we shall have

$$423.8$$
$$1.4$$
$$\underline{12.9}$$
$$438.1$$

We see that the two sums differ by one in the tenths place, and this difference could be much greater if more numbers were involved in the addition.

In order to help avoid this occurrence the following procedure is often adopted in discarding five's in the "rounding off" process. If more than one digit is to be dropped and the first (or left-most) digit to be dropped is a 5, increase the preceding digit by 1. For example, if we wish to round 3.254 to two digits we shall obtain 3.3. If only one digit is to be discarded and it is a 5, then increase the preceding digit by 1 if that digit is presently odd and do not increase it if it is presently even; for instance, 0.00135 would be rounded to 0.0014 and 0.00125 to 0.0012. The effect of this procedure is to increase about half the time, when discarding five's. Let us see how this rule works in our previous example. If we round to tenths we have

$$\begin{array}{r} 423.8 \\ 1.4 \\ \underline{12.8} \\ 438.0 \end{array}$$

which gives the same result, in this case, as rounding the original sum after addition. Hence, in general, we are justified in claiming that a sum is as precise as the least precise of the numbers being added.

EXERCISES

1. Add or subtract the following measures:
   (a) $42.36 + 578.1 + 73.4 + 37.285 + 0.62$
   (b) $7.3 - 6.28$
   (c) $5430 - 647$
   (d) $9.36 + 0.345 + 1713.06 + 35.27$
   (e) $38514 + 68000 + 29500 + 278500$
2. Perform the indicated operations on the given measures:
   (a) $85.42 + 7.30 + 16.015 + 36.4$ (b) $735 - 0.73$
   (c) $0.004 + 2.1 + 6.135$ (d) $5.03 - 4.2$

5.05 SIGNIFICANT DIGITS AND MULTIPLICATION

When we encounter the multiplication of two measured values, as we do in the computation of area, the procedure used is not the same as in addition. Let us suppose that the sides of a rectangle are measured as 2.3 and 123.6. Direct multiplication gives the area as 284.28. Since the dimension whose measure is 2.3 could vary between 2.25 and 2.35 and similarly the other measure could vary from 123.55 to 123.65, the smallest and largest possible values of the area would be $123.55 \times 2.25 = 277.9875$ and $123.65 \times 2.35 = 290.5775$, respectively. It is clear, therefore, that at least three digits of the answer, 284.28

are meaningless. Also it is evident that more work than was necessary has been done in obtaining the result, 280, which is all we are justified in concluding. Hence it is advisable for us to reduce the number of significant digits in 123.6, and the generally accepted procedure is to carry only as many significant digits as are in the factor containing the smallest number of significant digits. According to this rule we would have $2.3 \times 120 = 276$, which when rounded to the number of significant digits in either factor gives 280. This result is in agreement with the original answer, rounded to two digits. Our purpose always is to obtain the result with the justified accuracy and with the least effort. In general, a product of measures is as accurate as the least accurate of the factors.

Let us suppose that we wish to evaluate 29π, where 29 is an approximation. The product, $29 \times 3.1416 = 91.1064$, is 91 when rounded to two digits. However 29×3.1 gives 89.9 which rounds to 90. If we were to use three digits of π (where we have as many significant digits as we can ever need) we obtain $29 \times 3.14 = 91.06$ which rounds to 91 and gives the desired result accurate to two digits. For this reason the rule for multiplication is sometimes altered slightly, as follows, to provide greater accuracy. When two approximate numbers with differing numbers of significant digits are to be multiplied, it may be helpful to keep at most one more significant digit in one factor than is kept in the other factor.

It should be emphasized that no error but only excess labor is introduced if the number of significant digits retained in a factor is larger than the minimum number needed to give the required accuracy in the answer, provided the answer is rounded off properly. This is particularly applicable in division where it may be desirable to retain one or two additional digits in the dividend, if they are known to be significant, in order to obtain the desired accuracy in the quotient. The latter will, of course, be rounded off, if necessary, as in multiplication. For example, $\frac{1.142}{27} = 0.042$; again $\frac{3.142}{27} = 0.116$ which would round off to 0.12.

EXERCISES

1. Multiply the following measures, giving the answer to the proper accuracy:
    (a) 39.1×124.8 (b) 48.27π where $\pi = 3.14159\ldots$ (c) 0.0480×7.635
2. Multiply the following measures, giving the resulting product with the correct accuracy:
    (a) 4.1×36.9 (b) 3.6×4673 (c) $3.76 \times (2.9 \times 10^4)$
3. Divide the following measures:
    (a) $3.632 \div 0.83$ (b) $0.000344 \div 0.000301$ (c) $(3.14 \times 10^6) \div 8.006$

4. If π is given as 3.141593, find the circumferences of the circles whose diameters have the following measures:
   (a) 3.5   (b) 46.36   (c) 6
5. Find the area of a rectangular field whose sides have measures 835.5 and 305.
6. A machine stamps out parts, each weighing 0.625 pounds. How much do 75 of these parts weigh?
7. Assuming that water weighs 62.5 pounds per cubic foot what is the volume of 15,610 pounds of water?

5.06 SHORT MULTIPLICATION AND DIVISION

By way of conclusion it might not be inappropriate to devote a little space to a method of short multiplication. Let us examine the following multiplication of two measured values, each accurate to four significant digits.

$$\begin{array}{r} 1.872 \\ 23.64 \\ \hline 7{\vert}488 \\ 112{\vert}32 \\ 561{\vert}6 \\ 3744{\vert} \\ \hline 44.25{\vert}408 \end{array}$$

Since the answer is reliable only to four digits, it appears that the digits to the right of the vertical line represent unprofitable labor on our part, provided that we "carry" the proper amount in obtaining the digit immediately to the left of the vertical line.

We are going to illustrate a slight variation in form in the following multiplication of 24×36 in which we multiply first by the left-hand (in this case, ten's) digit* of the multiplier and then by the unit's digit:

$$\begin{array}{r} 24 \\ 36 \\ \hline 72 \\ 144 \\ \hline 864 \end{array}$$

---

*At the risk of boring the reader we note once again that we actually multiply by a number and not by a digit. However we choose to use the simpler language in order to avoid a complicated circumlocution.

Measurement and Approximation

If we use this procedure in our first example we obtain

$$
\begin{array}{r}
1.872 \\
23.64 \\
\hline
3744 \\
561|6 \\
112|32 \\
7|488 \\
\hline
44.25|408
\end{array}
$$

We see then that we may dispense with writing the digits to the right of the vertical line provided that we "carry" the proper quantity "across" that line. In order to help us "keep track" of the proper product to be recorded, it might be helpful to place a slanting line through successive digits of the upper factor beginning at the right following each multiplication by a digit of the multiplier. Consequently we obtain the following abbreviated form (compare with the previous multiplication to note where the "carrying" occurred):

$$
\begin{array}{r}
1.8\!\!\!/7\!\!\!/2\!\!\!/ \\
23.64 \\
\hline
3744 = 2 \times 1872 \\
562 = (3 \times 187) + 1 \\
112 = (6 \times 18) + 4 \\
7 = (4 \times 1) + 3 \\
\hline
44.25
\end{array}
$$

In the short procedure the decimal point must be located by approximating the original product (in this case, $2 \times 24 = 48$, hence 44.25). The final digit of the answer will generally be found to differ at most by 1 or 2 from the original result obtained by "rounding off." However this error would be expected to increase as the number of "roundings" increases. This is illustrated in the following example:

$$
\begin{array}{r}
0.19352 \\
483.26 \\
\hline
116112 \\
38704 \\
58056 \\
154816 \\
77408 \\
\hline
93.5204752
\end{array}
\qquad
\begin{array}{r}
0.1\!\!\!/9\!\!\!/3\!\!\!/5\!\!\!/2\!\!\!/ \\
483.26 \\
\hline
77408 \\
15482 \\
581 \\
39 \\
12 \\
\hline
93.522
\end{array}
$$

Question. Can you verify the preceding results by reversing the order of the factors in each of the products?

An analogous procedure is possible in division. Let us evaluate $\frac{23.64}{1.872}$ as a decimal fraction. We should obtain a quotient with four significant digits, and we can do it (in this case but not when the quotient is less than 1 when decimal points are disregarded) *without* rewriting 23.64 as 23.640 or 23.6400, and so on. (This is most desirable since we have no way of knowing what the actual digits are which lie to the right of 4.) After each subtraction step we eliminate a digit of the divisor beginning at the right, but remember to "carry," where necessary, when subtracting multiples of the divisor.

```
            12.63
    1.872 ) 23.64
            1872
             492
             374
             118
             112
               6
               6
```

Question. Can you verify by short multiplication that $1.872 \times 12.63 = 23.64$ with approximately four digit accuracy?

The slide rule and logarithms are two methods of multiplication in which the accuracy of the result may be limited by the procedure itself. In the case of the slide rule, about three digit accuracy is the maximum generally attainable. With regard to logarithms, tables in common use generally have four or five significant digits, but tables of greater accuracy are available.

EXERCISES

1. Use short multiplication to obtain the product of the following measures:
   (a) 38.754×2.9143 (b) 2.9143×38.754
2. Use the above short division procedure to obtain the quotients of the following measures:
   (a) $101.3 \div 23.75$ (b) $4.826 \div 1374$ (c) $0.0827 \div 0.00158$

6 *From Arithmetic to Algebra*

6.01 WHERE DOES ALGEBRA BEGIN?

For many decades arithmetic and algebra have been kept separate from each other and treated as distinct entities. Arithmetic was thought of as restricted to computations involving the carrying out of indicated operations on numbers. On the other hand, algebra was considered to be a higher level study, where the answers were obtained to questions requiring more devious solutions.

It is only relatively recently that we have come to recognize in a practical way that arithmetic is specialized algebra or that algebra is generalized arithmetic. Perhaps the introduction of the term, "sentence," to describe a mathematical statement which may be true or false and to provide an alternative expression for the term, "equation," may have helped to erase the distinction between the two areas.

Thus at one time the sentence $3 + 5 = 8$ would have been thought of as belonging to arithmetic and the sentence $x + 5 = 8$ as belonging to algebra. However $3 + 5 = 8$ is a true sentence and serves as a verification that the number three belongs to the solution set of the open sentence $x + 5 = 8$. Since these sentences are so closely related it seems unwise and unnecessary to deny ourselves the freedom of operation made available through the use of algebraic techniques.

6.02 GRAPHS

When we incorporate signs of inequality in our statements we obtain another type of sentence, for example, $3 + 5 < 9$. However the solution set of the open sentence $x + 5 < 9$ contains much more than the number three. Here, as always, it is essential to know clearly what our universe U is. If U is the set of natural numbers, then the solution set of the sentence $x + 5 < 9$ is $\{1,2,3\}$. If U is the set of integers, the solution set is $\{3,2,1,0,-1,-2,-3,...\}$. If U is the set of natural numbers greater than 5, the solution set is $\emptyset$. Unless otherwise stated we shall use the real numbers as our universe U from now on, and the solution set of the above sentence is then seen to be $\{x|x \in R$ and $x < 4\}$. It is quite possible for two different sentences to have the same solution set with respect to the same universe. When this is true we say the sentences are *equivalent sentences*. For example, $2x + 10 < 18$ and $x + 6 < 10$ are both equivalent to the above sentence $x + 5 < 9$.

It is helpful to represent the numbers of the solution set of a sentence by indicated circles or segments on the number line, thereby producing what is known as the *graph* of the solution set of the sentence, or, in short, the graph of the sentence or the graph of the locus. It should be emphasized that the graph is the picture while the locus is the set of points (for example, the solution set). On the number line a small circle is darkened or not darkened to indicate, respectively, that the number corresponding to the point belongs or does not belong to the solution set. Hence the graph of $x + 5 = 8$ is

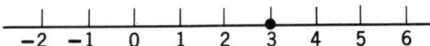

and the graph of $x + 5 < 9$ is

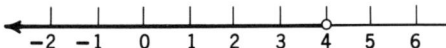

We may create more complicated open sentences by combining two clauses by "and" or "or." Note that $x + 6 \geqslant 4$ means $x + 6 > 4$ or $x + 6 = 4$. Then for the open sentence $[x + 6 \geqslant 4$ *and* $x + 3 < 9]$ a number will have to satisfy *both* clauses in order to belong to the solution set. Hence the solution set of the open sentence, $[x + 6 \geqslant 4$ *and* $x + 3 < 9]$, will be the *intersection* of the solution set of $x + 6 \geqslant 4$ and the solution set of $x + 3 < 9$, that is,

$\{x|x \in R$ and $x \geqslant -2\} \cap \{x|x \in R$ and $x < 6\} = \{x|x \in R$ and $-2 \leqslant x < 6\}$.

If we represent the two graphs of the intersection, separately, as

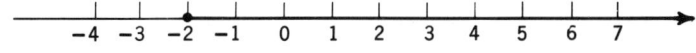

and

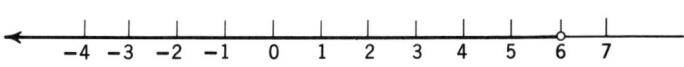

then the graph of our combination sentence is the set of points common to both graphs, that is, the points lying between -2 and 6 and including -2.

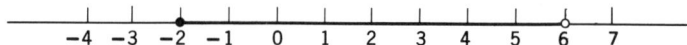

The reader will find another notation in rather common usage, namely that of "open" and "closed" interval. We will define four cases:

$[a,b] = \{x | x \in R \text{ and } a \leq x \leq b\}$ that is, a *closed interval* (*includes* both end-points)

$[a,b)$ or $[a,b[= \{x | x \in R \text{ and } a \leq x < b\}$ that is, a *half-open interval* (*includes* only one end-point)

$(a,b]$ or $]a,b] = \{x | x \in R \text{ and } a < x \leq b\}$ that is, a *half-open interval* (*includes* only one end-point)

(a,b) or $]a,b[= \{x | x \in R \text{ and } a < x < b\}$ that is, an *open interval* (*excludes* both end-points)

Hence the set $\{x | x \in R \text{ and } -2 \leq x < 6\}$ associated with the above graph may also be represented by the half-open interval $[-2, 6[$.

For the sentence $[x + 6 \geq 4 \text{ or } x + 3 < 9]$ the solution set is the *union* of the two individual solution sets, that is,

$\{x | x \in R \text{ and } x \geq -2\} \cup \{x | x \in R \text{ and } x < 6\} = \{x | x \in R \text{ and } x \geq -2 \text{ or } x < 6\}$

and hence is the complete universe R of real numbers. Its graph is the entire number line:

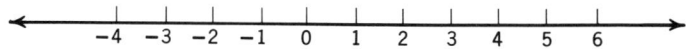

As a further illustration the sentence $[x + 6 \leq 4 \text{ or } x + 3 > 9]$ has as its solution set the set

$\{x | x \in R \text{ and } x \leq -2\} \cup \{x | x \in R \text{ and } x > 6\} = \{x | x \in R \text{ and } x \leq -2 \text{ or } x > 6\}$

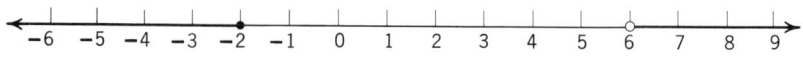

On the other hand the sentence $[x + 6 \leq 4 \text{ and } x + 3 > 9]$ has as its solution set the set

$\{x|x \in R \text{ and } x \leqslant -2\} \cap \{x|x \in R \text{ and } x > 6\} = \{x|x \in R \text{ and } x \leqslant -2 \text{ and } x > 6\} = \emptyset$, whose graph is the unshaded number line.

In preceding discussions we have stressed the principle of substitution of numbers from our replacement set or universe in an effort to arrive at the solution set of a given open sentence. Also, in Section 3.05 we demonstrated a constructive, formal approach to the solution of an equation of the form

$$ax + b = cx + d, a \neq c$$

It is the latter type of procedure which is representative of the general algebraic method. Although this type of operation will inevitably become almost automatic, and desirably so, a student when asked why he took a certain algebraic step should never have to answer, "That's the way the rule works," or words to that effect. Again, with reference to the solution of a sentence like $ax + b = cx + d$, $a \neq c$, we should note that the checking of the solution by substitution in the original sentence, actually verifies that the sentence obtained at each stage is truly equivalent to the original sentence.

Let us consider a sentence involving two variables*, for example, $x + y = 4$, and suppose that our universe is the set of whole numbers. Then the following pairs of numbers and only these pairs are seen to satisfy the equation: $x = 0$, $y = 4$; $x = 1$, $y = 3$; $x = 2$, $y = 2$; $x = 3$, $y = 1$; $x = 4$, $y = 0$. We may express the results more neatly by putting the numbers in ordered pairs, writing the x-value first and the y-value second, separated by a comma. The solution set is therefore $\{(0,4), (1,3), (2,2), (3,1), (4,0)\}$. In Section 4.09 we saw that such ordered pairs may be thought of as designating points in the plane. The graph of the sentence is seen at the right.

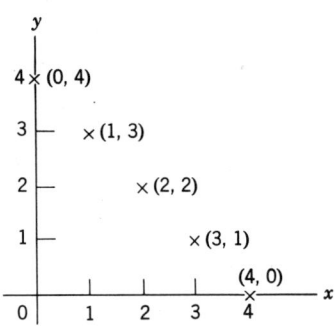

*The letters, x and y, which we use in equations like $x + 2 = 5$ or $x + y = 4$ play the role of "place-holders," that is, they indicate definitely where a substitution is to be made of a number or of numbers chosen from the replacement set or universe. Sometimes the word "unknown" is used to refer to these letters. However this is fundamentally an undesirable word since the solution set exists (even if it might be $\emptyset$) and is only temporarily unknown to the investigator. We believe the word "variable" is more suitable and we shall use it consistently.

122   From Arithmetic to Algebra

Question. How would the graph differ if the universe were the set of integers?

If the universe were the set of real numbers, we would find that our solution set consists of *all* the points on the complete line passing through the original five points.

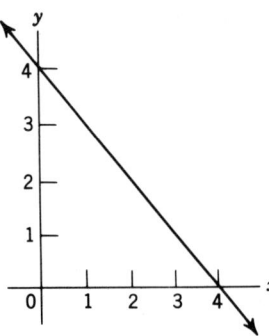

It is virtually impossible to overemphasize the important significance of the 1 : 1 correspondence between the set of points on the line (or locus) and the particular set of ordered pairs of real numbers which satisfy an equation such as $x + y = 4$.

EXERCISES

The universe in Exercises 1 through 4 is the set of real numbers.

1. Give the solution sets and draw the graphs for the following sentences:
   (a) $x - 2 \neq 3$ (b) $5x > 3 + 2x$ (c) $x + 3 = 3 + x$
   (d) $x^2 = 2x$ (e) $|x| < -3$

2. Give the solution sets and draw the graphs for the following sentences:
   (a) $7x + 9 = 10x - 4$ (b) $x + x \neq 2x$ (c) $x + 5 = 5 + |x|$
   (d) $x(x + 2) = 4x$ (e) $5x > 3 + |2x|$

3. Give the solution sets and draw the graphs for the following sentences:
   (a) $x^2 = 3|x|$ (b) $x^2 = -3|x|$ (c) $x + 5 < 5 + |x|$
   (d) $x^2 < 3|x|$ (e) $x + 5 > 5 + |x|$ (f) $|x - 3| + |x + 4| = 7$

4. Give the solution sets and draw the graphs for the following sentences:
   (a) $[|x| \geq 2 \text{ and } |x| \neq 5]$ (b) $[2 < |x| < 3 \text{ or } x^2 \geq 5x]$

5. Compare the graphs of the sentence, $y - 2x = 3$, with respect to the following universes for x and y:
   (a) the set of natural numbers
   (b) the set of whole numbers
   (c) the set of integers

6. Compare the graphs of the sentence $y + 2x + 4 = 0$ when the universe of x and y is
   (a) the set of whole numbers
   (b) the set of integers
   (c) the set of real numbers

7. On a half-hour television show the advertiser insists that there must be at least three minutes for commercials, and the network insists that there must be less than seven minutes for commercials. How much time must the program director provide for material other than commercials?

6.03 LINEAR EQUATIONS

There is no end of problems whose solution depends ultimately on finding the solution set of a linear equation. Perhaps the following example, chosen from the category of problems involving our positional notation, will illustrate how a descriptive statement may be expressed in terms of mathematical symbols and its solution obtained thereby.

In a certain two digit number* the tens' digit is twice as large as the units' digit. We are required to find the number if it is smaller by 36 when the digits are reversed. We begin by representing the number in question in the form $10y + x$; that is, by letting x represent the number of units and y the number of tens in the numeral for the number. From the statement of the problem we know that $y = 2x$; hence we may now describe our number in terms of a single variable x as

$$10(2x) + x = 21x$$

The number with the digits reversed is represented by

$$10x + 2x = 12x$$

Hence the final statement of the problem may be expressed in terms of x as follows:

$$21x - 12x = 36$$
$$9x = 36$$
$$x = 4, \quad y = 8$$

The required number is evidently 84. It is easily verified that 84 satisfies all the conditions of the problem.

It can be said quite rightly that the above problem involves not one but two variables and not one but two linear equations, namely,

$$(10y + x) - (10x + y) = 36$$

and
$$y - 2x = 0$$

It happens that the coefficients in the second equation are such as to make it a very simple procedure to substitute $2x$ for y in the first equation,

---

*This is a colloquial abbreviation of an expression like the following: "a number whose representation as a numeral in base ten requires two digits." In this problem we are seeking a number, not a two digit numeral, since it is numbers and not numerals which differ by 36.

From Arithmetic to Algebra

thus reducing the number of variables and equations from two to one.

Sometimes this sort of reduction is not quite as easy to carry out. Let us suppose that we arrive at or are given the following two equations:

$$3x - 5y = 7 \quad (1)$$
$$5x + 2y = 9 \quad (2)$$

From the second equation we may solve for y in terms of x as follows:

$$2y = 9 - 5x$$
$$y = \frac{1}{2}(9 - 5x)$$
$$= \frac{9}{2} - \frac{5}{2}x \quad (3)$$

If we substitute the latter expression for y in equation (1), we obtain

$$3x - 5\left(\frac{9}{2} - \frac{5}{2}x\right) = 7$$

Hence $\quad\quad 6x - 45 + 25x = 14$
That is $\quad\quad 6x + 25x = 14 + 45$
$$31x = 59$$
$$x = \frac{59}{31}$$

Now we may substitute $\frac{59}{31}$ for x in equation (3) and obtain

$$y = \frac{9}{2} - \frac{5}{2}\left(\frac{59}{31}\right)$$
$$= \frac{9(31) - 5(59)}{2(31)}$$
$$= \frac{279 - 295}{62}$$
$$= -\frac{16}{62}$$
$$= -\frac{8}{31}$$

Question. Can you verify that $x = \frac{59}{31}$ and $y = -\frac{8}{31}$ satisfy both equations (1) and (2) above?

Let us now apply the above procedure to the general case by considering the following two equations in the variables x and y:

$$ax + by = f$$
$$cx + dy = g$$

We know that not both a and c are zero, otherwise our equations would involve only one variable. Hence, if $a \neq 0$, we may obtain from the first equation

$$x = \frac{f}{a} - \frac{b}{a}y$$

Substituting in the second equation gives

$$c\left(\frac{f}{a} - \frac{b}{a}y\right) + dy = g$$

This latter equation has the solution $y = \frac{ag - cf}{ad - bc}$ if $ad - bc \neq 0$, and when this expression is substituted in the equation $x = \frac{f}{a} - \frac{b}{a}y$ we obtain $x = \frac{df - bg}{ad - bc}$, provided $ad - bc \neq 0$. Hence the solution of the equations is $x = \frac{df - bg}{ad - bc}$ and $y = \frac{ag - cf}{ad - bc}$, if $ad - bc \neq 0$. In fact another way of looking at the situation is to say that the equations

$$(ad - bc)x = df - bg$$

and

$$(ad - bc)y = ag - cf$$

are equivalent to the original two equations

$$ax + by = f$$
$$cx + dy = g, \text{ when } ad - bc \neq 0$$

and

Questions. 1. Can you verify that $x = \frac{df - bg}{ad - bc}$ and $y = \frac{ag - cf}{ad - bc}$ satisfy the above two equations?
    2. What happens if $a = 0$?
      Example: $2y = 7$
                     $3x + 4y = 11$

    3. What happens if $ad - bc = 0$?

Example: (a) $3x + 4y = 5$
$6x + 8y = 9$
(b) $3x + 4y = 5$
$6x + 8y = 10$

4. What happens if $a = 0$ and $ad - bc = 0$?

Another procedure which is quite effective involves multiplying, if necessary, the expressions on the left and right sides of each equation by some constant so that when the expressions on corresponding sides of the two equations are added, one of the variables will have coefficient zero. Let us use this approach with our previous example

$$3x - 5y = 7$$
$$5x + 2y = 9$$

If we multiply both sides of the first equation by 2 and both sides of the second equation by 5

we obtain $\qquad 6x - 10y = 14$
and $\qquad 25x + 10y = 45$

When we add corresponding sides of these equations

we obtain $\qquad 31x = 59$

and $\qquad x = \dfrac{59}{31}$

Then we have a choice of substituting this expression for x in one of the original equations and solving for y, or of repeating the original procedure, this time eliminating x and solving for y.

If we use this procedure with our two general equations

$$ax + by = f$$
$$cx + dy = g$$

the steps might be as follows:

$$adx + bdy = df$$
$$-bcx - bdy = -bg$$
$$(ad - bc)x = df - bg$$
$$x = \dfrac{df - bg}{ad - bc}, \text{ if } ad - bc \neq 0$$

We are again faced with a choice of methods for obtaining the solution for y.

Question. Can you obtain $y = \dfrac{ag - cf}{ad - bc}$ by eliminating the variable x in the above manner?

Let us recall that the solution set of the sentence $x + y = 4$ in the universe of real numbers, consisted of *all* ordered pairs corresponding to points on the straight line through the points $(0,4)$ and $(4,0)$. If we had had a second equation, say $x - y = 2$, we would have expected its solution set to consist of all ordered pairs corresponding to points on the line through the points $(0,-2)$ and $(2,0)$. Hence the solution set of $x + y - 4 = 0$ and $x - y - 2 = 0$ would be the intersection of the two individual solution sets. Evidently the pair $(3,1)$ belongs to the intersection set and investigation of the graphs of the two equations would lead us to the conclusion that this point is the only point of intersection of the two lines. This is a special case of the more general pair of equations whose solution set we have obtained in the previous paragraph.

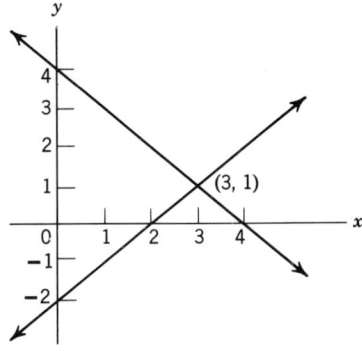

Question. In the language of geometry what can we say about the point

$$\left(\frac{df - bg}{ad - bc}, \frac{ag - cf}{ad - bc} \right) ?$$

If we introduce a new term called a (second order) determinant in the form of $\begin{vmatrix} a & b \\ c & d \end{vmatrix}$, defined simply as an alternative expression for the quantity, $ad - bc$, then we may represent the solution of the equations

$$ax + by = f$$
$$cx + dy = g$$

as

$$x = \frac{\begin{vmatrix} f & b \\ g & d \end{vmatrix}}{\begin{vmatrix} a & b \\ c & d \end{vmatrix}} \text{ and } y = \frac{\begin{vmatrix} a & f \\ c & g \end{vmatrix}}{\begin{vmatrix} a & b \\ c & d \end{vmatrix}},$$

that is, the solution set is

$$\left\{ \left(\frac{\begin{vmatrix} f & b \\ g & d \end{vmatrix}}{\begin{vmatrix} a & b \\ c & d \end{vmatrix}}, \frac{\begin{vmatrix} a & f \\ c & g \end{vmatrix}}{\begin{vmatrix} a & b \\ c & d \end{vmatrix}} \right) \right\}$$

Let us apply the determinant procedure to our previous example

$$3x - 5y = 7$$
$$5x + 2y = 9$$

We obtain

$$x = \frac{\begin{vmatrix} 7 & -5 \\ 9 & 2 \end{vmatrix}}{\begin{vmatrix} 3 & -5 \\ 5 & 2 \end{vmatrix}} = \frac{7(2) - (-5)(9)}{3(2) - (-5)(5)}$$

$$= \frac{14 + 45}{6 + 25} = \frac{59}{31}$$

and

$$y = \frac{\begin{vmatrix} 3 & 7 \\ 5 & 9 \end{vmatrix}}{\begin{vmatrix} 3 & -5 \\ 5 & 2 \end{vmatrix}} = \frac{3(9) - 5(7)}{3(2) - (-5)(5)}$$

$$= \frac{27 - 35}{6 + 25} = -\frac{8}{31}$$

Hence we may express the solution set as $\left\{ \left(\frac{59}{31}, -\frac{8}{31} \right) \right\}$

Now that we are aware of the close relationship between linear equations in two variables and straight lines in the plane, we should recognize the possibility that two such sentences or equations may possess (1) an empty solution set or (2) a solution set consisting of more than a single ordered pair of numbers. Case (1) is illustrated by the equations $2x + 3y = 5$ and $2x + 3y = 7$. Let us consider a particular ordered pair, (x_1, y_1), for which $2x_1 + 3y_1 = 5$. We say that the pair (x_1, y_1) satisfies the equation $2x + 3y = 5$. For example, $(1,1)$ satisfies the equation $2x + 3y = 5$. But $2x_1 + 3y_1 \neq 7$. Hence the two equations in question cannot be satisfied by any single ordered pair (x, y) and, therefore, the lines corresponding to the equations "never meet" and are said to be *parallel*. In case (2) the two lines are actually coincident, each point of one line is a point of the other line and the two individual solution sets are equal. An example of this situation is provided by the equations $2x + 3y = 5$ and $4x + 6y = 10$, in which the second equation is obtained by multiplying the equal expressions in the first equation by 2. In case (1) the determinant $\begin{vmatrix} a & b \\ c & d \end{vmatrix} = ad - bc$ is zero and we see that in this situation the equations

$$\begin{vmatrix} a & b \\ c & d \end{vmatrix} x = \begin{vmatrix} f & b \\ g & d \end{vmatrix} \text{ and } \begin{vmatrix} a & b \\ c & d \end{vmatrix} y = \begin{vmatrix} a & f \\ c & g \end{vmatrix}$$

have the empty set as their solution set. In case (2) all three determinants $\begin{vmatrix} a & b \\ c & d \end{vmatrix}, \begin{vmatrix} f & b \\ g & d \end{vmatrix}, \begin{vmatrix} a & f \\ c & g \end{vmatrix}$ are zero and hence every point of the given line satisfies the above pair of equivalent equations. Some additional material on determinants is to be found in Appendix B.

By way of concluding this section, we should like to illustrate a procedure connected with the solution of three linear equations in three variables. We have described a matrix (see Exercise 5, Section 3.09) as an array of entries and such an array may be square or rectangular in shape. If we compare the matrix

$$\begin{pmatrix} 1 & -1 & 2 & -9 \\ 2 & -3 & -1 & -5 \\ 3 & 2 & -1 & 4 \end{pmatrix}$$

with the equations

$$\begin{aligned} x - y + 2z &= -9 \\ 2x - 3y - z &= -5 \\ 3x + 2y - z &= 4 \end{aligned}$$

we see that the matrix describes all of the essential characteristics of the three equations. We sometimes refer to it as the *augmented matrix* since it contains the constants on the right side of the equalities as well as the coefficients of the variables.

There are certain standard operations such as
(1) interchanging two equations,
(2) multiplying the expression on each side of an equation by a number,
(3) adding the expressions on corresponding sides of two equations, which we may carry out on these equations and which produce an equivalent system of equations. The effect of each of these operations can be exhibited in the matrix. We are going to obtain the solution set for the three given equations and carry out, in parallel, the corresponding operations on the matrix. We shall then be in a position to see that the solution set for the equations could have been obtained by carrying out the matrix operations, by themselves, on the matrix.

From Arithmetic to Algebra

$$\begin{aligned}(1)\quad & x - y + 2z = -9 \\ (2)\quad & 2x - 3y - z = -5 \\ (3)\quad & 3x + 2y - z = 4\end{aligned} \qquad \begin{pmatrix} 1 & -1 & 2 & -9 \\ 2 & -3 & -1 & -5 \\ 3 & 2 & -1 & 4 \end{pmatrix}$$

We now eliminate the variable x in equation (2) by multiplying both sides of (1) by -2 and adding to the corresponding sides of (2).

$$\begin{aligned}(1)\quad & x - y + 2z = -9 \\ (4)\quad & - y - 5z = 13 \\ (3)\quad & 3x + 2y - z = 4\end{aligned} \qquad \begin{pmatrix} 1 & -1 & 2 & -9 \\ 0 & -1 & -5 & 13 \\ 3 & 2 & -1 & 4 \end{pmatrix}$$

In similar manner we eliminate x in (3) by multiplying both sides of (1) by -3 and adding to the corresponding sides of (3).

$$\begin{aligned}(1)\quad & x - y + 2z = -9 \\ (4)\quad & - y - 5z = 13 \\ (5)\quad & 5y - 7z = 31\end{aligned} \qquad \begin{pmatrix} 1 & -1 & 2 & -9 \\ 0 & -1 & -5 & 13 \\ 0 & 5 & -7 & 31 \end{pmatrix}$$

Let us multiply both sides of (4) by 5 and add to the corresponding sides of (5) to eliminate y in (5).

$$\begin{aligned}(1)\quad & x - y + 2z = -9 \\ (4)\quad & - y - 5z = 13 \\ (6)\quad & -32z = 96\end{aligned} \qquad \begin{pmatrix} 1 & -1 & 2 & -9 \\ 0 & -1 & -5 & 13 \\ 0 & 0 & -32 & 96 \end{pmatrix}$$

Multiply both sides of (4) by -1 and both sides of (6) by $-\frac{1}{32}$.

$$\begin{aligned}(1)\quad & x - y + 2z = -9 \\ (7)\quad & y + 5z = -13 \\ (8)\quad & z = -3\end{aligned} \qquad \begin{pmatrix} 1 & -1 & 2 & -9 \\ 0 & 1 & 5 & -13 \\ 0 & 0 & 1 & -3 \end{pmatrix}$$

Multiply both sides of (8) by -5 and add to the corresponding sides of (7).

$$\begin{aligned}(1)\quad & x - y + 2z = -9 \\ (9)\quad & y = 2 \\ (8)\quad & z = -3\end{aligned} \qquad \begin{pmatrix} 1 & -1 & 2 & -9 \\ 0 & 1 & 0 & 2 \\ 0 & 0 & 1 & -3 \end{pmatrix}$$

Multiply both sides of (8) by -2 and add to the corresponding sides of (1).

$$\begin{aligned}(10)\quad & x - y = -3 \\ (9)\quad & y = 2 \\ (8)\quad & z = -3\end{aligned} \qquad \begin{pmatrix} 1 & -1 & 0 & -3 \\ 0 & 1 & 0 & 2 \\ 0 & 0 & 1 & -3 \end{pmatrix}$$

Add the corresponding sides of (9) to the corresponding sides of (10).

$$
\begin{matrix}
(11) & x & & = -1 \\
(9) & & y & = 2 \\
(8) & & & z = -3
\end{matrix}
\qquad
\begin{pmatrix} 1 & 0 & 0 & -1 \\ 0 & 1 & 0 & 2 \\ 0 & 0 & 1 & -3 \end{pmatrix}
$$

The values of $x, y,$ and z determined by equations (8), (9), and (11) are checked, by substitution, as satisfying (1), (2), and (3). Hence, if $x, y,$ and z are named in that order, the solution set of equations (1), (2), and (3) is $\{(-1, 2, -3)\}$.

There is not any unique order for the above steps and, in practice, they could be combined, at some stages, into fewer steps.

Question. Can you obtain the solution set for the equations

$$
\begin{aligned}
3x + y - z &= -3 \\
x + 2y + z &= 0 \\
2x - 4y - 3z &= 5
\end{aligned}
$$

by working only with the augmented matrix?

EXERCISES

1. Find the solution sets for the following systems of equations:

   (a) $2x - y + z - 3 = 0$
   $x + 2y - z - 1 = 0$
   $3x + y + z - 6 = 0$

   (b) $3x + 2y - z - 1 = 0$
   $3x + 2y + 4z - 3 = 0$
   $x - 3y - z + 2 = 0$

   (c) $x + 2y - z - 1 = 0$
   $2x - y + z - 3 = 0$
   $2x + 4y - 2z - 5 = 0$

   (d) $2x - y + z - 3 = 0$
   $x + 2y - z - 1 = 0$
   $4x - 7y + 5z - 7 = 0$

   (e) $2x - y + z - 3 = 0$
   $x + 2y - z - 1 = 0$
   $4x - 7y + 5z - 4 = 0$

2. A bottle and a cork cost $1.10 together. If the bottle cost $1.00 more than the cork, find the cost of each.

3. John has five hours at his disposal. How far can he ride his bicycle into the surrounding hills at the rate of 8 miles per hour and return at the rate of 12 miles per hour?

4. A toy train is made up of engine, dining car, and caboose. The engine is three inches long. The dining car is as long as the caboose and engine

together. The caboose is as long as the engine and half the dining car together. Find the length of the train.

5. A store has 39 quarts of milk, some in pint cartons and some in half-pint cartons. There are 6 times as many pint cartons as half-pint cartons. How many half-pint cartons are there?

6. A man about to explode a charge of dynamite, set the fuse to cause the explosion to take place in 30 seconds. He ran back at the rate of 8 yards per second. If sound travels 1080 feet per second, how far did he run before he heard the sound of the explosion?

7. A man cashed a check at a bank and was given as many dollars as the check called for in cents and as many cents as the check called for in dollars. He spent $1.93 and then had twice the amount for which the check was written. What is the smallest amount for which the check could have been written?

8. If it costs one dollar a cord to have 4 foot lumber cut into 2 foot lengths, how much per cord will it cost to have 8 foot lumber cut into 2 foot lengths?

9. A man drives to work at an average speed of 35 miles per hour and drives home again, the same distance, at an average speed of 25 miles per hour. What is his average speed for the complete (two-way) trip?

10. Suppose we have a glass of water and a similar glass of wine. If a teaspoon of wine is transferred to the glass of water and then a teaspoon of the mixture is returned to the glass of wine, is there then more water in the wine or more wine in the water?

11. A man was bringing a wheelbarrow load of apples to town to sell. At each of three toll stations he was forced to give up half his apples and half an apple. If he arrived in town with twenty-five apples, how many did he have originally?

12. Of 1000 married couples, two-thirds of the husbands who are taller than their wives are also heavier, while three-quarters of the husbands who are heavier than their wives are also taller. If 120 wives are taller and heavier than their husbands, how many husbands are taller and heavier than their wives?

13. If a man drives up one side of a symmetric hill at an average speed of 20 miles per hour, at what average speed must he drive down the other side in order to average 40 miles per hour for the complete (up and down) trip?

6.04 QUADRATICS AND FACTORING

We have seen in Chapter 3 that if our universe is the set of complex numbers, we always have a nonempty solution set for the equation $ax^2 + b = 0$, where a and b are real numbers and $a \neq 0$.

Quadratics and Factoring

Question. What is the solution set for the sentence $ax^2 + b = 0 \ (a \neq 0)$?

This same type of equation may appear in the form $x^2 - m^2 = 0$. The left side of this equation may be rewritten as the product of two factors, as follows:

$$(x - m)(x + m) = 0$$

If we recall that in Chapter 3 we discussed the fact that $ab = 0 \iff a = 0$ or $b = 0$, then we see that $(x - m)(x + m) = 0 \iff x - m = 0$ or $x + m = 0$. Hence the solution set is $\{m, -m\}$. This solution set is also obtainable by equating the square root of each side of the equation $x^2 = m^2$, thereby obtaining $|x| = |m|$, that is, $x = m$ or $x = -m$. The standard abbreviation for this is $x = \pm m$. (*Note:* in order to avoid duplication, we only associate the $\pm$ sign with one side of the equation.)

We could have treated the equation $ax^2 + b = 0$ in this same way, multiplying first by $\frac{1}{a}$ to obtain $x^2 + \frac{b}{a} = 0$ and then rewriting the equation as $x^2 - \left(-\frac{b}{a}\right) = 0$ or $x^2 - \left(\sqrt{-\frac{b}{a}}\right)^2 = 0$. For example, if the given equation is $2x^2 + 5 = 0$, we may proceed as follows:

$$x^2 + \frac{5}{2} = 0$$

$$x^2 - \left(\sqrt{-\frac{5}{2}}\right)^2 = 0$$

$$\left(x - \sqrt{-\frac{5}{2}}\right)\left(x + \sqrt{-\frac{5}{2}}\right) = 0$$

Hence the solution set is $\left\{i\sqrt{\frac{5}{2}}, -i\sqrt{\frac{5}{2}}\right\}$. Again from $x^2 = -\frac{5}{2}$, we could have written immediately $x = \pm\sqrt{-\frac{5}{2}} = \pm i\sqrt{\frac{5}{2}}$.

The left side of the equation $x^2 - m^2 = 0$ is in the form of the difference of the squares of the two quantities and is a special case of a more general quadratic expression, $ax^2 + bx + c$, which we refer to as a trinomial; that is, a polynomial in which the number of terms is three. Let us consider a particular trinomial in the form

$$x^2 + (a + b)x + ab$$

134   From Arithmetic to Algebra

This expression is easily seen to have the factored form

$$(x + a)(x + b)$$

Question. What is the solution set for the sentence

$$x^2 + (a + b)x + ab = 0$$

So far we have observed that each of our quadratic equations has had two solutions, and this fact is in agreement with a very important theorem known as the *Fundamental Theorem of Algebra*. This theorem states that every algebraic equation of this type, that is, involving complex coefficients and nonnegative integral powers of x up to and including the nth, has n complex roots*, some or all of which may be real numbers. We can factor with ease a good many of the quadratic expressions we encounter, for example

$$x^2 - 7x + 12 = (x - 3)(x - 4)$$
$$x^2 + 4x - 12 = (x + 6)(x - 2)$$

Question. Can you factor $2x^2 - 5x - 12$?

However, there are many other examples where it is not at all easy to find the factored form by inspection, for example,

$$x^2 - 10x + 12$$

Let us proceed as follows to solve the equation

$$x^2 - 10x + 12 = 0$$

Adding -12 to each side, we have

$$x^2 - 10x = -12$$

It is now possible, by considering $(x - a)^2 = x^2 - 2ax + a^2$, to discover what number, namely 25, should be added to $x^2 - 10x$ to make it a square of an expression, often called a "perfect square"—in this case $(x - 5)^2$. We add 25 to each side of the equation and obtain

$$x^2 - 10x + 25 = -12 + 25$$
or
$$(x - 5)^2 = 13$$

---

*Whereas this has been the time-honored way of stating the theorem, it has a very significant weakness, illustrated by the following example: The equation $(x - 2)^{16} = 0$ has for its solution set the set $\{2\}$, that is, the equation has really only one root 2. In order to describe accurately the multiple feature which is present here, it is preferable to state that $(x - 2)^{16}$ has sixteen linear factors.

This equation may be treated in two ways. We may add -13 to both sides obtaining

$$(x-5)^2 - (\sqrt{13})^2 = 0$$

and then factor in the form

$$[(x-5) - \sqrt{13}][(x-5) + \sqrt{13}] = 0$$

to obtain the solution set $\{5 + \sqrt{13}, 5 - \sqrt{13}\}$. Or we may proceed more directly to the solution by taking the square root of both sides of the equation, as follows:

$$(x-5)^2 = 13$$
$$\sqrt{(x-5)^2} = \sqrt{13}$$
$$|x-5| = \sqrt{13}$$
$$x - 5 = \pm\sqrt{13}$$

Thus we obtain the same solution set as before.

Question. Can you carry through the above procedure for the equation $ax^2 + bx + c = 0$, if $a \neq 0$? (*Hint:* It is helpful to begin by multiplying both sides of the equation by $\frac{1}{a}$.)

Just as the sentence $x + y = 4$ was found to have a solution set consisting of an infinite number of ordered pairs, such as $(1,3)$, $(-\frac{7}{3}, \frac{19}{3}), (\frac{3}{2}, \frac{5}{2})$, and so on, similarly the equation $y = 2x^2 - 5x + 3$ has a solution set consisting of an infinite number of ordered pairs, including, for example, $(1,0), (-1,10), (2,1),$ .... In order to graph this equation it is helpful to make a table of ordered pairs. It is also helpful to write the equation as $y = 2(x - \frac{5}{4})^2 - \frac{1}{8}$. We see that this graph is symmetric with respect to the vertical line through the point $(\frac{5}{4}, -\frac{1}{8})$, that is, the line whose equation is $x = \frac{5}{4}$.

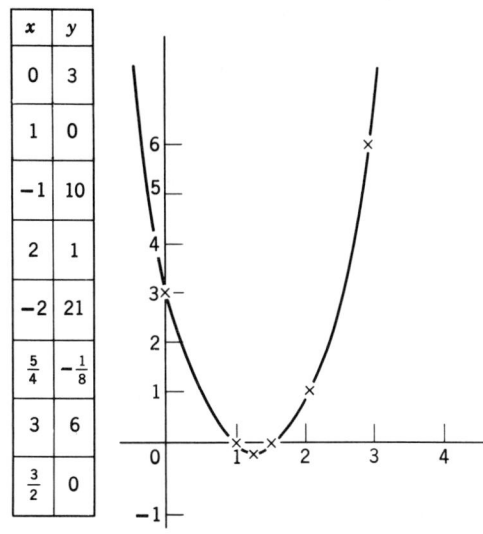

x	y
0	3
1	0
-1	10
2	1
-2	21
$\frac{5}{4}$	$-\frac{1}{8}$
3	6
$\frac{3}{2}$	0

136   From Arithmetic to Algebra

The graph of the equation $y = 2x^2 - 5x + 3$ is an example of a parabola, belonging to the family of conics (plane sections of a cone), and the points where the curve crosses the x-axis are $(1,0)$ and $(\frac{3}{2},0)$. It is no surprise, then, to find that $\{1,\frac{3}{2}\}$ is the solution set of the equation $2x^2 - 5x + 3 = 0$. Clearly the set of ordered pairs $\{(1,0), (\frac{3}{2},0)\}$ is the solution set of the *pair* of equations

$$y = 2x^2 - 5x + 3 \text{ and } y = 0$$

that is, the common point or points of intersection of the parabola and the x-axis. Incidentally, it is easily seen that the "lowest point" of this parabola is the point $(\frac{5}{4}, -\frac{1}{8})$, since $-\frac{1}{8}$ is the smallest value which $y = 2(x - \frac{5}{4})^2 - \frac{1}{8}$ can assume.

Questions. 1. Can you determine the point(s) of intersection of the parabola $y = 2x^2 - 5x + \frac{25}{8}$ and the x-axis?
2. What is the solution set of the sentence $2x^2 - 5x + 4 = 0$?

If $a \neq 0$, the general quadratic equation $ax^2 + bx + c = 0$ has the solution set

$$\left\{\frac{-b + \sqrt{b^2 - 4ac}}{2a}, \frac{-b - \sqrt{b^2 - 4ac}}{2a}\right\}$$

The quantity $b^2 - 4ac$ is called the *discriminant* of the quadratic expression. Since the discriminant appears under a square root sign it provides a good deal of information concerning the nature of the roots of the equation $ax^2 + bx + c = 0$, when a, b, and c are real numbers.

Question. Can you fill in the four vacant spaces in the table below with the proper adjectives, when $a, b,$ and c are assumed to be real numbers?

Discriminant	Roots real or nonreal	Roots equal or unequal
Negative	nonreal	
Zero		
Positive		unequal

The product of the factors $p - q$ and $p + q$ is $p^2 - q^2$. In similar fashion the product of the two roots of the general quadratic equation is given by

$$\left(-\frac{b}{2a}+\frac{\sqrt{b^2-4ac}}{2a}\right)\left(-\frac{b}{2a}-\frac{\sqrt{b^2-4ac}}{2a}\right)=\frac{b^2}{4a^2}-\frac{b^2-4ac}{4a^2}$$

$$=\frac{4ac}{4a^2}$$

$$=\frac{c}{a}$$

On the other hand, the sum of the two roots is

$$\frac{-b+\sqrt{b^2-4ac}}{2a}+\frac{-b-\sqrt{b^2-4ac}}{2a}=-\frac{2b}{2a}=-\frac{b}{a}$$

Hence we can determine the sum and product of the roots of any quadratic equation, without solving for the roots individually, merely by computing the quantities $-\frac{b}{a}$ and $\frac{c}{a}$, respectively. For example, with respect to the equation

$$3x^2-5x+6=0$$

the sum of the roots is $-(-\frac{5}{3})=\frac{5}{3}$ and the product of the roots is $\frac{6}{3}=2$.

Questions. 1. Can you write a quadratic equation for which the sum and product of the roots are $\frac{2}{3}$ and $-\frac{5}{3}$, respectively?
2. Can you find, in two ways, a quadratic equation whose roots are $-\frac{2}{3}$ and $\frac{3}{4}$?
3. What value should be given to a in the quadratic equation $ax^2+6x-4=0$, in order that one of the roots shall be twice the other?

EXERCISES

1. Compare the graph of the set $\{(-3,9), (3,9), (-2,4), (2,4), (-1,1), (1,1), (0,0)\}$ with the graph of the sentence $y=x^2$.
2. If ax^2+bx+c is a perfect square, what must be the relationship between $a, b,$ and c?
3. Find three positive integral values of K and also of M for which the following polynomials are factorable over the integers:

   (a) x^2+6x+K
   (b) $x^2+Mx+12$

4. Why is it true that if you square any positive integer and add this product to the number itself, the result will be an even number?

5. Comment on the following "proof" that $2 = 1$:

If $x = y$,
$$\therefore x^2 = xy$$
$$x^2 - y^2 = xy - y^2$$
$$(x+y)(x-y) = y(x-y)$$
$$x + y = y$$
$$2y = y$$
$$2 = 1$$

6. If possible, express each of the following as a product of linear factors with integral coefficients:
   (a) $x^2 + 2x - 8$
   (b) $5x^2 - 11xy + 2y^2$
   (c) $4x^2 + 9$
   (d) $(x+2)^2 - (x-7)^2$
   (e) $x^3 + 125$

7. Prove that if p and q are integers and if $x^2 + px + q$ is factorable, then $x^2 - px + q$ is also factorable.

8. Prove that if x and y are integers such that 17 is a factor of $2x + 3y$, then 17 is a factor of $9x + 5y$.

9. Prove that if d is a divisor of two numbers b_1 and b_2, then d is a divisor of $b_1 + b_2$ and $b_1 - b_2$.

10. (a) Show why $(a+1)^2 = a(a+2) + 1$
    (b) Can you give a geometric interpretation of the statement in (a)?

11. (a) Without solving the equation, find the sum of the squares of the roots of the equation

$$x^2 + 5x + 6 = 0$$

   (b) Verify (a) by obtaining the solution set for the equation.

12. (a) Without solving the equation, find the sum of the reciprocals of the roots of the equation

$$2x^2 - 3x + 7 = 0$$

   (b) Verify (a) by obtaining the solution set for the equation.

13. (a) Without solving the given equation write an equation, each of whose roots is 5 times as great as the corresponding root of the equation

$$x^2 + 2x - 15 = 0$$

   (b) Verify (a) by obtaining the solution set for the equation.

14. (a) Without solving the given equation, write an equation each of whose roots is smaller by 3 than the corresponding root of the equation

$$3x^2 - x - 4 = 0$$

(b) Verify (a) by obtaining the solution set for the equation.

6.05 MATHEMATICAL INDUCTION APPLIED TO SERIES

In Section 1.19 we introduced the concept of Mathematical Induction, concentrating its application in the areas of factoring, exponents, and inequalities. Let us recall briefly the statement of the Principle of Mathematical Induction: If, for a given set S of numbers, (1) $1 \in S$ and (2) S is inductive, that is, $k + 1 \in S$ whenever $k \in S$, then all the natural numbers belong to S. In Chapter 3 we had occasion to refer to a sequence of numbers, $a_1, a_2, a_3, \ldots$. Let us consider the sum of successive terms of such a sequence, that is, $a_1 + a_2 + a_3 + \cdots$ This is usually called a *series*. We would like now to apply the Principle in finding the sums of, for example, n terms of certain sequences. As an illustration let us show that the proposition $P(n)$ is true for all natural numbers, where $P(n)$ represents the statement

$$1^2 + 2^2 + 3^2 + \cdots + n^2 = \frac{n(n+1)(2n+1)}{6}$$

(Note that the nth term is n^2 and not n; in other words n serves to designate which term we are talking about.) Let S be the set of numbers for which $P(n)$ is true.

To Prove. S contains *all* the natural numbers.

Proof. (1) For $n = 1$, we have L.S. $= 1^2 = 1$ and R.S. $= \dfrac{1(2)(3)}{6} = 1$

$\therefore P(1)$ is true and $1 \in S$

(2) We shall now *assume* that $k \in S$. This means that

(i) $1^2 + 2^2 + 3^2 + \cdots + k^2 = \dfrac{k(k+1)(2k+1)}{6}$

We *wish to show* that $k + 1 \in S$. Hence we must show that

(ii) $1^2 + 2^2 + 3^2 + \cdots + k^2 + (k+1)^2$

$$= \frac{(k+1)[(k+1)+1][2(k+1)+1]}{6}$$

$$= \frac{(k+1)(k+2)(2k+3)}{6}$$

In order to establish (ii) we shall simply work with the expression on its left side, thus:

$$1^2 + 2^2 + 3^2 + \cdots + k^2 + (k+1)^2$$

$$= [1^2 + 2^2 + \cdots + k^2] + (k+1)^2$$

$$= \frac{k(k+1)(2k+1)}{6} + (k+1)^2, \text{ using (i)}$$

$$= \frac{(k+1)[k(2k+1) + 6(k+1)]}{6}$$

$$= \frac{(k+1)[2k^2 + 7k + 6]}{6}$$

$$= \frac{(k+1)(k+2)(2k+3)}{6}$$

Since we have now established equation (ii), we know that $k + 1 \in S$. Therefore we may apply the Principle of Mathematical Induction which guarantees that the set S contains all the natural numbers. Hence the original proposition is true for every natural number n, that is, $1^2 + 2^2 + \cdots + n^2 = \dfrac{n(n+1)(2n+1)}{6}$ for all natural numbers n.

The reader will certainly note soon, if he is not already aware of the fact, that, in applying the Principle of Mathematical Induction, he does not produce the proposition but, rather, verifies that a suspected proposition $P(n)$ is actually true for all natural numbers n. This is particularly true in finding the sum of terms of a sequence. It might therefore be interesting to see how the sums of terms of some, at least, of the sequences we shall be dealing with, can be arrived at. For example, let us obtain the sum of the first n natural numbers. We know that $(k+1)^2 = k^2 + 2k + 1$ is true for all numbers k. Hence

when $k = 0$, $\quad 1^2 = 0^2 + 2(0) + 1$
when $k = 1$, $\quad 2^2 = 1^2 + 2(1) + 1$
when $k = 2$, $\quad 3^2 = 2^2 + 2(2) + 1$

----

when $k = n - 1$, $n^2 = (n-1)^2 + 2(n-1) + 1$
when $k = n$, $(n+1)^2 = n^2 + 2n + 1$

When we add corresponding sides of these equalities we see that the expression $1^2 + 2^2 + 3^2 + \cdots + n^2$ appears on both sides, and may be eliminated by adding the negative of it to both sides.

Therefore, we have $(n + 1)^2 = 2(1 + 2 + 3 + \cdots + n) + (n + 1)$

$$\therefore 1 + 2 + 3 + \cdots + n = \frac{(n + 1)^2 - (n + 1)}{2}$$
$$= \frac{(n + 1)(n + 1 - 1)}{2}$$
$$= \frac{n(n + 1)}{2}$$

This approach can obviously be extended to establish the sums of squares, cubes, and higher powers.

EXERCISES

1. Use the Principle of Mathematical Induction to prove that
   (a) $1 + 2 + 3 + 4 \cdots + n = \frac{n(n + 1)}{2}$, for all natural numbers n,
   (b) $1 + 3 + 5 + 7 + \cdots + (2n - 1) = n^2$, for all natural numbers n.
   (c) $1^2 + 3^2 + 5^2 + 7^2 + \cdots + (2n - 1)^2 = \frac{n}{3}(4n^2 - 1)$, for all natural numbers n.
   (d) $3 + 5 \cdot 3 + 7 \cdot 3^2 + 9 \cdot 3^3 + \cdots + (2n + 1)3^{n-1} = n \cdot 3^n$, for all natural numbers n.
   (e) $1^3 + 2^3 + 3^3 + \cdots + n^3 = \frac{n^2(n + 1)^2}{4}$, for all natural numbers n.
   (f) $\frac{1}{2 \cdot 3} + \frac{1}{3 \cdot 4} + \frac{1}{4 \cdot 5} + \cdots + \frac{1}{(n + 1)(n + 2)} = \frac{1}{2} - \frac{1}{n + 2}$ for all natural numbers n.
   (g) $\frac{1}{3 \cdot 5} + \frac{1}{5 \cdot 7} + \frac{1}{7 \cdot 9} + \cdots + \frac{1}{(2n + 1)(2n + 3)} = \frac{1}{2}\left[\frac{1}{3} - \frac{1}{2n + 3}\right]$ for all natural numbers n.
2. (a) Suppose that we are trying to prove that $1 + 3 + 5 + \cdots + (2n - 1) = n^2 + (n - 1)(n - 2) = 2n^2 - 3n + 2$. Where does the induction procedure fail?
   (b) Similarly, if we were trying to establish the sum in (a) as $n^2 - 1$, where does the induction procedure fail?

6.06 EQUIVALENT SENTENCES

In Section 6.02 we defined equivalent sentences as those which have the same solution set relative to the same universe. It might be profitable at this point for us to examine a few standard algebraic procedures from the point of view of whether or not they produce equivalent sentences. We shall find it convenient to think of our sentence as $F(x) = G(x)$ where $F(x)$ and $G(x)$ are any algebraic expressions; for example, we might have $F(x) = 2x + 3$ and $G(x) = 5x - 7$. Then our sentence is $2x + 3 = 5x - 7$. The first question we wish to ask is:

(1) Do we obtain an equivalent sentence if we add to $F(x)$ and $G(x)$ some algebraic expression $P(x)$ of the form $P(x) = a_0 x^n + a_1 x^{n-1} + a_2 x^{n-2} + \cdots + a_{n-1} x + a_n$, where the a_i are real numbers and the exponents are natural numbers? The answer is seen to be *affirmative* as follows: If $x = a$ is any solution of the original equation then $F(a) = G(a)$, hence $F(a) + P(a) = G(a) + P(a)$ and, therefore, $x = a$ is a solution of the sentence $F(x) + P(x) = G(x) + P(x)$. Similarly if $x = b$ is any solution of $F(x) + P(x) = G(x) + P(x)$, then $F(b) + P(b) = G(b) + P(b)$; hence $F(b) = G(b)$ and b is a solution of $F(x) = G(x)$. It should be noted that the answer would not necessarily have been affirmative had we added a fractional algebraic expression to both sides of the equation, for example

$$2x - 1 + \frac{1}{x-2} = x + 1 + \frac{1}{x-2}$$

Since $\frac{1}{x-2}$ is not defined (does not exist) at $x = 2$, then $x = 2$ is not a solution of the above equation, whereas it is a solution of $2x - 1 = x + 1$.

(2) The next procedure we wish to check is the effect of multiplying $F(x)$ and $G(x)$ by a constant $K \neq 0$. Here again, $F(a) = G(a) \Rightarrow K[F(a)] = K[G(a)]$ and also, since $K \neq 0$, $K[F(b)] = K[G(b)] \Rightarrow F(b) = G(b)$. Therefore the sentence remains equivalent. Incidentally there are at least two ways of verifying the second of the two implications. Since $K \neq 0$, $\frac{1}{K}$ exists and we may multiply each side of the equation (of course, we mean the expression on each side of the equation) by $\frac{1}{K}$. On the other hand, we may add $-K[G(b)]$ to each side of the equation and apply the distributive law to obtain

$$K[F(b) - G(b)] = 0$$

Since at least one of the factors must be zero and $K \neq 0$ we know $F(b) - G(b) = 0$, that is, $F(b) = G(b)$.

(3) A different situation is involved if we contemplate multiplying $F(x)$

and $G(x)$ by an expression $P(x)$ described in (1). An example will suffice. Consider the two equations $2x - 1 = x + 1$ and

$$(x - 1)(2x - 1) = (x + 1)(x - 1)$$

The first equation has the solution set $\{2\}$ whereas the second one has $\{1,2\}$ as its solution set. Clearly it is quite easy to augment the solution set of an equation in this way.

(4) In an analogous fashion it is equally easy to lose solutions by multiplying $F(x)$ and $G(x)$ by $\frac{1}{P(x)}$. The previous example, in reverse order, indicates the danger as follows: $(x - 1)(2x - 1) = (x + 1)(x - 1)$ has the solution set $\{1,2\}$ whereas $\frac{(x - 1)(2x - 1)}{(x - 1)} = \frac{(x + 1)(x - 1)}{(x - 1)}$ has the solution set $\{2\}$, since, in the latter equation, the expression on each side of the equation is undefined at $x = 1$.

(5) A fifth procedure which we might be tempted to use carelessly is that of squaring the expression on either side of the equation. Again an example should make the situation clear. Suppose the original equation is $x + 1 = -2$ with solution set $\{-3\}$. On squaring we have $(x + 1)^2 = 4$ which may be treated as follows:

$$(x + 1)^2 - 4 = 0$$
$$(x + 1 - 2)(x + 1 + 2) = 0$$
$$(x - 1)(x + 3) = 0$$

The final equation has a solution set $\{1,-3\}$ and hence this equation is *not* equivalent to the original equation. It is perhaps not too surprising that this should happen when we consider that $[F(x)]^2 = [G(x)]^2$ could be obtained by squaring both sides of either $F(x) = G(x)$ or $F(x) = -G(x)$.

EXERCISES

Find and check the solution set for each of the following equations.

1. $x = \dfrac{8}{x - 7}$

2. $\dfrac{x}{3 - x} = \dfrac{2}{x - 3}$

3. $\dfrac{x^2}{x - 2} = \dfrac{2x}{x - 2}$

4. $\dfrac{x - 1}{x + 2} = \dfrac{4x + 1}{2(x + 1)}$

5. $\dfrac{x^2}{(x - 3)(x + 1)} = \dfrac{3}{x - 3} - \dfrac{3}{(x - 3)(x + 1)}$

6. $\dfrac{4}{x + 7} + \dfrac{9}{x + 3} = 1$

7. $x(x - 2) = 3(x - 2)$

8. $(x - 3)(x - 1) = (x - 3)(2x - 3)$

9. $\sqrt{x+9} = -5$
10. $\sqrt{x+9} = 5$
11. $\sqrt{3x} = 3x - 2$
12. $\sqrt{3x} = 2 - 3x$
13. $\sqrt{x-4} = 9 - \sqrt{x+5}$
14. $\sqrt{x-4} = \sqrt{x+5} - 9$
15. $\sqrt{3x-2} = \sqrt{x-1} - 1$
16. $\sqrt{x+3} + \sqrt{2x+7} = 1$
17. $\sqrt{6x+1} = 1 + \sqrt{4x-1}$
18. $\sqrt{6x+4} = 1 + \sqrt{6x}$
19. $\sqrt{x+1} + \sqrt{x-1} = 4$
20. $\sqrt{6x-2} - \sqrt{2x} + \sqrt{2x-1} = 0$

6.07 PROGRESSIONS

There are two types of sequence which are of considerable basic importance, since the terms of the sequence develop in such an orderly and elementary manner that we are able to find the sum of any finite number of terms of each with ease. In the first of these sequences, known as an *arithmetic progression,* successive terms are formed, in each case, by adding a particular number to the preceding term. In general, if the first term is a_1 and if the "common difference" between successive terms is d, then the nth term is given by

$$a_n = a_1 + (n-1)d$$

It is quite easy to find the sum, S_n, of n terms of this progression by reversing the order as follows:

Let $\quad S_n = a_1 + (a_1 + d) + (a_1 + 2d) + \cdots + [a_1 + (n-1)d]$

Then $\quad S_n = [a_1 + (n-1)d] + [a_1 + (n-2)d] + \cdots + a_1$

Adding gives $2S_n = [2a_1 + (n-1)d] + [2a_1 + (n-1)d] + \cdots$
$\qquad\qquad\qquad + [2a_1 + (n-1)d]$
$\qquad\qquad = n[2a_1 + (n-1)d]$

$$\therefore S_n = \frac{n}{2}[2a_1 + (n-1)d]$$

Question. Can you employ the Principle of Mathematical Induction to verify this result for the sum of n terms of the arithmetic progression?

For example, the sum of 100 terms of the arithmetic progression,

$$297, 291, 285, 279, \cdots,$$

may be written as

$$S_{100} = 297 + 291 + 285 + 279 + \cdots + (-297)$$

Then by the above
$$S_{100} = \frac{100}{2}[2(297) + 99(-6)]$$
$$= 50[594 - 594]$$
$$= 0$$

The other type of sequence that we wish to consider is known as a *geometric progression* and, in it, successive terms are formed by multiplying the preceding term by a particular number different from 1. If the first term is again designated by a_1 and if the "common ratio" of successive terms is r, then the nth term is given by

$$a_n = a_1 r^{n-1}$$

and n terms of this progression may be summed in the following way:

If $\qquad S_n = a_1 + a_1 r + a_1 r^2 + \cdots + a_1 r^{n-1}$
then $\qquad rS_n = a_1 r + a_1 r^2 + a_1 r^3 + \cdots + a_1 r^{n-1} + a_1 r^n$
Subtracting gives $\qquad (1-r)S_n = a_1 - a_1 r^n$

or
$$S_n = \frac{a_1(1-r^n)}{1-r} = a_1 \frac{(r^n-1)}{r-1}$$

Question. Why did we insert the condition $r \neq 1$ in our discussion of the geometric progression and not require $d \neq 0$ in considering the arithmetic progression?

It should be noted that we could have established this result more directly had we been aware of the factorization

$$1 - r^n = (1 + r + r^2 + \cdots + r^{n-1})(1-r)$$

In this case we could have proceeded as follows:

Since $\quad r \neq 1, S_n = a_1(1 + r + r^2 + \cdots + r^{n-1})\frac{(1-r)}{(1-r)} = a_1\frac{(1-r^n)}{(1-r)}$

For example, the sum of 15 terms of the geometric progression $1, 2, 4, 8, 16, \cdots$, may be written as $S_{15} = 1 + 2 + 4 + 8 + 16 + \cdots + 16384$.

Then by the above
$$S_{15} = \frac{1(2^{15} - 1)}{2-1}$$
$$= 2^{15} - 1$$
$$= 32{,}767$$

146   From Arithmetic to Algebra

It may be interesting to note that, for this progression, S_n is always $a_{n+1} - a_1$.

Question. Can you establish the validity of the sum of n terms of the geometric progression by use of the Principle of Mathematical Induction?

This latter result is of particular interest when $|r| < 1$ because, in this case, $|r^n|$ becomes not only steadily smaller, but, in fact, as small (or as close to zero) as we wish, as n becomes indefinitely large. We wish to state this more precisely by saying that $|r^n|$ can be made to differ from zero by as small a positive quantity as we wish; that is, we can make $|r^n|$ less than any positive number by taking n sufficiently large.

Question. How large must n be to make $(0.5)^n < 0.01$? or $(0.5)^n < 0.0001$?

In more sophisticated mathematical language we are saying that the *limit* of r^n is zero as n becomes infinitely great, that is, $\lim_{n \to \infty} r^n = 0$ (see Section 3.07). This means that when $|r| < 1$, S_n becomes as close as we wish to $\dfrac{a_1}{1-r}$ as n increases indefinitely, and in this sense we say that we are able to find the "sum" of an infinite number of terms of the sequence, when the common ratio is less than one in absolute value. We shall meet this topic again when we consider repeating decimal fractions, although we shall have recourse at that time to an alternative procedure as well.

Clearly, when $|r| > 1, S_n = \dfrac{a_1(r^n - 1)}{r - 1}$ will become larger than any number we may care to name, as n is allowed to increase indefinitely.

Question. What is the "sum" of an infinite number of terms of the following geometric progression:

$$1, \frac{1}{2}, \frac{1}{4}, \frac{1}{8}, \frac{1}{16}, \dots$$

Before leaving this immediate discussion let us consider the following very special sequence, known as the *harmonic sequence*, which bears a deceptive resemblance to the sequence in the previous *Question*; that is, we wish to consider the sum S of an infinite number of terms of the sequence, $1, \frac{1}{2}, \frac{1}{3}, \frac{1}{4}, \frac{1}{5}, \frac{1}{6}, \frac{1}{7}, \frac{1}{8}, \dots$; hence

$$S = 1 + \frac{1}{2} + \frac{1}{3} + \frac{1}{4} + \frac{1}{5} + \frac{1}{6} + \frac{1}{7} + \frac{1}{8} + \dots$$

Progressions 147

It might appear at first glance as if n terms of this sequence might have a sum which would approach a limit as n became infinitely great. However, let us group the terms of the sum as follows:

$$1 + \frac{1}{2} + \left(\frac{1}{3} + \frac{1}{4}\right) + \left(\frac{1}{5} + \frac{1}{6} + \frac{1}{7} + \frac{1}{8}\right) + \left(\frac{1}{9} + \frac{1}{10} + \cdots + \frac{1}{16}\right) + \cdots$$

We see that $\frac{1}{3} > \frac{1}{4}$ and, therefore, $\frac{1}{3} + \frac{1}{4} > \frac{1}{4} + \frac{1}{4} = \frac{2}{4} = \frac{1}{2}$. Similarly, $\frac{1}{5} + \frac{1}{6} + \frac{1}{7} + \frac{1}{8} > \frac{1}{8} + \frac{1}{8} + \frac{1}{8} + \frac{1}{8} = \frac{4}{8} = \frac{1}{2}$ and $\frac{1}{9} + \frac{1}{10} + \cdots + \frac{1}{16} > \frac{8}{16} = \frac{1}{2}$. In this sum we can continue to associate sufficiently large numbers of terms together so that the sum of each group of numbers is greater than $\frac{1}{2}$. It is evident, then, that we can take n large enough so that the sum of n terms will be greater than 1 plus as many $\frac{1}{2}$'s as we wish, that is, as large as we wish. The sequence we have just been considering is a special case of a more general sequence known as a *harmonic progression*. This is a sequence with the property that the reciprocals of the terms of the sequence form an arithmetic progression.

EXERCISES

1. Obtain the 23rd term in each of the following arithmetic sequences:
   (a) $-66, -63, -60, -57, \cdots$ (b) $111, 104, 97, 90, \cdots$

2. Find the sum of the first 30 terms of each of the sequences associated with parts (a) and (b) of Exercise 1.

3. Mr. Brown is employed at an initial salary of $5400, with an annual increase of $300, while Mr. Black starts at the same time at an initial salary of $6300, with an annual increase of $150. At the end of how many years will the two men be earning the same salary?

4. Find the 16th and 17th terms and the sum of 20 terms of the geometric sequence $1, \sqrt{2}, 2, 2\sqrt{2}, 4, \ldots$.

5. For the geometric sequence $1, -\frac{1}{2}, \frac{1}{4}, -\frac{1}{8}, \frac{1}{16}, \cdots$, show

   (a) that the sum of the first 10 terms is $\frac{2}{3}\left(\frac{1023}{1024}\right)$

   (b) that the sum of the first 20 terms is $\frac{2}{3}\left(\frac{1023}{1024}\right)\left(\frac{1025}{1024}\right)$

   (c) that the "sum" of the terms of the infinite sequence is $\frac{2}{3}$.

6. Two trains are 300 miles apart and each is traveling toward the other at 50 miles per hour. At this instant a bee flies from the front end of one train to the front end of the other train, back and forth at 200 miles per hour. How far will the bee have travelled when the trains meet?

148   From Arithmetic to Algebra

7. Imagine an infinite set of discs, each of which has on it a numeral for a single natural number. Suppose that

at one minute to 12 we put into a box discs No. 1,2,..., 10 and take out disc No. 1;

at one-half minute to 12 we put into the box discs No. 11,12,...,20 and take out disc No. 2;

at one-third minute to 12 we put into the box discs No. 21,22,...,30 and take out disc No. 3;

and so on. How many discs are in the box at 12 o'clock?

6.08 BINOMIAL THEOREM

It may be noted that successive applications of the distributive property allow us to obtain the following equalities:

$$(a+x)^2 = a^2 + 2ax + x^2$$
$$(a+x)^3 = a^3 + 3a^2x + 3ax^2 + x^3$$
$$(a+x)^4 = a^4 + 4a^3x + 6a^2x^2 + 4ax^3 + x^4$$

We can continue the process of multiplication by more factors of $(a+x)$ as long as we wish and in the process a striking pattern for the coefficients develops, namely

$$
\begin{array}{ccccccccc}
 & & & & 1 & & & & \\
 & & & 1 & & 1 & & & \\
 & & 1 & & 2 & & 1 & & \\
 & 1 & & 3 & & 3 & & 1 & \\
1 & & 4 & & 6 & & 4 & & 1
\end{array}
$$

This pattern is known as *Pascal's Triangle* and, in it, any coefficient different from 1 is seen to be the sum of the two numbers immediately above it. The general result which makes use of the coefficients occurring in the $n+1$st row is called the *Binomial Theorem*, the statement of which follows:

$$(a+x)^n = a^n + na^{n-1}x + \frac{n(n-1)}{1 \cdot 2} a^{n-2}x^2 + \cdots + \frac{n(n-1) \cdots (n-r+1)}{1 \cdot 2 \cdot 3 \cdots r} a^{n-r}x^r + \cdots + nax^{n-1} + x^n$$

In Appendix D the proof of the Binomial Theorem (by Mathematical

Induction) is given for any natural number n. In using the theorem one should note among other things that
  (1) There are $n+1$ terms in the expansion of $(a+x)^n$.
  (2) The coefficients symmetrically located from each end, are equal.
  (3) In each term the exponents of a and x add up to n.
  (4) The coefficient of *any term* is equal to the product of certain numbers obtainable from the *previous term*, viz., the coefficient times the exponent of a divided by 1 more than the exponent of x.

For example, if $n = 5$,

$$(a+x)^5 = a^5 + 5a^4x + \frac{5\cdot 4}{1\cdot 2}a^3x^2 + \frac{5\cdot 4\cdot 3}{1\cdot 2\cdot 3}a^2x^3 + \frac{5\cdot 4\cdot 3\cdot 2}{1\cdot 2\cdot 3\cdot 4}ax^4 + \frac{5\cdot 4\cdot 3\cdot 2\cdot 1}{1\cdot 2\cdot 3\cdot 4\cdot 5}x^5$$
$$= a^5 + 5a^4x + 10a^3x^2 + 10a^2x^3 + 5ax^4 + x^5$$

Question. Can you foresee what form the binomial expansion may assume when n is other than a positive integer?

EXERCISES

1. Expand by the Binomial Theorem:
   (a) $(x+2y)^5$ (b) $(2a-b)^6$ (c) $(1.01)^5$
2. Use the Binomial Theorem to simplify:
   (a) $(\sqrt{2}+1)^4 + (\sqrt{2}-1)^4$ (b) $(\sqrt{a}+\sqrt{b})^5 - (\sqrt{a}-\sqrt{b})^5$

6.09 PERMUTATIONS

When we place the letters A, B, C in the particular order ABC we have an arrangement or *permutation* of these three letters. ACB is another permutation of the same letters and there are four more distinct permutations, namely, BCA, BAC, CAB, CBA. We are, of course, interested only in permutations, any two of which are distinguishable from each other. Consequently there are six possible permutations of three different objects. If there were four distinct objects, we could proceed in more than one way to determine the total number of possible permutations. If we think of four empty squares in a row, to be filled with the letters A, B, C, D, it is clear that one of the squares (it makes no difference which one we think of) can be filled in four ways. For each of those four choices the remaining three letters can be permuted in six ways in the remaining three squares making a total of twenty-four

possibilities. An alternative procedure would be to think of three of the four letters as permuted in the six possible ways, after which, for each of the six ways, the fourth letter could be placed in any one of four available places indicated by blank squares:

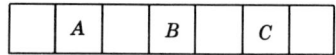

Hence the number of permutations of four distinct objects is twenty-four.

The notation $n!$, read "n factorial," is commonly used to represent the product of all integral factors from 1 through n, where n is any natural number, that is,

$$n! = n(n-1)(n-2) \cdots (3)(2)(1)$$

Question. Can you prove that $n! = n[(n-1)!]$ provided $n > 1$?

The formula for $n!$ applies only when n is a natural number but it is customary to give a definition for $0!$. The above *Question* provides the motivation for defining $0! = 1$.

Questions. 1. Can you employ the Principle of Mathematical Induction to prove that the number of permutations of n different objects is $n!$?

2. Can you show that the number of permutations of r different objects, taken s at a time, where $s < r$, is $\dfrac{r!}{(r-s)!}$?

(*Hint:* Let Q be the required number of permutations and assume that Q is known. Then adjoin to each of the Q permutations the remaining $r - s$ objects permuted among themselves in all possible ways.)

The symbol $P_{r,s}$ is often used to denote the number of arrangements of r different objects, s at a time, that is,

$$P_{r,s} = \frac{r!}{(r-s)!}$$

Permutations 151

For example, the number of permutations of the letters of the word "becloud" is $P_{7,7} = 7! = 5040$. On the other hand if only three of these letters are to be used *at one time*, then the number of such possible arrangements is

$$P_{7,3} = \frac{7!}{4!} = 210$$

Question. What is the total number of permutations of $p + q + r$ objects of which p are alike of one kind, q alike of another kind, and r alike of a third kind?

EXERCISES

1. Simplify
   (a) $\dfrac{10!}{7!}$
   (b) $\dfrac{12!}{6!6!}$
   (c) $\dfrac{n!}{(n-1)!}$
   (d) $\dfrac{n!(n-3)!}{(n-1)!(n-2)!}$
   (e) $\dfrac{101! + 99!}{100!}$

2. Show that
   (a) $n(n!) = (n+1)! - n!$
   (b) $(n+1)! = n(n^2 - 1)[(n-2)!]$
   (c) $\dfrac{n^2}{n!} = \dfrac{1}{(n-1)!} + \dfrac{1}{(n-2)!}$

3. (a) Show that $P_{n+1, r+1} = (n+1)P_{n,r}$
   (b) Demonstrate in a way other than algebraic that the statement in (a) is true.

4. In how many ways can ten boys stand in a row if (a) A and B must be together? (b) A and B must not be together?

5. There are six reserves on a team. How many different seatings of the reserves are possible on the bench (a) if the bench seats 5? (b) if the bench has room only for 4?

6. How many numerals of five digits each can be formed from the digits 1,2,3,4, using each digit as often as desired in a numeral?

7. How many proper four digit numerals can be formed from the five digits, 0,1,2,3,4? (a) using each digit as often as desired in a numeral? (b) using each digit at most once in a numeral?

8. How many numbers between 3000 and 5000 can be formed with the digits 1,3,5,7,9, with no digit being repeated in a given numeral?

9. Find the number of permutations of the letters a, a, a, b, b, c, d, when used all at a time.

10. In how many ways can seven identical quarters and five identical dimes be given to twelve boys, in such a way that each boy receives one coin?

11. (a) How many permutations are there of the letters of the word "serene" taken all together?
    (b) How many of them begin with e?
    (c) With two e's?
    (d) With three e's?
    (e) With just two e's?
12. How many permutations are there of the letters in the word Mississippi, when taken all together?

6.10 COMBINATIONS

Closely related to the concept of permutation is the idea of combination, that is, selection without arranging in any order. The problem here is to discover the number of ways of choosing s objects from r different objects. We denote this number by $C_{r,s}$. The answer is easy to obtain if we think of permuting each of the $C_{r,s}$ selections in its $s!$ ways. Then the total number of possible permutations is $(C_{r,s})(s!)$ which must also equal $P_{r,s}$. Hence

$$(s!)(C_{r,s}) = P_{r,s}$$

We may multiply both sides of the equation by $\frac{1}{s!}$, obtaining

$$C_{r,s} = \frac{P_{r,s}}{s!} = \frac{r!}{s!(r-s)!}$$

For example, the number of triangles formed by joining 10 points, no three of which are collinear (and disregarding intersections of joins) is given by

$$C_{10,3} = \frac{10 \cdot 9 \cdot 8}{1 \cdot 2 \cdot 3} = 120$$

Again, the number of diagonals in a regular decagon (polygon of 10 sides) is given by

$$C_{10,2} - 10 = 45 - 10 = 35$$

This result may be checked by noting that each vertex has 7 diagonals associated with it. But each diagonal will be counted once for each vertex. Hence the number of diagonals is $\frac{10 \cdot 7}{2} = 35$.

Questions. 1. Should we expect that $C_{r,s} = C_{r,r-s}$? Why?
2. Can you show that

$$C_{r,s} = C_{r-1,s} + C_{r-1,s-1}$$

   (i) by using the algebraic formula for $C_{r,s}$?
   (ii) by using an intuitive argument?

3. How many diagonals are there in an n-sided regular polygon?

$\binom{r}{s}$ is a combination symbol in common use as an alternative to $C_{r,s}$. It may be easily verified that the coefficients of the binomial expansion (see Section 6.08) are combination symbols and the reader will often see the results given in the following form:

$$(a+x)^n = \binom{n}{0}a^n + \binom{n}{1}a^{n-1}x + \binom{n}{2}a^{n-2}x^2 + \cdots$$
$$+ \binom{n}{r}a^{n-r}x^r + \cdots$$
$$+ \binom{n}{n-1}ax^{n-1} + \binom{n}{n}x^n$$

where $\binom{n}{0}$ is defined as 1.

EXERCISES

1. Find the value of $C_{100,98} - C_{99,97}$.
2. If $C_{n,3} = C_{n,4}$, what is n?
3. In how many ways can a hostess make up a party of six from a list of nine friends?
4. In how many ways can a party of sixteen be conveyed in two cabs, one of which will not hold more than eight people and the other not more than ten?
5. Out of 16 different consonants and 5 different vowels, how many words can be formed containing 4 consonants and 1 vowel? In how many words will the vowel be the middle letter?
6. A box contains fifteen tags numbered from 1 to 15. In how many ways can six tags be selected if 1 is included and 2 and 3 are excluded?
7. In how many ways can a selection be made from ten different books? In how many ways if at least two books must be chosen?
8. There are six different textbooks on a shelf and three copies of each. In how many ways can a selection be made from them?

9. Prove that

$$\binom{n}{0} + \binom{n}{1} + \binom{n}{2} + \cdots + \binom{n}{n-2} + \binom{n}{n-1} + \binom{n}{n} = 2^n$$

[*Hint:* Let $x = 1$ in the binomial expansion of $(1 + x)^n$.]

10. Prove that

$$\binom{n}{1} + 2\binom{n}{2} + 3\binom{n}{3} + \cdots + (n-2)\binom{n}{n-2} + (n-1)\binom{n}{n-1} + n\binom{n}{n} = n \cdot 2^{n-1}$$

[*Hint:* Let $x = 1$ in the binomial expansion of $n(1 + x)^{n-1}$.]

11. Prove that

$$\binom{n}{0}^2 + \binom{n}{1}^2 + \binom{n}{2}^2 + \cdots + \binom{n}{n}^2 = \binom{2n}{n}$$

[*Hint:* Examine the coefficient of x^n in each of $(1 + x)^{2n}$ and $(1 + x)^n(1 + x)^n$.]

12. Show that $C_{r,s} = C_{r-2,s} + 2C_{r-2,s-1} + C_{r-2,s-2}$ (a) algebraically, (b) intuitively.

6.11 PROBABILITY

When the weather forecaster announces that there is a one-tenth chance of rain, he is stating the likelihood or probability of the occurrence of a particular event. As used in mathematics the word probability has a very definite meaning. If an event can occur in w different, equally likely ways, of which f of these ways are thought of as favorable or desirable, then we say that the probability of the favorable occurrence is its frequency relative to the total frequency of all possible occurrences, that is, $\frac{f}{w}$. For example, suppose that we are required to find the probability of two particular boys being together when 12 boys stand in a row. We know that the 12 boys can be arranged in a row in 12! ways. In order to find the number of arrangements with the two boys in question together, let us tie them together, figuratively speaking, so that it is really a matter of arranging 11 boys in a row. Since the two boys, A and B, can stand either as AB or as BA, the number of possible permutations in this case will be $2(11!)$. The probability of the two boys, A and B, being together is therefore $\frac{2(11!)}{12!} = \frac{1}{6}$. If the event can also occur in u unfavorable ways, then $u+f=w$ and the probability of the unfavorable event occurring is $\frac{u}{w}$. We see therefore, that $\frac{u}{w}+\frac{f}{w}=\frac{u+f}{w}=1$. This is another way of saying that the probability of an event occurring or not occurring is 1. Hence the probability of an event that is certain to occur is 1, whereas, on the other hand, the probability of an event which cannot happen is zero.

There are many happenings in our own experience for which it is impossible to state relative frequencies as a result of any theoretical analysis. In such cases, we usually make use of the observed relative frequencies of past occurrences of the event. In the case of the manufacture of large quantities of a single object, we may obtain the probability of the product being satisfactory by examining various samples of the production. Insurance mortality tables illustrate this procedure and are an excellent example of the use of probability in the business world. From our discussion we have seen that a probability is a fraction lying between 0 and 1, inclusive. Consider the tossing of a two-sided coin. If either side is equally likely to turn up, then the probability of "heads" occurring is $\frac{1}{2}$ and the probability of "tails" is also $\frac{1}{2}$. This means that in 1000 tosses of the coin, "heads" should occur approximately 500 times and "tails" roughly as often.

Suppose that we are tossing two coins. We might be tempted to argue that there are three possible results, each with a probability of $\frac{1}{3}$, which can be described as follows, if H stands for "heads" and T for "tails":

$$HH, HT, TT$$

However, further analysis of the problem will lead us to the conclusion that tossing two coins is not intrinsically different from tossing one coin twice and that the "heads-tails" combination may occur both as HT and TH. Hence there are really four equally likely possibilities, HH, HT, TH, TT, as a result of which the probability of one "head" and one "tail" showing is $\frac{2}{4}$ or $\frac{1}{2}$, the remaining events each having a probability of $\frac{1}{4}$. This illustrates how important it is to be sure that the events whose frequencies we are comparing are actually equally likely to occur.

We shall be interested in computing probabilities which involve the occurrences of more than one event. First of all, if two events are mutually exclusive, that is, cannot both occur in one trial, we might want to know the probability of one or the other event occurring. By way of illustration let us consider two of several contestants in a race. Suppose the probability of A winning is $\frac{1}{3}$ and of B winning is $\frac{1}{4}$. This means that in a large number, n, of races with the same contestants,

A might be expected to win $\frac{n}{3}$ times and B to win $\frac{n}{4}$ times. Hence A or B would be expected to win approximately $\frac{n}{3} + \frac{n}{4}$ of the n races and the probability of A or B winning is $\frac{\frac{n}{3}+\frac{n}{4}}{n} = \frac{1}{3} + \frac{1}{4} = \frac{7}{12}$. Let us suppose that the event, P, has a probability p and the event, Q, has a probability q. Then in r trials the expected numbers of occurrences of P and Q are pr and qr, respectively. Hence the expected number of occurrences of the event, "P or Q," is pr + qr and the relative frequency is $\frac{pr+qr}{r} = p + q$. Hence the probability of one event or the other occurring is given by the sum of the probabilities of the separate events. The coin-tossing example illustrated this principle when we observed that the probability of TH or HT is $\frac{1}{4} + \frac{1}{4} = \frac{1}{2}$. It was also illustrated in the first paragraph in the discussion of favorable and unfavorable events where

$$\frac{u}{w} + \frac{f}{w} = 1.$$

Question. When two coins are tossed what is the probability of at least one "head" showing?

On the other hand, suppose we are dealing with independent events, P and Q, both of which may occur in one trial. Let us again assign the individual probabilities p and q to P and Q, respectively, and consider the problem of determining the probability of the event, "P and Q." In r trials, the expected number of events, P, will be pr and in these pr trials the expected number of events, Q, will be pqr. Hence in r trials the expected number of events, "P and Q," will be pqr and the relative frequency or probability of this event will be $\frac{pqr}{r} = pq$; that is, the product of the two individual probabilities. The above example of the tossing of two coins illustrates this principle in establishing the probability, $\frac{1}{4} = \frac{1}{2} \cdot \frac{1}{2}$, for each of the events, HH, HT, TH, TT.

As a more interesting example, consider the problem of tossing a six-sided die, numbered in the usual way. In three tosses the probability of obtaining first a six, then a five, and then a four is $(\frac{1}{6})^3$. However if we are permitted to disregard the order of the events, we may think of tossing three dice at one time and then the probability of throwing a six, a five, and a four is $(3!)(\frac{1}{6})^3 = \frac{1}{36}$. We may look at this problem in another way. On the first throw the probability of a six or a five or a four occurring is $3(\frac{1}{6}) = \frac{1}{2}$. On the next throw the probability of obtaining one of the remaining two numbers is $2(\frac{1}{6}) = \frac{1}{3}$. Hence in two throws the probability of obtaining two of the three desired numbers is $\frac{1}{2} \cdot \frac{1}{3} = \frac{1}{6}$. On the third throw the probability is $\frac{1}{6}$ that the third desired number will appear. The probability for the event is then $\frac{1}{6} \cdot \frac{1}{6} = \frac{1}{36}$.

Question. Can you determine the probability of obtaining at least 15 in a single throw of three dice?

Until now we have been dealing with independent events. Let us consider a situation where the probabilities of successive events are affected by the preceding events. Let us suppose that a bag contains five red marbles and ten white marbles. In three successive drawings without replacement the probability of getting a red marble each time will be $(\frac{5}{15})(\frac{4}{14})(\frac{3}{13})$.

Question. What is the probability in the above example of drawing one white and two red marbles?

The above is obviously only an exceedingly brief summary of an elementary introduction to probability.

EXERCISES

1. If a die is thrown, what is the probability that the number showing will be 4? That it will be more than 4? That it will be less than 4?
2. A person holds one ticket in a lottery where there are 6 winning tickets and 24 losing tickets. What is the probability that he will win a prize? That he will not win a prize?
3. The letters of the word "absurd" are placed in a row. Find the probability that the two vowels come together.
4. From a bag containing four white and five black marbles, three are drawn at random. What is the probability that the three will all be black?
5. A woman has six nickels, three dimes, five pennies, and three bus tokens in her purse. What is the probability that she will draw a bus token on her first try?
6. When two dice are thrown what is the probability that one dice will show a 3 and the other a 4?
7. If a coin is thrown three times, what is the probability that it will fall heads and tails alternately?
8. The probability that A can solve a problem is $\frac{1}{3}$ and that B can solve it is $\frac{1}{4}$, what is the probability that it will be solved if both work separately at it?
9. A, B, C run in a race with other competitors. Excluding ties, the probability that A will win is $\frac{1}{6}$, that B will win is $\frac{1}{5}$, and that C will win is $\frac{1}{4}$. What is the probability that one of them will win? That someone other than $A, B,$ or C will win?

10. The probability that a certain event will happen is $\frac{2}{7}$ and that another event, independent of the former, will happen is $\frac{4}{11}$. Find the probability that one, at least, of the events will happen.
11. Four men, A, B, C, D leave their coats, a, b, c, d, in a check room. When they return, the room is in darkness. Find the probability that, by choosing at random, nobody gets his right coat.

7 Fractions and Fractional Exponents

7.01 NUMBER AND NUMERAL

In Chapter 1 we drew attention, in the particular case of natural numbers, to the important distinction between number and numeral, that is, between the abstract idea and any of the many possible symbols used to represent it. The same distinction holds among the various concepts associated with rational and irrational numbers. This emphasis will be new to many teachers who may not have been led to give much consideration to these matters. Unfortunately there is no uniformity with respect to nomenclature, and both the new and the experienced teacher are advised to check carefully the words employed to describe these concepts in the texts they will be using.

In Chapter 3 the reader was introduced to the idea of fraction as the indicated quotient, $\dfrac{b}{c}$, of two numbers, b and $c, c \neq 0$, together with the conditions of equality of two fractions. These definitions were presented in a form sufficiently general to extend to fractions like $\dfrac{\sqrt{2}}{3}, \dfrac{\pi}{4}, \dfrac{\sqrt[3]{5}}{\sqrt[4]{7}}$, as well as fractions like $\dfrac{3}{7}$. We find that the complete set of fractions may be partitioned into equivalence classes (Section 3.04) of equal fractions, like $\left\{\dfrac{2}{3}, \dfrac{4}{6}, \dfrac{6}{9}, \dfrac{8}{12} \cdots\right\}, \left\{\dfrac{\sqrt{3}}{2}, \dfrac{2\sqrt{3}}{4}, \dfrac{3\sqrt{3}}{6}, \dfrac{4\sqrt{3}}{8}, \cdots\right\}$, and so on. When we limit our attention, as in the first of these two sets, to fractions, $\dfrac{b}{c}$, where b and c are integers with $c \neq 0$, the equivalence class defines a rational number, that is, an abstract idea to which; in this case, we give the name "two-thirds." Any one of the symbols $\tfrac{2}{3}, \tfrac{4}{6}$, and so on, is a numeral which may represent that rational number. On the other hand, the second of the two given equivalence classes necessarily defines an irrational number.

160   Fractions and Fractional Exponents

In some texts the term fraction is used to describe the idea while the symbol for it is given the name of fractional numeral. A good many modern texts develop the idea of rational number very beautifully through the use of ordered pairs (b, c), and some writers have introduced new terms such as rate-pair. No attempt will be made here to provide universally applicable definitions. It is almost inevitable that there will be a certain amount of ambiguity incurred in speaking and writing about rational numbers. For example, numbers and not numerals are added but, occasionally, we shall want to add numerators or denominators of particular fractions, regardless of the fact that these are obtained from the fractional numerals for the numbers. When we write $\frac{2}{3} = \frac{4}{6} = \frac{6}{9} = \ldots$ we are saying that these are all names for the same number. Very often it will be necessary to distinguish, from the context, between an interpretation as numeral or number, and the reader is advised that he may encounter a variety of fine distinctions in usage. In the present material the effort has been made to present the concept of rational number in as simple a manner as possible consistent with maintaining a clear distinction between the ideas of number and numeral, a distinction which students generally find not difficult to accept.

Very often the term *ratio* is reserved for the purpose of comparing two numbers. "The ratio of b to c" is expressed in symbols as "$b:c$" and is equal to $b \div c$; the equality of two ratios is known as a *proportion*. For example, the problem of determining the cost, x, of a dozen oranges when they are selling three for ten cents may be handled effectively as follows: $x : 12 = 10 : 3$ or $\frac{x}{12} = \frac{10}{3}$, whence $x = 40$. The following might be a more striking example: An electric storm knocked out 150 radio stations, which represented two-thirds of the stations in a particular system. What is the total number of stations in the system? If there are n stations in the system, then

$$\frac{150}{n} = \frac{2}{3}$$

and

$$n = \frac{3}{2} \times 150$$
$$= 225$$

EXERCISES

1. Determine x if
   (a) $x : 4 = 2 : 5$
   (b) $8 : 3 = 12 : x$

2. If a missile travels at a speed of 18,000 m.p.h.
   (a) In how many hours will it travel 40,000 miles?
   (b) How many miles will it travel in 18 minutes?
3. If $x : y = 2 : 5$, find the ratio of $7x - 2y : 6x - 2y$.
4. The ratio of the weight of an object to the weight of an equal volume of water is its specific gravity. A particular type of wood has a specific gravity of 0.6667.
   (a) If a piece of this wood weighs 120 grams, what is the weight of an equal volume of water?
   (b) What does a piece of this wood weigh, if an equal volume of water weighs 90 grams?
5. Two numbers are in the ratio 6 : 7. If three times the first exceeds twice the second by 24, find the numbers.
6. A board is divided in the ratio 1 : 4. If the longer piece is 10 feet long, how long was the original board?
7. A certain warship exhausts her total fuel capacity when she burns 96 tons of fuel per day while cruising at a moderate speed for 20 days. How many days can she stay at sea if she increases her speed and uses 120 tons of fuel per day?
8. The distance between two objects on the earth may be calculated from an aerial photograph by means of the following:

$$\frac{\text{distance on photo (in in.)}}{\text{distance on earth (in ft.)}} = \frac{\text{distance from lens to plate (in in.)}}{\text{distance from lens to ground (in ft.)}}$$

On a photo taken at 4000 feet two buildings appear 4 inches apart. If the distance between the lens and the plate is 6 inches, find the actual distance between the buildings on the ground.

7.02 HOW MANY?

In Section 1.01 we considered the problem of counting the objects in a finite set by establishing a 1 : 1 correspondence between these objects and the natural numbers in the set $\{1, 2, 3, \ldots, n\}$. Even when dealing with finite sets it is not always necessary for us to know the exact number of objects in a set but merely whether two sets contain the same number of objects. This is illustrated by the familiar example of having an audience in a hall sit in the available seats in order to determine whether or not the number of chairs matches the number of people.

We employ the latter idea in dealing with infinite sets and any set of numbers which is capable of a 1 : 1 correspondence with the natural

162   Fractions and Fractional Exponents

numbers is said to possess the *countability* of the natural numbers or to be *countable* or *denumerable* or *countably* or *denumerably infinite*. (Any finite set is also said to be countable or denumerable.) Many apparent paradoxes result from establishing correspondences between the natural numbers and one of its subsets; for example, the 1 : 1 correspondence, $n \leftrightarrow 2n$, leads to the conclusion that there are "as many" even numbers as there are natural numbers. This illustrates the fact that, after some elements of a set have been removed the resulting set may have "as many" elements as the original set (in the sense of 1 : 1 correspondence). The existence of a 1 : 1 correspondence between a set and a proper subset of itself is a sufficient condition that both sets contain an infinite number of elements.

We would like now to demonstrate that not only the positive integers but also, in fact, all the integers comprise a countable set. We are motivated to do this not only by our desire to establish this fundamental result but also by the opportunity it affords to exhibit a procedure which will be useful in subsequent sections.

We know the positive integers are countable; hence the negative integers are likewise countable (since a 1 : 1 correspondence certainly exists). Consider the sequence $0, 1, -1, 2, -2, 3, -3, 4, -4, \ldots, k, -k, \ldots$ formed by starting with 0 and then taking the first number in the sequence of positive integers followed by the first number in the sequence of negative integers and continuing to take succeeding numbers, alternately, from the two sequences, each being in its natural order. The constructed sequence evidently contains all the integers and is in 1 : 1 correspondence with the natural numbers since $0 \leftrightarrow 1, 1 \leftrightarrow 2, -1 \leftrightarrow 3, 2 \leftrightarrow 4, -2 \leftrightarrow 5, 3 \leftrightarrow 6, -3 \leftrightarrow 7, 4 \leftrightarrow 8, \ldots, k \leftrightarrow 2k, -k \leftrightarrow 2k+1, \ldots$. Hence the complete set of integers is countable.

7.03 COUNTABILITY OF RATIONAL NUMBERS

It is appropriate at this time to consider the problem of "counting" the rational numbers. We shall employ the classical procedure originated by Georg Cantor in which a 1 : 1 correspondence is established between the set of natural numbers and the set of all positive fractions, $\frac{b}{c}$, where b and c are positive integers with $c \neq 0$.

The correspondence is established in the order indicated by the arrows and, indeed, to each positive fraction corresponds a definite natural number. For example, the fraction $\frac{3}{2}$, corresponds to the natural number 8 and the natural number 12 corresponds to the fraction $\frac{2}{4}$. The set of positive fractions is, therefore, countable. In fact it is possible to determine the natural number corresponding to any positive fraction $\frac{p}{q}$ or the particular fraction corresponding to any natural number n. The reader has already observed that in this correspondence

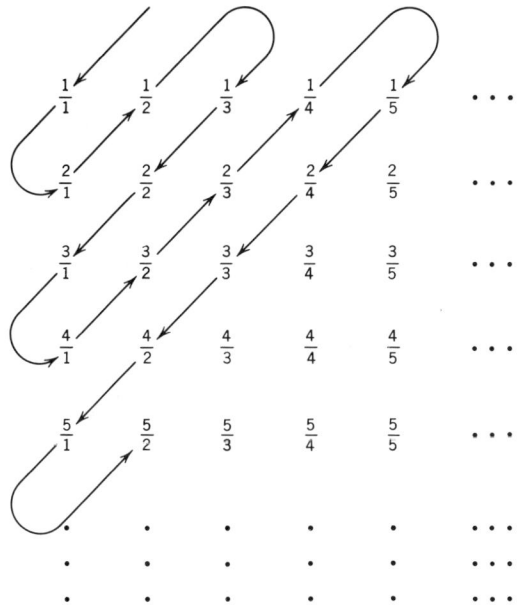

a place is reserved for each positive fraction, not merely for each positive rational number. It follows, therefore, that the positive rational numbers themselves cannot fail to be countable.

Question. How would you establish the previous statement?

If desired, the procedure can be modified by eliminating from the correspondence, as they are encountered, those fractions which are equal to a fraction met earlier. In this way the resulting 1 : 1 correspondence would have indicated directly the countability of the positive rational numbers. For example, under these circumstances, fractions such as $\frac{2}{2}, \frac{2}{4}, \frac{3}{3}, \frac{4}{2}, \frac{4}{4}, \frac{5}{5}, \ldots$ would be eliminated and the fraction, $\frac{3}{2}$, would correspond to the natural number, 7, whereas the natural number, 12, would correspond to the fraction, $\frac{5}{2}$. Since we know that the positive rational numbers are countable, we know equally well that the negative rational numbers are also countable. Hence we may employ the same procedure which we used in Section 7.02 to demonstrate the countability of the integers, in order to show that the set of

164   Fractions and Fractional Exponents

all rational numbers is countable. We have, therefore, answered the question, "How many rational numbers are there"?

EXERCISES

1. Are the following sets denumerable?
    (a) $\left\{\dfrac{3}{5}, \dfrac{6}{5}, \dfrac{9}{5}, \dfrac{12}{5}\right\}$
    (b) $\left\{\text{the positive integral multiples of } \dfrac{4}{11} \text{ which are } \leq \dfrac{144}{11}\right\}$
    (c) {the positive integral multiples of $5\sqrt{2}$}
    (d) {the reciprocals of the positive even integers}
    (e) $\left\{\dfrac{n+2}{n+1} \bigg| n \text{ is a positive integer}\right\}$
    (f) {the even positive integers} ∪ {the multiples of $\sqrt{2}$ by the even positive integers}

7.04 MORE ABOUT DECIMAL FRACTIONS

In Section 3.06 we introduced decimal fractions and discussed briefly a few details having to do with decimal fraction computations.

Many decimal fractions do not terminate, that is, they involve an infinite number of digits without there being any digit to the right of which all the digits are zero. Of special interest are those nonterminating decimal fractions in which, to the right of some digit, all the digits consist of a particular finite sequence of digits repeated continually. Such a "repeating decimal" fraction is equal to a fraction representing a rational number, as the following example will illustrate.

Let us consider the repeating decimal $0.353535\ldots$ which we shall represent as $0.\dot{3}\dot{5}$, where it is understood that the pair of digits 35 repeats indefinitely. This repeating decimal is merely another way of writing the sum of the terms of the sequence

$$0.35, 0.0035, 0.000035, \ldots$$

The terms of this infinite sequence form a geometric progression with first term 0.35 and common ratio 0.01. In Section 6.07 we discovered that for such a progression as this one (since $r = 0.01 < 1$), the sum of the first n terms of the sequence has a limit as n approaches infinity and this limit we call the "sum" of the terms of the sequence. If we apply that result to this sequence we obtain the sum

$$S = \frac{a_1}{1-r}$$
$$= \frac{0.35}{1-0.01}$$
$$= \frac{0.35}{0.99}$$
$$= \frac{35}{99}$$

Once we are certain that such a repeating decimal represents a unique real number, we may represent the number $0.\dot{3}\dot{5}$ as N and determine N in the following way:

$$100 N = 35 + 0.\dot{3}\dot{5}$$
$$= 35 + N$$
$$99 N = 35$$
$$N = \frac{35}{99}$$

The importance of our knowing that $0.\dot{3}\dot{5}$ is a unique number (which is another way of saying that the sum of terms of the sequence 0.35, 0.0035, 0.000035,... "converges"), cannot be overrated. To see that this is the case, let us consider the sequence

$$1, 2, 4, 8, 16, \ldots$$

Clearly the terms of the infinite sequence $1, 2, 4, 8, 16, \ldots$ have no "sum" since they continue to add up to a number larger than any number of which we can conceive. However if we should make the mistake of treating the sum as a number N, then we would have

$$N = 1 + 2 + 4 + 8 + 16 + \cdots$$
$$= 1 + 2(1 + 2 + 4 + 8 + \cdots)$$
$$= 1 + 2N$$

from which we obtain the erroneous result $N = -1$.

On the other hand we know that the sum of the terms of the sequence

$$1, 1/2, 1/4, 1/8, 1/16, \ldots$$

166   Fractions and Fractional Exponents

does approach a limit as the number of terms increases beyond all bound (since $r = 1/2 < 1$) and

$$N = 1 + 1/2 + 1/4 + 1/8 + 1/16 + \cdots$$
$$= 1 + 1/2(1 + 1/2 + 1/4 + 1/8 + \cdots)$$
$$= 1 + 1/2N$$
$$\therefore N = 2$$

Question. What result do you obtain for N if you write

$$N = 1 + 1/2 + 1/4(1 + 1/2 + 1/4 + \cdots)$$

Let us consider a second example $N = 2.78\dot{3}\dot{5}\dot{4}$. Here

$$100{,}000N = 278354.\dot{3}\dot{5}\dot{4}$$
$$100N = 278.\dot{3}\dot{5}\dot{4}$$

Subtracting gives

$$99{,}900N = 278076$$
$$\therefore N = \frac{278076}{99900}$$

Question. Can you verify by long division that each of the previously obtained fractions has the given repeating decimal as quotient?

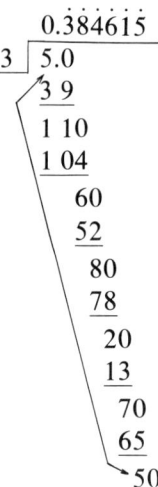

Although these examples do not constitute a proof, they are indicative of the fact that any repeating decimal fraction is equal to a rational fraction.

The inverse problem involves the question of the possible representation of any rational number by a decimal fraction. Again let us investigate this matter by looking at an illustration, for example, the fraction $\frac{5}{13}$. As we begin the long division procedure of dividing 5 by 13, the first digits of the quotient are 0.384615. At this point in the division we see that the remainder is 5 for the first time since the beginning of the division. It is therefore automatically true that the next six digits in the quotient will again be 384615 and that this sequence of digits will repeat indefinitely. Is this just an accidental situation or should such a result be expected in general?

More about Decimal Fractions   167

Question. Can you verify that $0.\dot{3}8461\dot{5}$ is equal to $\frac{5}{13}$ by evaluating the repeating decimal fraction?

Let us consider the numbers which might possibly be obtained as remainders in the above division procedure. There are only 13 such numbers, namely the natural numbers 0 through 12. Whenever a number occurs a second time as a remainder, we may be sure that a particular repetition of digits must begin at that point in the quotient. Since only a finite number of distinct remainders is available, it is inevitable that one of them will be repeated within a finite number of steps. Therefore a repetition of some sequence of digits is bound to occur in the quotient which, accordingly, assumes the form of a repeating decimal fraction. The proof in the general case employs an argument similar to the above procedure. Hence we may say that every terminating or repeating decimal is equal to a rational fraction and conversely every rational fraction has a representation as either a repeating or a terminating decimal fraction (the latter might be termed "repeating" by affixing zeros).

A special case of interest occurs when the sequence of repeating digits is a sequence of 9's. For example, if

$$N = 0.\dot{9}*$$

then
$$10N = 9.\dot{9}$$
$$= 9 + N$$

and
$$9N = 9$$
$$N = 1$$

Question. What result do you obtain by treating $0.\dot{9}$ as an infinite geometric progression?

In another example, if $\quad N = 2.38\dot{9},$

then $\qquad\qquad 1000N = 2389.\dot{9}$

and $\qquad\qquad 100N = 238.\dot{9}$

Hence $\qquad\qquad 900N = 2151$

That is $\qquad\qquad N = \dfrac{2151}{900}$

$\qquad\qquad\qquad = 2.39$

*Note that we are assuming in this procedure that $0.\dot{9}$ is a unique real number, a result which you are asked to verify in the following *Question*.

168   Fractions and Fractional Exponents

Therefore we are able to say that, for any terminating decimal fraction, there is an alternative representation as a repeating decimal, obtained by reducing the extreme right-hand digit by 1 and adjoining to it an infinite sequence of 9's.

EXERCISES

1. Express each of the following as a repeating decimal fraction:

    (a) $\frac{15}{8}$ (b) $\frac{6}{5}$ (c) $\frac{22}{7}$ (d) $\frac{103}{33}$

2. Express each of the following in the form of a fractional numeral:

    (a) $0.\dot{7}$ (b) $17.1\dot{8}$ (c) $14.3\dot{2}1\dot{4}$

3. What will be the natural numbers c for which $\frac{1}{c}$ can be expressed as a terminating decimal, in base ten? in base eight? in base six?

4. If $\frac{1}{3} = 0.\dot{3}$, (a) Does $3 \times \frac{1}{3} = 0.\dot{9}$? (b) What does $4 \times \frac{1}{3} = ?$

5. Does the addition of the decimal fraction expansions for $\frac{1}{9}$ and $\frac{1}{7}$ give the decimal fraction expansion for $\frac{16}{63}$?

6. (a) Verify that $\frac{1}{7} = 0.\dot{1}4285\dot{7}$

    $\frac{3}{7} = 0.\dot{4}2857\dot{1}$

    $\frac{2}{7} = 0.\dot{2}8571\dot{4}$

    Can you explain why the repeated digits occur in the same order in the above three decimal fractions?

    (b) What multiple of $0.\dot{1}4285\dot{7}$ is $0.\dot{8}5714\dot{2}$?

    (c) Would $8(0.\dot{1}4285\dot{7})$ contain only the digits 1,2,4,5,7,8?

7. With reference to Exercise 17 in Section 1.17, express the repeating binary fraction $0.1\dot{0}11\dot{0}$ as a ratio of numbers represented in binary notation and finally as a rational number in the decimal system.

8. In traveling any unit distance, a person might consider that he first travels half the distance, then half of the remaining distance, followed by half of that remaining distance, and so on.

    (a) Represent the total distance in the form of a binary numeral.

    (b) Obtain the rational number which is equal to the number obtained in (a), by either of the methods employed in this section.

7.05 NONCOUNTABILITY OF THE SET OF IRRATIONAL NUMBERS

We have seen in Chapter 3 that $\sqrt{2}$ can be approximated more and more closely, but never expressed exactly, by a sequence of decimal fractions. Since $\sqrt{2}$ is irrational we know that the sequence of digits in its decimal representation cannot terminate nor can any subsequence of these digits repeat indefinitely. Hence for an irrational number we know that the digits in its decimal fraction representation must continue indefinitely in no repeating pattern.

It is an interesting question to consider how many irrational numbers there are. To be more exact, we would like to know whether or not there are too many irrational numbers for us to be able to establish a 1 : 1 correspondence between them and the natural numbers.

Let us suppose that it is possible to establish a 1:1 correspondence between the set of natural numbers and the set of *all* real numbers (rational and irrational) between 0 and 1. We shall assume that the real numbers are represented by nonterminating decimal fractions and that the correspondence appears at the beginning as follows (where the a_{ij} are whole numbers less than 10):

$$.a_{11}a_{12}a_{13}\cdots a_{1n}\cdots$$
$$.a_{21}a_{22}a_{23}\cdots a_{2n}\cdots$$
$$.a_{31}a_{32}a_{33}\cdots a_{3n}\cdots$$
$$\cdots\cdots\cdots\cdots\cdots$$

We shall also assume that each number which is equal to a terminating decimal fraction is expressed in terms of a repeating sequence of 9's. For example, $0.25000\ldots$ is written as $0.24999\ldots$. Now let us consider the number

$$N = 0.b_{11}\,b_{22}\,b_{33}\,b_{44}\cdots b_{kk}\cdots b_{nn}\cdots,$$

where $b_{kk} = 1 + a_{kk}$ if $a_{kk} \neq 9$ and $b_{kk} = 1$ if $a_{kk} = 9$, for any natural number k. Then N is a real number between 0 and 1 which is not represented in the original set of nonterminating decimal fractions, since N differs in at least one digit from each member of that set. This contradicts our assumption that *all* the real numbers between 0 and 1 appear in the correspondence. Therefore the real numbers between 0 and 1 are not countable. Hence it is certainly not possible to establish a 1:1 correspondence between the natural numbers and all the real numbers. Therefore the latter set is uncountable.

Question. Where does the previous argument fail when applied to the rational numbers between 0 and 1, when the latter have been represented as nonterminating decimal fractions?

The question remains concerning the countability of the set R'' of irrational numbers.* Let us suppose that the latter set is denumerable.

---
*Cf. "Infinity" by Hans Hahn in *The World of Mathematics*, published by Simon and Schuster, Vol. 3, pp. 1593–1611.

170   Fractions and Fractional Exponents

We already know that the set R' of rational numbers is countable. Hence let us imagine each set as having been put, separately, in $1:1$ correspondence with the natural numbers. From here on the procedure is similar to the one we used in Section 7.02 to show that the integers are countable. We establish a $1:1$ correspondence between the natural numbers and all the real numbers as follows: First take the first-listed number from the set R' (that is, the number which corresponds to 1 in that $1:1$ correspondence), then the first-listed number from the set R'', next the second-listed number from R', then the second listed number from R'', and continue taking numbers alternately from each set. The resulting sequence comprises all the real numbers and is, therefore, in $1:1$ correspondence with the natural numbers, in contradiction to the result established in the previous paragraph. Hence our assumption that the irrational numbers are countable is untenable. Thus, in this sense, *most* real numbers are irrational.

EXERCISES

1. It is possible to construct nonterminating, nonrepeating decimal fractions as follows:
   (a) 0.01001000100001 ... where each sequence of 0's contains one more 0 than the sequence to the left of it.
   (b) 3.556655566655556666 ... where each sequence of 5's and 6's to the right of the first such sequence contains one more 5 and one more 6 than the sequence immediately to the left of it. Are these numbers in (a) and (b) rational or irrational numbers?
2. Use the comments in Exercise 1 to make plausible the following statement: Between any two rational numbers there is always an irrational number.

7.06   RADICALS AND FRACTIONAL EXPONENTS

In presenting the material of this section, it is not desirable to attempt to state an all-inclusive universe, within which *all* the definitions will apply, since any such common universe would necessarily be unduly restrictive with respect to some procedures. In general the universe will be the set of real numbers, restricted where indicated, to the set of positive real numbers (see footnote on p. 171).

As a result of the introduction in Chapter 1 of the notation b^n, where n is a natural number, to represent the product of n factors, each of which is b, we were able to discover that $b^m \cdot b^n = b^{m+n}$,

Radicals and Fractional Exponents   171

where m and n are both natural numbers. In addition it may be proved (see Section 1.19, Exercise 10) that

$$(b^m)^n = b^{mn}, (ab)^n = a^n b^n, \left(\frac{a}{b}\right)^n = \frac{a^n}{b^n}$$

and

$$\frac{b^m}{b^n} = b^{m-n} \text{ if } m > n$$

or

$$\frac{b^m}{b^n} = \frac{1}{b^{n-m}} \text{ if } n > m, \text{ where } b \neq 0$$

The next question to be faced is how to handle $\frac{b^m}{b^n}$ when $m = n$. We have before us the rule $\frac{b^m}{b^n} = b^{m-n}$ when $m > n$, whose consistency we would like to maintain. With this goal as motivation we make the definition $b^0 = 1$ and follow it up by defining $b^{-n} = \frac{1}{b^n}$, for $b \neq 0$. Thus, for example, $b^{-2} = \frac{1}{b^2}$. We can then make the broader statement that $\frac{b^m}{b^n} = b^{m-n}$ for *all* integral m and n.

We have defined $\sqrt{a}$ (see Section 3.07) when $a > 0$, as that positive number x such that $x^2 = a$. When we come to define the general radical, $\sqrt[q]{a}$, we have to consider two cases:
(1) if q is an odd natural number, then $\sqrt[q]{a}$ is that real number t for which $t^q = a$.
(2) If q is an even natural number and $a \geq 0$, then $\sqrt[q]{a}$ is that nonnegative real number t for which $t^q = a$. (In the latter case we recognize the fact that there exists a negative real number y such that $y^q = a$, when $a \geq 0$, and we deliberately choose the nonnegative number t.) For example, $\sqrt[4]{16} = 2$ and $\sqrt[4]{16} \neq -2$, although we have both $2^4 = 16$ and $(-2)^4 = 16$. To illustrate further

$$\sqrt{4} = 2, \sqrt{4} \neq -2, \sqrt{2^2} = \sqrt{4} = 2, \sqrt{(-2)^2} = \sqrt{4} = 2 \neq -2$$

In each case the root which we have defined above is called the *principal* root and $\left(\sqrt[q]{a}\right)^q = a$. When a and b are ≥ 0,* it follows from the above definition that $\sqrt[q]{ab} = \sqrt[q]{a}\sqrt[q]{b}$, since $\sqrt[q]{a}\sqrt[q]{b} \geq 0$ and

*In more general terms we could say: when a and b are such that the expressions are defined, since, for example $\sqrt[3]{-27}\sqrt[3]{-27} = \sqrt[3]{(-27)(-27)}$, that is, $(-3)(-3) = \sqrt[3]{(27)(27)} = 9$.

172   Fractions and Fractional Exponents

$\left(\sqrt[q]{a}\sqrt[q]{b}\right)^q = \left(\sqrt[q]{a}\right)^q\left(\sqrt[q]{b}\right)^q = ab$ and similarly, if $b \neq 0$, $\sqrt[q]{\frac{a}{b}} = \frac{\sqrt[q]{a}}{\sqrt[q]{b}}$.

As an illustration of the concept of principal root, we should note that $\sqrt[3]{a^3} = a$, $\sqrt[5]{a^5} = a$, and so on but $\sqrt{a^2} = |a|$, $\sqrt[4]{a^4} = |a|$, and so on. We now wish to introduce the idea of a fractional exponent for the purpose of simplifying many of our procedures. Since $\left(\sqrt[q]{b}\right)^q = b$ by definition and since we would like to have the relation $(b^m)^n = b^{mn}$ continue to hold, it is a very natural step for us to define $b^{1/q} = \sqrt[q]{b}$; clearly $(b^{1/q})^q = b = b^{1/q \cdot q}$, if $q \neq 0$. We also define $b^{p/q} = \sqrt[q]{b^p} = \left(\sqrt[q]{b}\right)^p$, where p and q are integers with $q > 0$. The latter expression is the more desirable one to use from the point of view of computation. Hence with the previous results and the latter definitions we can establish the following rules, when x and y are any rational numbers and a and b are any real numbers for which the expressions are defined:

(1) $b^{-x} = \frac{1}{b^x}$, where $b \neq 0$

(2) $b^x \cdot b^y = b^{x+y}$

(3) $(ab)^x = a^x b^x$

(4) $(b^x)^y = b^{xy}$ or $|b^{xy}|$. Note that with $b < 0$, $(b^3)^{1/3} = b$, but $(b^2)^{1/2} = |b|$. For example, $(5^3)^{1/3} = 125^{1/3} = 5$, $[(-5)^3]^{1/3} = (-125)^{1/3} = -5$, $(5^2)^{1/2} = 25^{1/2} = 5 = |5|$, $[(-5)^2]^{1/2} = 25^{1/2} = 5 = |-5|$.

(5) $\left(\frac{a}{b}\right)^x = \frac{a^x}{b^x}$, where $b \neq 0$.

Let us establish the first of these results. If $x = \frac{m}{n}$, $n > 0$, then

$$b^{-x} = b^{\frac{-m}{n}} = \sqrt[n]{b^{-m}}$$

$$= \sqrt[n]{\frac{1}{b^m}} = \frac{1}{\sqrt[n]{b^m}}$$

$$= \frac{1}{b^{\frac{m}{n}}} = \frac{1}{b^x}$$

Question. Can you prove the above rules (2), (3), (4), and (5)?

It follows that computations involving radicals may frequently be handled more conveniently by first changing to fractional exponent form. It should not be overlooked, however, that, for example, $\sqrt[3]{a^3} = a$ directly.

EXERCISES

1. Which is greater $\frac{2\sqrt{2}}{11}$ or $\frac{3}{8\sqrt{2}}$? $\frac{23}{11\sqrt{3}}$ or $\frac{9\sqrt{3}}{13}$?
2. Rationalize denominators* and simplify:

   (a) $\frac{1}{\sqrt{2}} - \frac{1}{\sqrt{8}}$ (b) $\frac{1}{\sqrt{3}} - \frac{1}{\sqrt{7}}$ (c) $\frac{4}{\sqrt{3} - \sqrt{2}}$

3. Show $(\sqrt{3} + 1) : (2\sqrt{3} + 4) = (6\sqrt{3} + 10) : (16\sqrt{3} + 28)$.
4. Do you think $\sqrt{2}$ is larger or smaller than $\sqrt[3]{3}$? Why?

7.07 PER CENT

The nomenclatures that we have for real numbers are adequate for all purposes but it is convenient to have an additional one, namely, *per cent*. We would like to hope that per cent is not a deep topic requiring a lengthy and special treatment but rather that we might simply make the definition:

$$K \text{ per cent} = K\% = \frac{K}{100}$$

Thus any number M can be rewritten as $\left(\frac{100}{100}\right)M = 100M\%$, whenever it is desirable to have M expressed in terms of per cent. In view of the ease with which a number may be transformed from per cent to its fractional form or in the reverse direction, in our opinion the person who is able to work efficiently with fractions should encounter no serious difficulty in working with per cent.

Traditionally there have been three types of problems associated with per cent. We shall illustrate all three types from which it will hopefully become evident that essentially one and only one principle, namely $Q = (K\%)B = \left(\frac{K}{100}\right)B$ is operating in every case. We shall also indicate the alternative approach, in each problem, by way of ratio.

Example 1. What is 150% of 38? Here K is given as 150 and B as 38, hence

$$Q = \left(\frac{150}{100}\right) \times 38$$
$$= 1.5 \times 38$$
$$= 57$$

Alternatively, we may write $\frac{Q}{38} = \frac{150}{100}$ and obtain the result that 150% of 38 is 57.

---
*By "rationalize denominators" is meant, transform the given fractions into equivalent fractions, each of whose denominators is a rational number.

Fractions and Fractional Exponents

Example 2. What per cent of 75 is 225? Here Q is given as 225 and B as 75.

Hence $$225 = \left(\frac{K}{100}\right) \times 75$$

and $$K = 225 \times \left(\frac{100}{75}\right)$$
$$= 300$$

In terms of ratios we may write $\frac{K}{100} = \frac{225}{75}$ which also leads us to the conclusion that 225 is 300% of 75.

Example 3. 25 is 0.01% of what number? In this case Q is given as 25 and K as 0.01 and we have

$$25 = \frac{0.01}{100} \times B$$

Hence $$B = 25 \times \left(\frac{100}{.01}\right)$$
$$= 250{,}000$$

In the ratio approach we would write

$$\frac{25}{B} = \frac{0.01}{100}$$

and arrive equally well at the fact that 25 is 0.01% of 250,000.

It is our opinion that all problems involving per cent are merely variations of a single, fundamental relation and therefore yield easily to standard elementary algebraic procedures.

EXERCISES

1. How much of 10 gallons of a 10% solution of alcohol in water should be withdrawn and replaced by a 40% solution to yield 10 gallons of a 20% solution?
2. In Lower Slabovia, the income tax is 4% of the net income, that is, the income after all deductions are made. One of the allowable deductions is the amount of the tax itself. If R is the income after all deductions are made except that of the tax itself, what, in terms of R, is the amount of the tax?
3. A men's clothing merchant sold two shirts for $3.75 each. On the first he lost 25% of the cost and on the second he gained 25% of the cost. How much did he gain or lose on the two sales or did he break even?

8 *More Informal Geometry*

8.01 CONGRUENCE

The study of geometry involves not only the investigation of abstract properties possessed by sets of points but also has to do with matters of shape and size. These latter considerations are exceedingly important in areas such as architecture, engineering, and machine tooling, which are concerned with problems of design and construction. We think of two plane figures as being *congruent* if one is a "carbon copy" of the other. For many years it was considered a satisfactory procedure to place one figure above the other, if not literally, at least figuratively, in order to see if they matched exactly. But there were many persons who realized that this process of "superposition" really entailed a theory of motion and when it was attempted to spell this out in the form of postulates, it was found to be undesirably complicated. Hence it has been considered much more satisfactory to assume a very limited number of basic postulates which relate directly to congruence rather than to a procedure to justify superposition. It will be seen also that congruence of compound figures can be described in terms of congruence of more elementary figures in a very effective way.

We are going to find that there are two principal ways of approaching the idea of congruence,* (1) metrically, as a defined concept and (2) synthetically, as an undefined concept. Let us think first of congruence of segments. If we decide, as is done in some presentations, to assume a 1:1 correspondence between points on the line and the set of real numbers, then we may proceed to postulate that to every pair of different points there corresponds a unique positive number. It is necessary to describe carefully, as we did in Section 4.08, how a scale is associated with a line, that is, how a coordinate C_P is to be assigned to each point P. Once this is done, we may define the distance PQ, between points P and Q, that is, the measure $m(\overline{PQ})$ of the segment $\overline{PQ}$ as the absolute value of the difference of the coordinates

---

*A more detailed treatment is to be found in *Elementary Geometry from an Advanced Standpoint* by Edwin Moise, published by Addison-Wesley.

corresponding to P and Q. Thus we define $m(\overline{PQ}) = PQ = |C_P - C_Q|$. For example, if P and Q are assigned coordinates 6 and 10, respectively, then $PQ = |6 - 10| = 4$. We are then in a position to define $\overline{AB}$ congruent to $\overline{CD}$, written, $\overline{AB} \cong \overline{CD}$, as follows:

$$\overline{AB} \cong \overline{CD} <=> AB = CD, \text{ that is, } m(\overline{AB}) = m(\overline{CD})$$

It should be observed here that congruence is a defined relation between geometric figures, whereas the equality of measure is the statement that the two numbers, $m(\overline{AB})$ and $m(\overline{CD})$, are equal. The only time we permit a sign of equality to be placed between two geometric figures occurs when the figures are identical, for example $\overline{AB} = \overline{CD} <=> (A = C \text{ and } B = D) \text{ or } (A = D \text{ and } B = C)$.

In the second of the two ways of considering congruence, as applied to segments, we merely adopt the necessary postulates to guarantee that the undefined concept of congruence shall have the properties we would like it to have. For example we would want to be certain that we could reproduce a segment, $\overline{A'B'}$, on a particular line and having a particular point, A, as end-point so that $\overline{A'B'} \cong \overline{AB}$. In this connection we would wish to have sufficient postulates to make congruence of segments an equivalence relation (see Section 3.04). And, finally, we would find it very desirable to assume postulates which would make possible the addition and subtraction of segments. Under this system, by means of a rather lengthy development based on Euclid's concept of ratio, it is possible to define the distance AB, between two points A and B, in such a way that the following is true:

$$AB = CD \text{ or } m(\overline{AB}) = m(\overline{CD}) <=> \overline{AB} \cong \overline{CD}$$

There is a considerable analogy between the treatment of segments and that of angles. The discussion of congruence of angles can be handled in two ways, (1) metrically, by definition and (2) synthetically, by postulate. In (1), the measure of an angle is established by assuming the following two postulates: (a) To every angle there corresponds a real number between 0 and 180, and, conversely, to every real number between 0 and 180 there corresponds a unique set of angles; (b) the measure of the sum of two angles is the sum of the measures of the two angles. As a consequence of postulate (b) and the fact that, by definition, the two rays of an angle cannot be in the same line, it follows that the numbers 0 and 180 must be excluded from the above set of measures. Two angles are then defined to be congruent if and only if they have the same measure. In the alternate approach, (2), the ability to reproduce an angle with one side in a given line and with a given point in the line as vertex is postulated. As might be expected, we wish to have the postulates which establish that congruence of angles is an equivalence relation and, further, those which describe the addition and the subtraction of angles.

Since in either approach we are able to discuss the congruence of segments and angles, we are now able to consider the congruence of triangles, the next simplest geometric figure in the plane. When we say that $\triangle ABC$ is congruent to $\triangle A'B'C'$ and write "$\triangle ABC \cong \triangle A'B'C'$", we mean that there is a $1:1$ correspondence of vertices, $A \leftrightarrow A'$, $B \leftrightarrow B'$, $C \leftrightarrow C'$, such that $\overline{AB} \cong \overline{A'B'}$, $\overline{BC} \cong \overline{B'C'}$, $\overline{CA} \cong \overline{C'A'}$; and $\angle A \cong \angle A'$, $\angle B \cong \angle B'$, $\angle C \cong \angle C'$. If there should be any possibility of confusion regarding which angle is intended to be designated by $\angle B$, then the angle should be described by means of three letters (see Section 4.07).

A little exploratory work will convince us that there are essentially three different combinations of congruent segments and congruent angles which will yield congruent triangles. The first of these involves the congruence of two pairs of corresponding sides of two triangles, and the congruence of the angles consisting of the rays containing those particular sides. Since we have eliminated the possibility of employing superposition, we must assume a postulate here. It is interesting, however, to note that we have the following alternatives: We may accept, as a postulate, the complete "side-angle-side" (SAS), statement, namely, "If in $\triangle ABC$ and $\triangle A'B'C'$, $\overline{AB} \cong \overline{A'B'}$, $\overline{AC} \cong \overline{A'C'}$, and $\angle A \cong \angle A'$, then $\triangle ABC \cong \triangle A'B'C'$". Or, on the other hand, we may accept a slightly weaker postulate which states, "If in $\triangle ABC$ and $\triangle A'B'C'$, $\overline{AB} \cong \overline{A'B'}$, $\overline{AC} \cong \overline{A'C'}$, and $\angle A \cong \angle A'$, then $\angle B \cong \angle B'$ and $\angle C \cong \angle C'$", from which the SAS theorem may be proved rather easily.

It is not our purpose to involve the reader in the details of geometric proof but rather to provide an overview of the high points of the subject from an intuitive point of view—but still in keeping with the modern way of treating plane geometry. The two other most important theorems on congruence of triangles are the "angle-side-angle" (ASA) theorem and the "side-side-side" (SSS) theorem, both of which may be proved as a result of the SAS postulate. It is assumed that the reader will have no trouble in formulating the ASA and SSS theorems by analogy with the statement of the SAS postulate.

EXERCISES

1. If two triangles are each congruent to a third, are they congruent to each other?

178   *More Informal Geometry*

2. If $\overline{AC} \cong \overline{AB}$ and $\overline{CD} \cong \overline{BD}$ in the figure below, show that $\angle ACD \cong \angle ABD$.

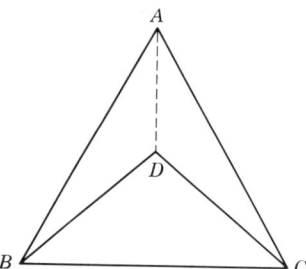

3. Is the following statement true? If $\overleftrightarrow{AB}$ and $\overleftrightarrow{CD}$ intersect at O, then $\angle AOC \cong \angle BOD$. When and when not?
4. Explain why a triangular gate is rigid whereas a rectangular gate is not generally so.
5. Does a quadrilateral figure become rigid when one vertex is joined to *any* point (not a vertex on either side containing the original vertex) of one of the opposite sides?

8.02 EXISTENCE OF PARALLEL LINES

Until now we have been interested mainly in lines which intersect and in the relations between segments thus formed. If we think of a sheaf of planes all having one line in common, then we may pick out any particular plane in the sheaf by choosing a point on that plane which does not lie on the line. Hence a line and a point not on the line determine a plane. It is, therefore, also true that two distinct intersecting lines lie in a plane since either line and a point on the other line, different from the intersection point, must determine a plane which necessarily contains both lines.

Question. Why must two intersecting lines, as described in the preceding sentence, lie in the same plane? (*Hint:* If points A and B lie in a plane S, what about line $\overleftrightarrow{AB}$?)

Accordingly, if two lines intersect they must be coplanar, that is lie in the same plane. If we examine the contrapositive of this statement we conclude that, if two lines are not coplanar, then they do not intersect.

Existence of Parallel Lines 179

We are interested in the possible behavior of two coplanar lines. We know they may coincide or intersect in one point and it is an intriguing question whether or not there exist distinct coplanar lines which do not intersect. We refer to lines such as the latter, as *parallel* lines.

Let us approach this problem by first seeking the answer to the question: Can two distinct lines be perpendicular* to a third line at a single point of the latter line? If this were possible, we would then have two angles with the same vertex and a common ray and lying on the same side of that ray, with each having a measure of 90. Our intuition suggests that this is impossible and the possibility is actually eliminated by the assumption (or its equivalent) that there is a 1 : 1 correspondence between angles and real numbers between 0 and 180, that is, only one angle can have a measure of 90.

Let us now use this fact and our fundamental congruence theorems to establish a second basic result, namely, that there cannot be two distinct lines through a point not lying on a given line and perpendicular to that line. Let us suppose that this is possible, that is, that lines $\overleftrightarrow{PR}$ and $\overleftrightarrow{PT}$ are both perpendicular to line m. Locate point Q on $\overleftrightarrow{PR}$ on the opposite side of R from P such that $PR = RQ$. Since $\angle TRQ$ must also have a measure of 90 and $\overline{RT}$ is a common side, we know $\triangle PRT \cong \triangle QRT$ by SAS. Consequently we know that $\angle PTR \cong \angle QTR$ and hence $m(\angle QTR) = 90$. However line $\overleftrightarrow{PT}$ is perpendicular to m, and, therefore, we have two lines $\overleftrightarrow{QT}$ and $\overleftrightarrow{PT}$ perpendicular to m at T, which is not possible as we have seen in the previous paragraph. Accord-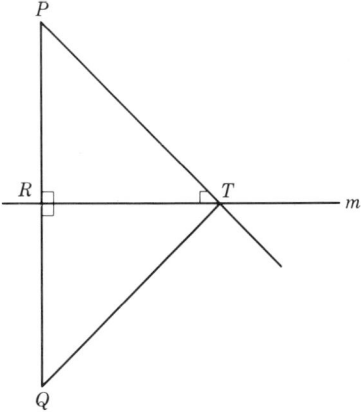ingly we have demonstrated that there cannot be two distinct lines from a point perpendicular to the same line.

We are now ready to demonstrate that parallel lines exist. To be specific, consider a line m and a point P, not lying on m. Let line l,

---

*In the complete development, two angles may be defined to be supplementary if they are congruent, respectively, to a pair of angles which have one ray in common and the other two rays lying in the same line. It is then postulated that the sum of the measures of two supplementary angles is 180. Hence, if two supplementary angles are congruent to each other, each must have a measure of 90 and is called a *right angle*. Two lines which contain two rays forming a right angle are said to be *perpendicular*.

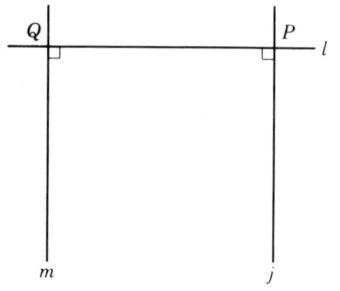

through P, be perpendicular to m at Q. Then let line j be perpendicular to line l at P. Therefore lines j and m are both perpendicular to l. Let us suppose that lines j and m have an intersection point, R. Then there would be two distinct lines through R perpendicular to l and we have seen that this is impossible. Hence we know that there always exists at least one line parallel to m through P, where P is a point not lying on m. The significant fact is that we do not know that this line is unique. We have merely employed *one* procedure for achieving such a line through P parallel to m. In order to illustrate the point under consideration, let k be the line perpendicular to m at T, a point on m distinct from Q. Then let s be the line through P perpendicular to k at V. Hence, by the previous argument, s and m are parallel lines. Therefore s and j are both parallel to m and pass through P and we have no way of knowing whether or not they are distinct lines. It should also be observed that we have before us two quadrilaterals, namely $PQTW$ and $PQTV$, each containing three right angles and we are unable to determine whether or not either quadrilateral is a rectangle, that is, whether or not the remaining angle is a right angle.

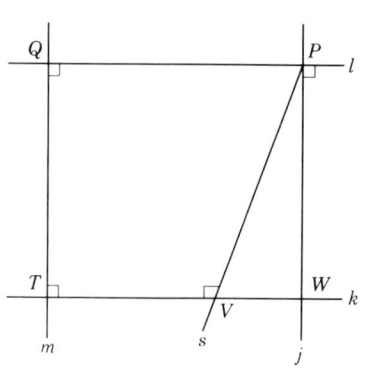

Before concluding this section we would like to give a brief description of a more general method of producing a line through P parallel to m. It can be proved at the present stage of development of our geometry that the measure of an exterior angle of a triangle is larger than the measure of either opposite interior angle; for example, $m(\angle RAC)$ is greater

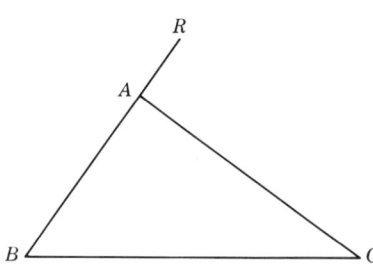

than either $m(\angle B)$ or $m(\angle C)$. Suppose any line k is drawn through P, intersecting line m in Q. Let G be a point on m distinct from Q and let $\angle QPS$ be congruent to $\angle PQG$, with S and G on opposite sides of k. The $n \overleftrightarrow{SP}$ is parallel to m.

Question. Can you demonstrate that $\overleftrightarrow{SP}$ is parallel to m if $\angle QPS \cong \angle PQG$? (*Hint*: Suppose that $\overleftrightarrow{SP}$ and m have a common point T.)

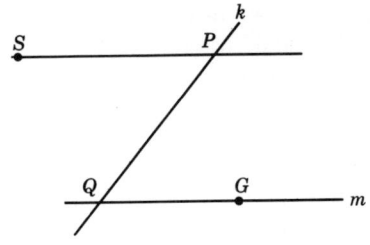

It must be emphasized, however, that if $\overleftrightarrow{SP}$ is merely known to be parallel to m, then we are *not* able to say that opposite interior angles are congruent, that is, we do *not* then know that $\angle QPS \cong \angle PQG$.

EXERCISES

1. In how many ways may two distinct lines in a plane be located relative to each other? Three distinct lines?
2. How many planes will contain three points if no line contains these three points?
3. If $\overrightarrow{OR}$ and $\overrightarrow{OS}$ are opposite rays (that is, lie in line $\overleftrightarrow{RS}$ and ROS) and $\overrightarrow{ON}$ is a ray such that $m(\angle RON) = m(\angle SON)$, what can be concluded regarding $\overleftrightarrow{ON}$ and $\overleftrightarrow{RS}$? Explain.
4. In how many ways may two distinct planes be located relative to each other? Three distinct planes?
5. On a level floor, why will a four-legged table sometimes rock, while a three-legged table is always steady?
6. How many lines can be drawn through 4 coplanar points, taken 2 at a time, if no 3 of the points are collinear? How many lines can be drawn if exactly 3 of the 4 points are collinear?

8.03 DO WE HAVE RECTANGLES?

It is a rewarding effort to investigate the geometry which exists without any assumption regarding the number of lines parallel to a line m, through a point P, not on m. In the previous section we discussed the fact that there is at least one such line. This geometry is sometimes called "neutral or absolute geometry," and may be described as a geometry sufficient to provide lines through a given point parallel to a given line but not sufficient to guarantee the uniqueness of such lines. In order to give the reader some idea of this kind of geometry we shall list a few of the more interesting theorems. In our informal approach we have made no attempt to give a complete listing of postulates and, accordingly, it is not possible to give proofs of these theorems here.

The following theorems have been selected in order to provide a sampling of the flavor of "neutral geometry":

(1) The angle measure sum of any triangle is less than or equal to 180.
(2) If one particular rectangle is known to exist, then every rectangle (that is, with sides of any preassigned lengths) exists.
(3) If one particular rectangle exists, then every triangle has an angle measure sum of 180.
(4) If one particular rectangle exists, then Euclid's Parallel Postulate (of a unique line through P parallel to m) holds.
(5) If there exists one particular triangle with angle measure sum of 180, then there exists a rectangle.

These theorems are important in that they demonstrate the close relationship which exists between the angle measure sum of a triangle, the existence of a single rectangle, and Euclid's Parallel Postulate. It might be well to note here that if we wish to make possible a geometry in which there is no line through a point parallel to a given line, it then is necessary to eliminate certain postulates which form a part of "neutral geometry," notably the postulate that states that there is only one line containing any two distinct points.

8.04 EUCLID'S PARALLEL POSTULATE

We have seen that, within the bounds of "neutral geometry," we encounter no trouble in producing a line parallel to a given line m, through a point not on m.

We are now ready to make a choice of postulate concerning parallel lines. If we decide to assume that there can be *at most* one line through P parallel to m, this is equivalent to saying that there is *only one* such possible line, and we are then on the way to developing Euclidean Geometry. If, on the other hand, we choose at this point the postulate which states that through any point P, not on m, there are at least two lines, l_1 and l_2, parallel to m, then we shall have taken the critical step

Euclid's Parallel Postulate

in the direction of the non-Euclidean geometry known as "hyperbolic."*

From now on we shall assume that we have adopted the Euclidean Axiom of Parallels and we shall investigate a few of the consequences of this choice. One of the first results to be obtained concerns the existence of rectangles. Let us recall the figure in Section 8.02 associated with the argument that there could be more than one line through P parallel to m. Note that in Section 8.02 we were unable to prove that the fourth angle, $\angle QPV$, of the quadrilateral $PQTV$ is a right angle, when the other three angles are known to be right angles. However, $\angle WPQ \cong$ a right angle and we know now that $\overleftrightarrow{PV}$ and $\overleftrightarrow{PW}$

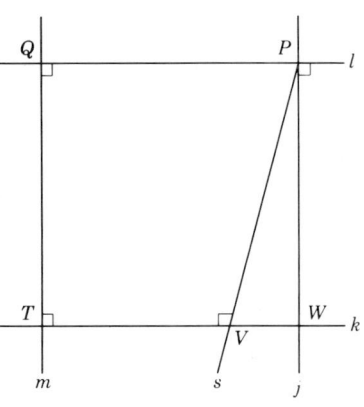

must coincide since there is only one line through P parallel to m. Therefore $\angle QPV$ is a right angle and $PQTV$ is a rectangle, the same rectangle as $PQTW$.

An equally significant consequence of the Euclidean Parallel Postulate concerns the sum of the measures of the angles of a triangle. Let m be the unique line through A parallel to $\overleftrightarrow{BC}$, in relation to $\triangle ABC$. Let P and Q be two points on m on opposite sides of A. From the discussion at the end of Section 8.02 we know that we can conclude that $\angle PAB \cong \angle B$ and $\angle QAC \cong \angle C$. Since the sum of the measures of $\angle PAB$, $\angle BAC$, and $\angle QAC$ is 180,** we know, therefore, that the

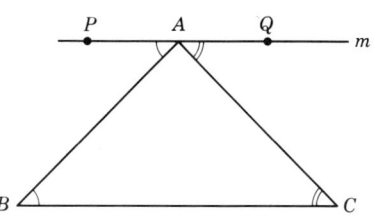

sum of the measures of $\angle A$, $\angle B$, and $\angle C$ is 180. It follows that the angle measure sum for any quadrilateral is 360.

---

*This is the geometry discovered independently by Bolyai and Lobachevsky (a Hungarian and a Russian mathematician, respectively). This is not the only non-Euclidean geometry, since it is possible to assume that there are no lines through P parallel to m. However, as we noted at the end of Section 8.03, this assumption could not be made without eliminating at the same time certain basic postulates which it contradicts.

**See footnote, Section 8.02.

$$m(\angle PAB) + m(\angle BAC) = m(\angle PAC)$$
$$m(\angle PAC) + m(\angle QAC) = 180$$
$$\therefore m(\angle PAB) + m(\angle BAC) + m(\angle QAC) = 180$$

8.05 AREA OF A TRIANGLE*

We have noted earlier our assumption that to every polygonal region there corresponds a unique positive number which is its area. It is entirely reasonable (but needs to be stated) that we should assume that congruent polygonal regions have equal areas and that areas are additive; that is, the area of the union of two polygonal regions is the sum of the areas of the two regions, provided the intersection of these two regions contains only vertices or segments of the boundary. The reader will recall that, as a result of elementary considerations, we defined the area of a rectangle to be the product of the lengths of its sides, when those lengths are relative to the same linear unit. Since either diagonal evidently separates any rectangular region into two congruent triangular regions, we may conclude that the area of a right triangle is one-half the product of the lengths of its two perpendicular sides.

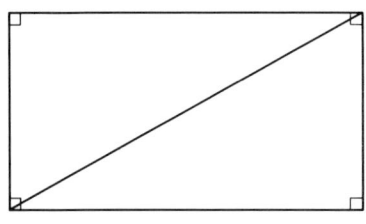

When we come to consider the area of a general triangle, there are three cases to be treated, illustrated by the following three diagrams:

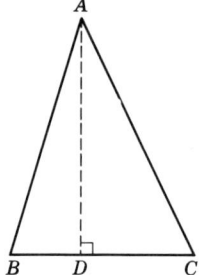 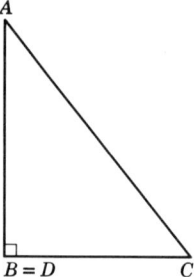 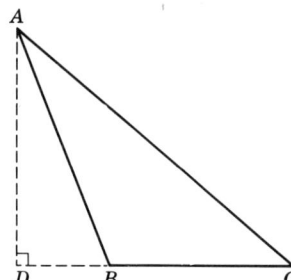

Any side of a triangle may be thought of as its base. For convenience let us consider $\overline{BC}$ as the base in the above figures. Then $\overline{AD}$ will be called the altitude of $\triangle ABC$ with respect to the base $\overline{BC}$, where $\overline{AD}$ is the segment from A perpendicular to $\overleftrightarrow{BC}$ at D.

---

*Technically, areas are associated with polygonal regions (see Section 4.08) rather than with polygons. However, for the sake of brevity, we shall use the term area of a triangle, or rectangle, to represent the area of a triangular or rectangular region, respectively.

Questions. 1. Can you deduce that the area of any triangular region is one-half the product of the lengths of its base and its altitude?
2. Can you show that the area of a parallelogram* is equal to the area of the rectangle on the same base and having the same altitude?

8.06 SIMILARITY

In Section 8.01 we discussed the congruence, that is, the identical size and shape, of geometric figures, particularly triangles. A very important and considerably more general relationship is that of *similarity*, in which the shape but not the size of figures is maintained. For example, all squares are *similar* to each other as are also all equilateral triangles. To be specific, $\triangle ABC$ is similar to $\triangle A'B'C'$, written $\triangle ABC \approx \triangle A'B'C'$

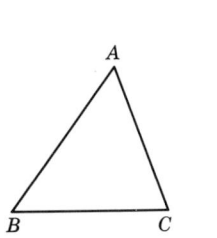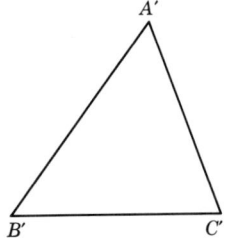

(or the correspondence $ABC \leftrightarrow A'B'C'$ is a similarity), if and only if $\angle A \cong \angle A'$, $\angle B \cong \angle B'$, $\angle C \cong \angle C'$ and $\dfrac{AB}{A'B'} = \dfrac{BC}{B'C'} = \dfrac{CA}{C'A'}$.

Hence we may say that $\triangle ABC \approx \triangle A'B'C'$ if and only if corresponding angles are congruent and corresponding sides are proportional.

The principal reason for delaying the discussion of similarity until we have assumed the Parallel Postulate lies in the fact that the following important theorem is now provable, although we shall not give the proof here: If a line $\overleftrightarrow{DE}$, parallel to the line $\overleftrightarrow{BC}$ containing one side $\overline{BC}$ of a triangle, $\triangle ABC$, intersects the other two sides in distinct points, D and E, then the

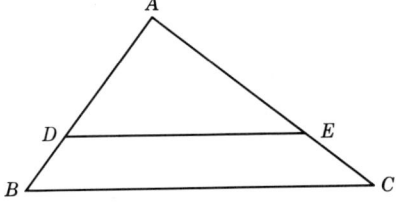

---

*A parallelogram is defined as a quadrilateral, or four-sided plane polygon, in which pairs of opposite segments are parts of parallel lines.

correspondence $ABC \leftrightarrow ADE$ is a similarity. It can be proved, further, that if corresponding angles of two triangles are congruent, then the triangles are similar.

We wish now to establish a very important result concerning the areas of similar triangles, and, by analogy, the areas of similar figures in general, namely, the areas of similar triangles are proportional to the squares of corresponding sides.

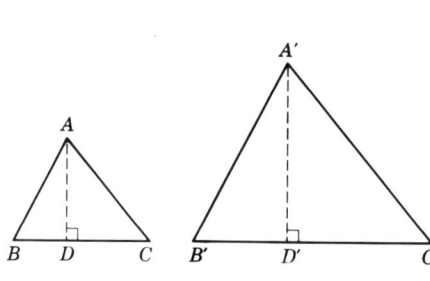

If $\triangle ABC \approx \triangle A'B'C'$, then $\frac{AB}{A'B'} = \frac{BC}{B'C'}$. Let $\overline{AD}$ and $\overline{A'D'}$ be corresponding altitudes of the two triangles. Since $\angle B \cong \angle B'$ and $\angle D \cong \angle D' \cong$ a right angle, then $\angle BAD \cong \angle B'A'D'$. Hence $\triangle ABD \approx \triangle A'B'D'$. Therefore $\frac{AD}{A'D'} = \frac{AB}{A'B'}$. Hence we have $\frac{BC}{B'C'} = \frac{AD}{A'D'}$. If we suppose each of these ratios equal to k, then $BC = k \cdot B'C'$; $AD = k \cdot A'D'$ and area of $\triangle ABC$
$= \frac{1}{2} BC \cdot AD$
$= \frac{1}{2} k^2 \cdot B'C' \cdot A'D'$
$= k^2 \cdot$ area of $\triangle A'B'C'$

Hence we have

$$\frac{\text{area of } \triangle ABC}{\text{area of } \triangle A'B'C'} = k^2 = \left(\frac{BC}{B'C'}\right)^2$$

or

$$\frac{\text{area of } \triangle ABC}{(BC)^2} = \frac{\text{area of } \triangle A'B'C'}{(B'C')^2}$$

Therefore the areas of similar triangles are proportional to the squares of corresponding sides.

EXERCISES

1. How would you divide a line segment into five congruent segments?
2. The line through a vertex of a triangle and the midpoint of the opposite side is called a median. What can you say about the areas of the two triangles into which any triangle is divided by a median?

3. If the base of a triangle is trisected and the points of trisection are joined to the opposite vertex, what can you say about the areas of the three smaller triangles so formed?
4. Prove that either diagonal of a parallelogram is trisected by the lines joining the remaining vertices to the midpoints of opposite sides.

8.07 THE THEOREM OF PYTHAGORAS

It is a curious fact that the so-called *Theorem of Pythagoras*, "The square on the hypotenuse of a right triangle is equal to the sum of the squares on the other two sides," was proved by Euclid and is the only theorem whose proof is directly ascribed to him.

There are many proofs of this theorem, some of which are based on considerations of area, whereas others employ algebraic procedures often depending on the consequences of similarity.

We shall limit ourselves to five proofs of the theorem beginning with the proof due to Euclid:

(1) In the figure, $\overline{AH}$ is perpendicular to $\overline{BC}$ and $\overleftrightarrow{AG}$ is parallel to

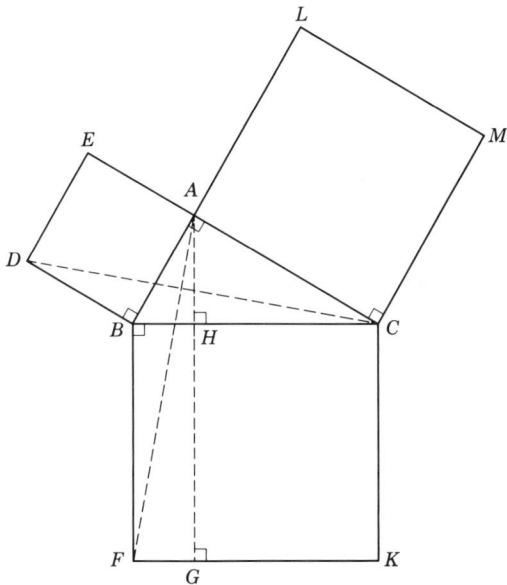

$\overleftrightarrow{BF}$. $\triangle ABF \cong \triangle DBC$ (SAS). $\therefore$ area of $\triangle ABF = \frac{1}{2}$ area of rectangle $BFGH$, area of $\triangle BCD = \frac{1}{2}$ area of square $BAED$. $\therefore$ area of rectangle

$BFGH$ = area of square $BAED$. In an exactly similar fashion it may be shown that area of rectangle $GKCH$ = area of square $ACML$. Since area of rectangle $BFGH$ + area of rectangle $GKCH$ = area of square $BFKC$, it follows that area of square $BAED$ + area of square $ACML$ = area of square $BFKC$.

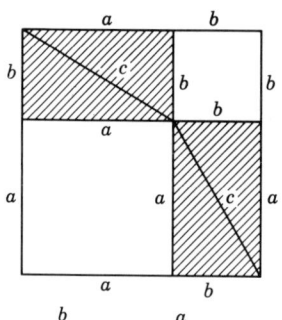

(2) Let a, b, and c represent the lengths of the sides and hypotenuse, respectively, of a right triangle. Let us consider two congruent squares, whose sides have length $a + b$ and which are dissected in the two ways indicated at the left. When the four (thatched) triangles are removed from each large square, it is evident that the remaining areas are equal, that is, $a^2 + b^2 = c^2$.

Question. In the second figure at the left how are we certain that the inner quadrilateral is truly a square?

(3) In the second figure of (2), the area of each triangle is $\tfrac{1}{2}ab$. Hence
$$(a + b)^2 = 4(\tfrac{1}{2}ab) + c^2$$
$$\therefore a^2 + 2ab + b^2 = 2ab + c^2$$
$$\therefore a^2 + b^2 = c^2$$

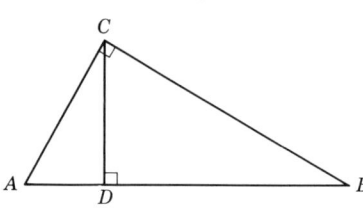

(4) The standard proof, based on similarity, proceeds as follows: In the figure at the left it is easy to check that all three triangles, $\triangle ABC$, $\triangle ACD$, and $\triangle CBD$ are similar.

Hence we know that

$$\frac{AD}{AC} = \frac{AC}{AB} \text{ since } \triangle ACD \approx \triangle ABC$$

and

$$\frac{DB}{BC} = \frac{BC}{AB} \text{ since } \triangle CBD \approx \triangle ABC$$

$$\therefore AD = \frac{(AC)^2}{AB}; \; DB = \frac{(BC)^2}{AB}$$

Hence

$$AB = AD + DB$$
$$= \frac{(AC)^2}{AB} + \frac{(BC)^2}{AB}$$

and
$$(AB)^2 = (AC)^2 + (BC)^2$$

(5) The following is the most elegant proof of which this writer is aware: Let us make use of the diagram in (4) and note again that $\triangle ABC \approx \triangle CBD \approx \triangle ACD$. As a result of the final argument in Section 8.06 we know that

$$\frac{\text{area of } \triangle ACD}{(AC)^2} = \frac{\text{area of } \triangle ABC}{(AB)^2} = \frac{\text{area of } \triangle CBD}{(CB)^2} = q, \text{ for example.}$$

Since the triangular region ABC is obviously the union of the two smaller triangular regions ACD and CBD, we have

$$\text{area of } \triangle ACD + \text{area of } \triangle CBD = \text{area of } \triangle ABC$$
$$\therefore q \cdot (AC)^2 + q \cdot (CB)^2 = q \cdot (AB)^2.$$

Since $q \neq 0$, it follows that $(AC)^2 + (CB)^2 = (AB)^2$.

8.08 CONSTRUCTIONS

It is appropriate that we examine some simple ruler and compass constructions, both for their intrinsic usefulness and also for the sake of the careful argument involved in their justification. (A good operating rule in approaching a geometric construction is to assume that the construction has been completed and then take a careful look at it to see how it might have been accomplished.)

(1) Let us first consider the matter of constructing an angle congruent to a given angle. In other words we are given an angle C and a ray with end-point A. We wish to construct an angle congruent to $\angle C$, with vertex A and with the given ray as one side and lying in one of the half-planes determined by the line containing the given ray. To begin with, the existence of the angle to be constructed is assured by postulate; consequently we are not attempting the impossible.

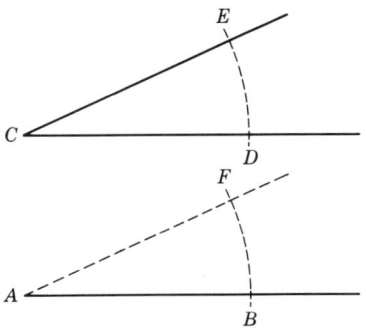

Let us draw a circle of radius r with center C. This circle will

190   More Informal Geometry

intersect both rays of ∠C at D and E, for example, since a point is guaranteed, by postulate, to exist on each ray at a distance r from C. With the same radius r and center A, we draw a second circle intersecting the given ray at B. Again, with radius DE and center B we draw a circle which our intuition tells us should intersect the previous circle in two points, one of which is F in the desired half-plane. We wish to consider this matter rather carefully from two points of view; first, must the two circles intersect and, second, if they do, is it true that ∠BAF ≅ ∠C?

First of all, we are assured by postulate of the existence of ∠BAF ≅ ∠C and of the points B and F, so located that $\overline{AB} \cong \overline{AF} \cong \overline{CD} \cong \overline{CE}$. Therefore △BAF ≅ △DCE by (SAS) and, hence, $\overline{BF} \cong \overline{DE}$. We already know that AF = r and thus we have established that the point F is a distance r from A and a distance DE from B. It is true, then, that F is a point lying on each of the two circles in question and hence we are assured that the circles intersect.

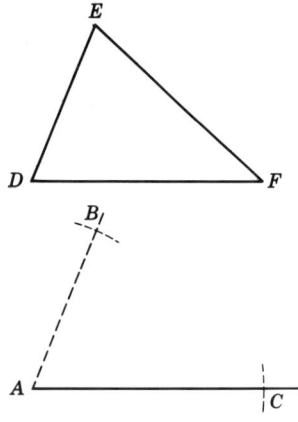

Having obtained the point F as one of the intersection points of the two circles, let us draw the ray $\overrightarrow{AF}$. We have △BAF ≅ △DCE by (SSS) and, therefore, ∠BAF ≅ ∠DCE.

(2) Let us now consider the problem of constructing a triangle congruent to a given △DEF, given one vertex A and one side lying in a given ray from A.

We may begin by constructing at A an angle congruent to ∠D. We may then obtain points B and C, on the two sides of ∠A, by drawing the appropriate circles, such that $\overline{AB} \cong \overline{DE}$ and $\overline{AC} \cong \overline{DF}$. Then △ABC ≅ △DEF by (SAS).

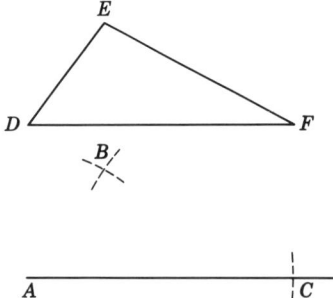

(3) There is another procedure for copying a triangle which would occur immediately to the reader. With the same hypothesis as in (2), let us locate point C on the given ray, such that $\overline{AC} \cong \overline{DF}$. Then, with center A and radius DE and also with center C and radius EF, draw two

circles. Let the point of intersection of the circles in the desired half-plane be B. Then $\triangle ABC \cong \triangle DEF$.

Questions. 1. In the previous construction can you prove (a) that the circles in question must intersect? (b) if they intersect at B, that $\triangle ABC \cong \triangle DEF$?
2. Can you develop a similar construction procedure for copying a triangle based on the (ASA) congruence theorem? Be sure to include the proofs that any intersections, of a type not already met, actually exist and also that the final triangle is congruent to the original triangle.

(4) We wish now to consider the problem of constructing a line perpendicular to a given line m at a point P on m. First locate two points R and S on m, on opposite sides of P such that $RP = PS$. Then, with centers R and S and radius $r > RP$, draw two circles. These circles must intersect for the following reason. We know the line k exists, perpendicular to m at P. Locate the point T on k such that $PT = \sqrt{r^2 - (RP)^2}$. Then, by the Pythagorean Theorem

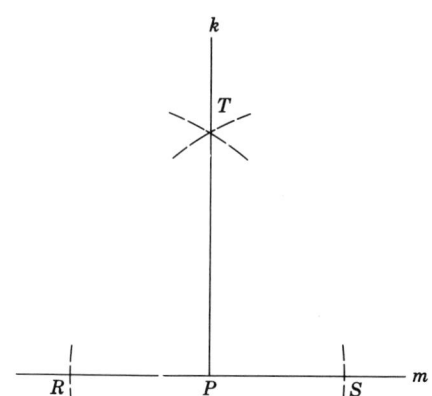

$$RT = \sqrt{(RP)^2 + (PT)^2} = r$$
$$ST = \sqrt{(SP)^2 + (PT)^2} = r$$

Hence $RT = ST$ and we are assured that the circles intersect. (It may also be shown that there is a second intersection point on the other side of m). If T is the intersection point of the two circles, then $\overleftrightarrow{TP}$ is the required line through P perpendicular to m.

Question. Can you complete (4) by proving that $\overleftrightarrow{TP}$ is perpendicular to m?

(5) Rather closely related to (4) is the problem of constructing the perpendicular bisector of a segment, that is, the line perpendicular to a segment at its midpoint. Let the given segment be $\overline{MN}$. With centers M and N and any radius $r > \frac{1}{2}MN$, draw two circles. These circles

192   More Informal Geometry

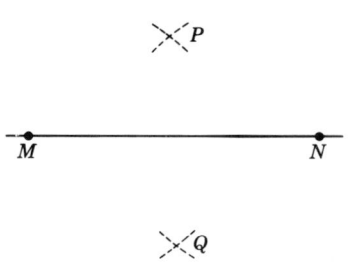

intersect in two points, P and Q, on opposite sides of $\overleftrightarrow{MN}$.

In order to show that the circles must intersect we shall make use of the fact that a point C certainly exists between M and N such that $MC = CN$. From here on the argument is identical with that used in (4).

The line $\overleftrightarrow{PQ}$ is the required perpendicular bisector of $\overline{MN}$.

Question. Can you complete the proof that $\overleftrightarrow{PQ}$ is the perpendicular bisector of $\overline{MN}$?

(6) The next problem is one of constructing the line perpendicular to a given line m through a given point P not on m. If we choose any point R

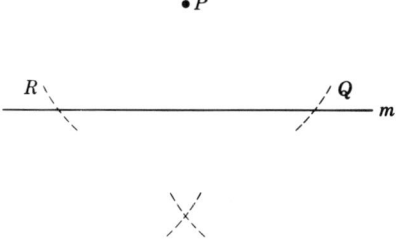

on m and draw the circle with center P and radius RP we shall obtain a second point, Q, of intersection of the circle with m. The perpendicular bisector of $\overline{RQ}$ can be constructed by (5) and provides the required perpendicular line from P to m.

There are three things to be demonstrated here, namely, the existence of the perpendicular line we are seeking, assurance of the second point of intersection of the line and circle, and, finally, the proof that the constructed line passes through P.

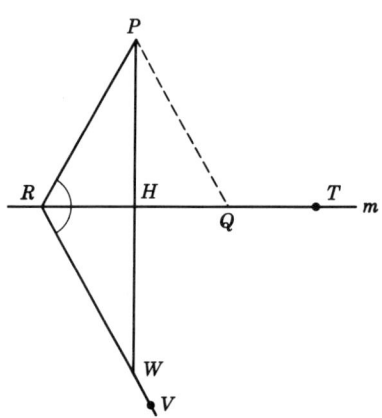

Let us begin by choosing any two points R and T on m. On the opposite side of m from P construct $\angle VRT \cong \angle PRT$. Let W be a point on ray $\overrightarrow{RV}$ such that $RW = RP$. The segment $\overline{PW}$ must intersect m in H, for example. $\overleftrightarrow{PH}$ is perpendicular to m, as required.

Question. Can you prove that $\overleftrightarrow{PH}$ is perpendicular to m?

In order to proceed with the second of our three requirements we note that, if $R \neq H$, there exists a point Q on m on the side of H opposite to R and such that $RH = HQ$. Then $RP = QP$, and Q is, accordingly, the second point of intersection of m with the circle having center P and radius RP.

Question. Can you prove that $RP = QP$?

Finally we know that the perpendicular bisector passes through H and is perpendicular to m and that $\overline{PH}$ is likewise perpendicular to m at H. Hence, by the uniqueness of the ray forming the right angle with m, we know that P must be on the perpendicular bisector of $\overline{RQ}$.

(7) The last construction we wish to describe is that of bisecting a given angle A. The procedure will be to locate two points, P and Q, on the rays forming the given angle A, such that $AP = AQ$. Then construct the perpendicular bisector of $\overline{PQ}$, and let R be any point in the interior of $\angle A$ and lying on the perpendicular bisector. The ray $\overrightarrow{AR}$ is the required bisector of $\angle A$. This is proved by observing that $\triangle APR \cong \triangle AQR$ by (SSS). Hence $\angle PAR \cong \angle QAR$.

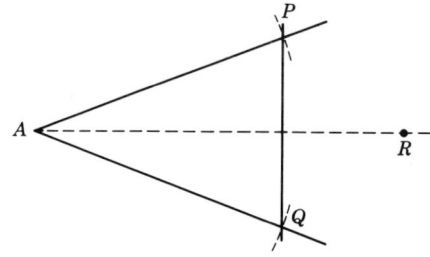

EXERCISES

1. Draw several triangles and find the angle bisectors for each triangle. Can you draw a conclusion regarding their intersection?
2. Same as Exercise 1 for the perpendicular bisectors of the sides of a triangle.
3. Same as Exercise 1 for the altitudes of a triangle. (See Section 8.05 for definition of altitude. For the purposes of this exercise, it may be necessary to extend the altitudes beyond the foot of the perpendicular.)
4. Same as Exercise 1 for the medians of a triangle. (See Exercise 2 in Section 8.06 for definition of median.)

8.09 VOLUMES OF SOLIDS

It is our purpose here to give the reader an idea of one approach to the volumes of solids by tracing very briefly the development of the concept of volume from parallelepiped through prism to pyramid.

194   More Informal Geometry

First of all we should recall that in Section 4.08 we defined the volume of a rectangular parallelepiped as the product of the lengths of the three perpendicular edges, when these lengths are related to the same linear unit. Let us suppose next that we wish to compare the volumes of two irregularly shaped solids. We shall assume that they are held rigidly and that we are able to examine plane sections* of both solids, by a particular plane, wherever we wish. Let us suppose, when plane sections of both solids are made by planes which remain always *parallel to some given plane,* that *the areas of pairs of corresponding sectional regions are equal,* in each case, without the shapes necessarily being the same.

If these plane sections are taken as close together as we wish, we would be inclined to think of corresponding thin slices in the two solids as having very nearly equal volumes, and hence we would expect the volumes of the solids themselves to be approximately equal. The concept which has been presented here in a very rough and intuitive way is known as *Cavalieri's Principle*, and we wish to assume it as a postulate. Cavalieri's Principle states: *Given two solids and a plane, if for every plane which intersects the solids and is parallel to the given plane, the two intersections have equal areas, then the two solids have equal volumes.* Note that this is a statement of *sufficiency. If* there exists such a plane for which the stated condition holds, *then* the volumes of the two solids are equal; if otherwise, then we have no information concerning the volumes.

What is meant by applying the principle is that any plane, which is parallel to the given plane, and has any nonempty intersection with one of the solids, is expected to have an intersection of equal cross-sectional area with the other solid. If the sectional areas are unequal in even one case then Cavalieri's Principle cannot be applied. The same is true in the situation where a plane parallel to the given plane does not intersect one of the solids (that is, the intersection is the empty set which, by definition, has zero area). In neither of these cases have the volumes been shown to be equal or unequal and another given plane of different orientation relative to the solids should be employed. We wish to apply this principle in obtaining the volumes of prisms and pyramids.

First of all we need to define a prism. Suppose that we have two parallel planes, E_1 and E_2, a line l in space, l not parallel to E_1 and E_2, and K, a polygonal region in E_1, not intersecting l. For each point P in K let PP' be a segment of a line $\overleftrightarrow{PP'}$ parallel to l and intersecting E_2 in P'. The union of all such segments PP' we call a prism.

---

*A plane section (or cross section as it is sometimes called) is the set of points belonging to the region common to the plane and the solid.

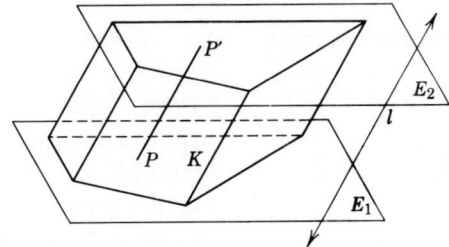

It can be shown that all cross sections of a prism by a plane parallel to its base are congruent to the base polygonal region and hence have the same area. Let us imagine a rectangular parallelepiped whose altitude is equal to the altitude of the prism and whose base has the same area as the base of the prism. Since all the plane sections parallel to the base in each solid figure have the same area, we may conclude by Cavalieri's Principle that the two volumes are equal. Hence *the volume of the prism is given by the product of its altitude and the area of its base.*

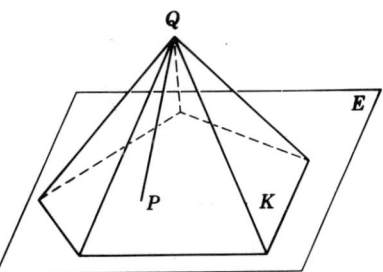

A pyramid is formed as follows: consider a polygonal region K in a plane E, and a point Q not lying in E. The union of the segments PQ for all points P in K is called a pyramid. From considerations of similarity it can be shown that two pyramids with equal altitudes and bases having equal areas must have corresponding plane sections of equal area and hence have equal volumes: it remains to discover how the volume of a pyramid is related to the volume of a particular prism.

We are going to begin with a triangular pyramid $PQRS$ on base

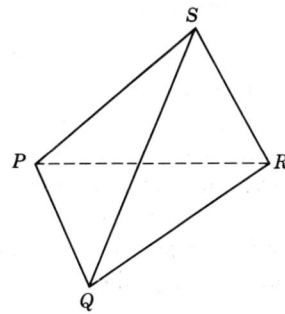

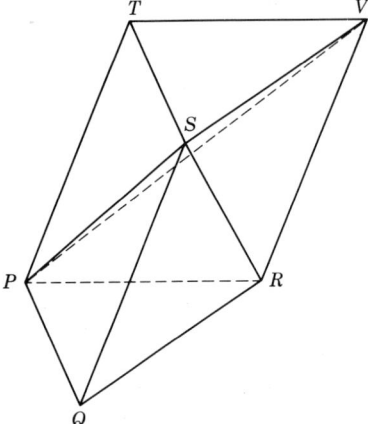

△PQR, with vertex S. We then wish to construct from it a prism, PQRSTV, on △PQR as base and with its parallel segments in lines parallel to $\overleftrightarrow{SQ}$ and having the same altitude as the pyramid. It is possible to dissect this prism PQRSTV, into three pyramids, one of which is PQRS, such that each of the other two pyramids has a face and corresponding altitude equal to a face and corresponding altitude, respectively, of PQRS. The three pyramids (a), (b), and (c) which go together to make the prism PQRSTV are shown below.

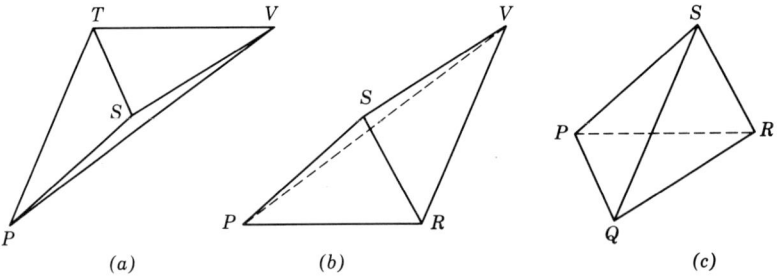

Question. Can you verify that the three pyramids have equal volumes? (*Hint:* To show that (a) and (c) have equal volumes, compare the areas of △TVS and △PRQ and corresponding altitudes. To show that (b) and (c) have equal volumes, compare the areas of △SRV and △RSQ and corresponding altitudes.)

If the *Question* has been answered correctly, it has been established that all three pyramids have equal volume, namely one-third the volume of the prism PQRSTV. Hence *the volume of any pyramid is given by one-third the product of its altitude and the area of its base.*

The volumes of cylinders and cones may be shown to be very closely related, by arguments based on limits, to the volumes of prisms and pyramids, respectively. We hope the above considerations have indicated a fruitful line of attack on a fascinating set of problems.

9 More Algebra

9.01 THE DIVISION ALGORITHM

When we divide 7 by 2, for example, we obtain a quotient, 3, and a remainder, 1, so that we may write $7 = 3(2) + 1$. In general, given any two natural numbers, N and D, we may find nonnegative integers Q and R such that $N = Q \cdot D + R$ and $0 \leq R < D$. Thus $7 = 3(2) + 1$ and $0 \leq 1 < 2$; $8 = 4(2) + 0$ and $0 \leq 0 < 2$; $7 = 0(8) + 7$ and $0 \leq 7 < 8$. The fact that such a representation of N is always possible may be proved from the axioms concerning nonnegative integers; here, however, we shall accept it as another axiom, commonly called the *division algorithm*. It plays a fundamental role in a great many theoretical considerations, two of which will be illustrated in Sections 9.03 and 9.06.

Question. Can you show that Q and R are unique for given N and D?

The following example will illustrate the use of the algorithm in the familiar "long division" procedure.

```
          3897
     23)89637
         69
         ---
         206
         184
         ---
         223
         207
         ---
         167
         161
         ---
           6
```

Hence we have

$$89637 = (23)(3897) + 6$$

197

More Algebra

It is relatively difficult to explain to one unfamiliar with the process, the significance of the steps in this traditional "repeated subtraction" procedure. However the form of the operation may be changed in such a way as to make the individual steps much clearer. This is demonstrated below, where the partial quotients are listed in a column at the right and the multiples of the divisor are written out completely. The advantage of this arrangement lies in the fact that it is self-correcting. A partial quotient is no longer "wrong" if it is too small, but it may be completed in a second or third stage. The final quotient is obtained by adding the column of partial quotients.

```
        23 | 89637
             46000         2000
             43637
             23000         1000
             20637
             13800          600
              6837
              4600          200
              2237
              2070           90
               167
               138            6
                29
                23            1
                 6         3897
```

Hence $89637 = (23)(3897) + 6$

We may arrange this alternative procedure in the form shown below which is more similar to the traditional process but still possesses the advantages noted above.

$$
\begin{array}{r}
7 \\
90 \\
800 \\
3000 \\
\underline{3897} \\
23\,\overline{)89637} \\
\underline{69000} \\
20637 \\
\underline{18400} \\
2237 \\
\underline{2070} \\
167 \\
\underline{161} \\
6
\end{array}
$$

We have, as before

$$89637 = (23)(3897) + 6$$

9.02 THE CONCEPT OF FUNCTION

We have seen the number of ways in which mathematics employs the idea of correspondence between elements of two sets. It is probably no exaggeration to say that there is no concept which is employed more often than this one throughout mathematics and particularly at the advanced levels.

We have defined a relation (Section 3.04) as a subset of the Cartesian product (Section 1.06), and we now define a *function* as a relation in which no two ordered pairs have the same first element. What we have done then is set up a correspondence between the set of first elements and the set of second elements of the set of ordered pairs. The function, then, specifies a rule or instruction which tells what is the unique image of any given element and, in fact, a function is often thought of as a mapping or transformation. The set, $\{(1,3),(2,4),(3,5),(4,5)\}$ is an example of a function, as is the set $\{(1,2),(2,4),(3,6),(4,8),\ldots\}$, where the second member of each pair is twice the first. However the set $\{(1,2),(1,3),(2,4),(3,5)\}$ is a relation which is not a function since the second element is not unique for a given first element: (1,2) and (1,3) are both members of the set; $1 = 1$ but $2 \neq 3$.

In terms of the mapping approach the function $\{(1,3),(2,4),(3,5),(4,5)\}$ would be written as

$$f: 1 \rightsquigarrow 3, 2 \rightsquigarrow 4, 3 \rightsquigarrow 5, 4 \rightsquigarrow 5$$

and the function

$$\{(1,2),(2,4),(3,6),(4,8),\ldots\}$$

as

$$f: 1 \rightsquigarrow 2, 2 \rightsquigarrow 4, 3 \rightsquigarrow 6, 4 \rightsquigarrow 8, \ldots$$

It is easy to see that we may pass readily from the representation of a function as a set of ordered pairs to the representation of a function as a mapping and conversely. Which representation is used is a matter of convenience and taste.

Sometimes, but certainly not always, we may find that the function can be described by a formula as, for example, when the ordered pairs are all of the type (x, x^2), where x is any real number. Then x^2 corresponds to x under the mapping, f, which is the rule for determining the correspondence.

In general, regardless of the existence of a formula for the mapping, we may describe by $f(x)$ the image of x under the function f. We are accustomed to calling $f(x)$ the *value* of the function, f, at x. The set of numbers from which x is selected is called the *domain* and the set of numbers into which the various numbers of the domain are mapped by the function is called the *range* of the function. The function f is therefore the set of ordered pairs $\{(x, f(x))\}$, where x takes any value in a given domain. Hence for the function $\{(1,3),(2,3),(3,5),(4,5)\}$, the domain is $\{1,2,3,4\}$ and the range is $\{3,5\}$; $f(1) = 3, f(2) = 3, f(3) = 5$, and $f(4) = 5$. For the function, $f = \{(x, x^2) | x \in \text{set of real numbers}\}$, $f(x) = x^2$ and the range is the set of nonnegative real numbers. Alternatively we may also denote such a function as this one by $\{(x,y) | y = x^2, x \text{ a real number}\}$ or by $f: x \rightsquigarrow x^2$ or by $f: f(x) = x^2$. But whether or not there is a formula, the function f determines the "map" or image, $f(x)$, of x, for each x in the domain.

Questions. (1) For the function $f = \{(1,2),(2,4),(3,6),\ldots\}$, previously discussed, the domain is the set of natural numbers.

    (a) What is the range of f?
    (b) What is the "map" of 5?
    (c) What is $f(12)$?
    (d) If $f(x) = 42$, what is x?

(2) If $f(x) = 2^x$, can you show that $f(y) \cdot f(w) = f(y + w)$?

EXERCISES

1. If $f(x) = 3x + 2$, show that $f(4y + 2) = 4f(y)$.
2. If $f(x) = x^2$, show that $f(y^3) = [f(y)]^3$.
3. If $f(x) = \frac{1}{x}$, show that $f(y + a) - f(y - a) = \frac{2a}{a^2 - y^2}$.
4. If $f(x) = \frac{1}{\sqrt{x+1}}$, show that $f(y - 1) - f(y) = \frac{1}{y\sqrt{y+1} + (y+1)\sqrt{y}}$.
5. With suitable restrictions in the domain of real numbers to avoid division by zero,

   (a) if $f(x) = \frac{x-1}{x+1}$, show that $f(y+2) \cdot f(y) = f\left(\frac{y+1}{2}\right)$

   (b) if $f(x) = \frac{x+3}{x-2}$, show that $f(y+1) \cdot f(y-4) = f\left(\frac{y}{2} - 1\right)$

   (c) if $f(x) = \frac{x-2}{x+1}$, show that $f(y+3) \cdot f(y) = f\left(\frac{y+2}{2}\right)$.

6. Find a formula for the function $f = \{(-2,-11),(-1,-8),(0,-5),(1,-2),(2,1),(3,4),(4,7)\}$.

   (a) What is the domain of f?
   (b) What is the range of f?

   (Note that the formula for f, along with the domain, provides a complete description of the function.)

9.03 THE REMAINDER THEOREM

A polynomial is an expression like

$$a_n x^n + a_{n-1} x^{n-1} + \ldots + a_1 x + a_0$$

where the coefficients $a_i, i = 0, 1, 2, \ldots, n,$ are real numbers and the exponents are whole numbers.

There is a natural extension of the division algorithm (discussed in Section 9.01) to polynomials: If $P(x)$ and $D(x)$ are polynomials, then there exist polynomials, $Q(x)$ and $R(x)$, such that $P(x) = D(x)Q(x) + R(x)$, where the degree of $R(x) <$ the degree of $D(x)$. (The degree of a polynomial is the exponent of the variable in the term containing the highest power of the variable; the degree of the constant polynomial $P(x) = c$, is defined to be zero.) The standard "long division" procedure produces $Q(x)$ and $R(x)$. In this procedure multiples of the divisor

More Algebra

polynomial $D(x)$ by the proper power of x are subtracted from the dividend $P(x)$, in order to eliminate, by successive stages, terms of $P(x)$ beginning with that of highest degree. The following example will illustrate the procedure:

$$
\begin{array}{r}
3x^2 + 6x + 11 \\
x^2 - 2x - 1 \overline{\smash{\big)}\, 3x^4 - 4x^2 + 5} \\
3x^4 - 6x^3 - 3x^2 \\
\hline
6x^3 - x^2 \\
6x^3 - 12x^2 - 6x \\
\hline
11x^2 + 6x + 5\\
11x^2 - 22x - 11\\
\hline
28x + 16
\end{array}
$$

Here $P(x) = 3x^4 - 4x^2 + 5$; $D(x) = x^2 - 2x - 1$
$Q(x) = 3x^2 + 6x + 11$; $R(x) = 28x + 16$

and $3x^4 - 4x^2 + 5 = (x^2 - 2x - 1)(3x^2 + 6x + 11) + (28x + 16)$

We are particularly interested in the case where the divisor polynomial $D(x) = ax + b (a \neq 0)$; that is, where $D(x)$ is linear. Then the remainder $R(x)$ will necessarily have degree zero* and hence will be a constant.

$$\therefore P(x) = (ax + b)Q(x) + r$$

This sentence is true when x is replaced by any number and in particular, when x is replaced by $-\dfrac{b}{a}$. Then

$$P\left(-\frac{b}{a}\right) = 0 \cdot Q\left(-\frac{b}{a}\right) + r, \text{ and } r = P\left(-\frac{b}{a}\right)$$

Therefore we may write

$$P(x) = (ax + b)Q(x) + P\left(-\frac{b}{a}\right)$$

This statement is known as the *Remainder Theorem* and is particularly useful when we are looking for factors of $P(x)$. Whenever

---

*If $R(x)$ has degree zero, then (see Section 1.17) $R(x) = kx^0$, a constant.

$P\left(-\dfrac{b}{a}\right)$ is zero we know immediately that $ax + b$ is a factor of $P(x)$. In simpler notation,
$$P(t) = 0 \iff P(x) = (x - t)Q(x)$$

For example, if
$$P(x) = x^4 + 8x^3 + 14x^2 - 8x - 15$$
we observe that $P(1) = 0$ and $P(-1) = 0$. Hence $x - 1$ and $x + 1$ are factors of $P(x)$. We may divide $P(x)$ by $(x + 1)(x - 1) = x^2 - 1$ to obtain the quotient, $x^2 + 8x + 15 = (x + 3)(x + 5)$. Hence
$$P(x) = (x - 1)(x + 1)(x + 3)(x + 5)$$

When used for this purpose the Remainder Theorem is sometimes referred to as the *Factor Theorem*. When $P(t) = 0$ we often call t a *zero* of $P(x)$ as well as a *root* of $P(x) = 0$.

EXERCISES

1. If two polynomials $P_1(x)$ and $P_2(x)$ have degrees n_1 and n_2 respectively, what is the degree of the polynomial obtained by multiplying $P_1(x)$ by $P_2(x)$?
2. Show that $Q(x)$ and $R(x)$ are unique in the Division Algorithm.
3. For $f(x) = 2x^3 + x^2 - 22x + 24$,
   (a) Evaluate $f(1), f(-2), f(-1), f(2), f(3), f(-\tfrac{1}{2}), f(\tfrac{3}{2}), f(-3), f(4), f(-4)$.
   (b) Express $f(x)$ in factored form.
4. What conclusion can you draw from the fact that $f(x)$ is a polynomial and $f(a) < 0$ but $f(b) > 0$?

9.04 SYNTHETIC DIVISION AND SYNTHETIC SUBSTITUTION

The labor of dividing a polynomial by $x - t$ can be reduced considerably by eliminating the symbols that occur repetitiously in the procedure. Let us consider the following division:

$$
\begin{array}{r}
4x^3 + 5x^2 + 3x + 2 \\
x - 2 \overline{\smash{)}\, 4x^4 - 3x^3 - 7x^2 - 4x - 9} \\
\underline{4x^4 - 8x^3 } \\
5x^3 - 7x^2 \\
\underline{5x^3 - 10x^2 } \\
3x^2 - 4x \\
\underline{3x^2 - 6x } \\
2x - 9 \\
\underline{2x - 4} \\
-5
\end{array}
$$

204 More Algebra

We may streamline this division, as follows, leaving out the various powers of x but maintaining the coefficients in their proper places.

$$\begin{array}{r} 4532 \\ -2\overline{\smash{)}4-3-7-4-9} \\ \underline{-8} \\ 5 \\ \underline{-10} \\ 3 \\ \underline{-6} \\ 2 \\ \underline{-4} \\ -5 \end{array}$$

The above arrangement may be "collapsed" to give the following:

$$\begin{array}{r} -2\overline{\smash{)}4-3-7-4-9} \\ \underline{-8-10-6-4} \\ 4532-5 \end{array}$$

Note that:
$$\begin{aligned} -8 &= 4(-2) \\ -10 &= 5(-2) \\ -6 &= 3(-2) \\ -4 &= 2(-2) \end{aligned}$$

Since it is generally easier to add than to subtract, we shall replace -2 by 2 and add, rather than subtract, in each column beginning with the second from the left. Hence we have the final streamlined division known as *synthetic division*:

$$\begin{array}{r} 2\overline{\smash{)}4-3-7-4-9} \\ \underline{81064} \\ 4532-5 \end{array}$$

There are several points to be noted in connection with this procedure:

(1) The number in the upper left-hand corner is "t", if we are dividing by $x - t$.

(2) The top row consists of coefficients of terms of the dividend polynomial in order of descending degree. Any missing term in the sequence must be indicated by a zero coefficient. For example, we shall treat $5x^4 + 3x$ as $5x^4 + 0x^3 + 0x^2 + 3x + 0$.

(3) The left-hand coefficient in the top row is merely "brought down" to the third row.
(4) The procedure is then one of "multiply by t and add."
(5) The third row, except for the right-hand number, consists of the coefficients of powers of x in the quotient polynomial, in order of descending degree.
(6) The right-hand number in the third row is the remainder, when the divisor is $x - t$, which, by the Remainder Theorem, also represents the value of the dividend polynomial at $x = t$.
(7) In view of the Remainder Theorem the process is known equally well as *synthetic substitution*.

If the reader should have any doubt that the right-hand number in the third row is actually $P(2)$, where

$$P(x) = 4x^4 - 3x^3 - 7x^2 - 4x - 9$$

it may be checked independently as follows. The synthetic division procedure in this case may be written in the form:

(a) $\qquad 2(2[2\{2(4) + (-3)\} + (-7)] + (-4)) + (-9)$

Direct replacement of 2 for x in $P(x)$ gives

(b) $\qquad 4(2)^4 - 3(2)^3 - 7(2)^2 - 4(2) - 9$

Question. Can you verify that the numbers represented by (a) and (b) are equal?

EXERCISES

1. When $f(x) = 4x^4 - 3x^3 - 7x^2 - 4x - 9$ is divided by $x - 3$, synthetically, the division looks like this:

$$\begin{array}{r|rrrrr} 3 & 4 & -3 & -7 & -4 & -9 \\ & & 12 & 27 & 60 & 168 \\ \hline & 4 & 9 & 20 & 56 & 159 \end{array}$$

(a) If $a > 3$, is it possible for $f(a)$ to be zero?
(b) What conclusion can be drawn from the fact that the third row consists only of positive numbers?

More Algebra

2. When the polynomial $f(x)$ in Exercise 1 is divided by $x + 2$, synthetically, the division appears as follows:

$$\begin{array}{r|rrrrr} -2 & 4 & -3 & -7 & 4 & -9 \\ & & -8 & 22 & -30 & 68 \\ \hline & 4 & -11 & 15 & -34 & 59 \end{array}$$

(a) If $b < -2$, could $f(b) = 0$?

(b) Of what importance is it in this case that the numbers in the third row alternate in sign?

3. Give the complete statements of the Division Algorithm illustrated (a) In Exercise 1, (b) In Exercise 2.

9.05 FACTORING AND THE DISTRIBUTIVE PROPERTY

We discussed in Section 6.04 a very elementary type of factoring, namely the difference of squares, $x^2 - m^2 = (x - m)(x + m)$, and some applications of it, including the factorization of the general quadratic polynomial in one variable. We would like to point out again the important role that the distributive property plays in all factoring situations. For instance,

$$\begin{aligned} x^2 - m^2 &= x^2 + mx - mx - m^2 \\ &= x(x + m) - m(x + m) \\ &= (x - m)(x + m) \end{aligned}$$

is simply a consequence of the distributive law. It is an obvious statement that the correctness of any factorization is verified by multiplying the factors by use of the distributive property.

We might observe in passing that the ability to factor an expression depends greatly on the basic universe in which we are working. Let us consider the polynomial, $x^4 - 25$, and let us suppose that we are given the universe of integers. Then $x^4 - 25$ may be factored as

$$(x^2 - 5)(x^2 + 5)$$

If, instead, the universe should include all the real numbers, the expression may be factored further, as

$$(x - \sqrt{5})(x + \sqrt{5})(x^2 + 5)$$

If, finally, the universe should consist of the set of complex numbers, then $x^4 - 25$ may be factored as

$$(x - \sqrt{5})(x + \sqrt{5})(x - i\sqrt{5})(x + i\sqrt{5})$$

Let us examine $ax^2 + 3b + bx + 3a + bx^2 + ax$ in the universe of real numbers. Here we may use the distributive law and obtain

$$(a + b)(x^2) + (a + b)x + (a + b)3$$
$$= (a + b)(x^2 + x + 3)$$

Since the discriminant of the quadratic factor is negative we cannot factor further in the real number domain (see Section 5.04).

Question. How does $x^2 + x + 3$ factor in the universe of complex numbers?

Let us consider $P(x) = x^3 - a^3$. Since $P(a) = 0$, we know that $x - a$ is a factor of $P(x)$. By division we obtain

$$x^3 - a^3 = (x - a)(x^2 + ax + a^2)$$

Similarly, if $M(x) = x^3 + a^3$, then $M(-a) = 0$ and hence $x + a$ is a factor of $M(x)$. We find that

$$x^3 + a^3 = (x + a)(x^2 - ax + a^2)$$

(It might be pointed out here that the quadratic factors in both cases are factorable into linear factors only if the universe is the set of complex numbers.)

Let us consider $B(x) = x^n - a^n$, where n is a positive integer. $B(a) = 0$ so we know that $x - a$ is a factor. We may build up the other factor by a constructive process. We know its first term must be x^{n-1} and its last term a^{n-1}. If we begin to multiply the factors, using the distributive property on

$$(x - a)(x^{n-1} + \ldots + a^{n-1})$$

we obtain $x^n - ax^{n-1}$ for the first two terms. We need a term ax^{n-1} to balance the one just obtained with a negative sign. This would be supplied if we included the term ax^{n-2} in the second factor; thus

$$(x - a)(x^{n-1} + ax^{n-2} + \ldots + a^{n-1})$$
$$= x^n - ax^{n-1} + ax^{n-1} - a^2x^{n-2} + \ldots$$

and we continue adding terms to the second factor, finally obtaining

$$(x - a)(x^{n-1} + ax^{n-2} + a^2x^{n-3} + a^3x^{n-4} + \ldots + a^{n-2}x + a^{n-1})$$
$$= x^n - ax^{n-1} + ax^{n-1} - a^2x^{n-2} + a^2x^{n-2} - a^3x^{n-3} + a^3x^{n-3} + \ldots$$
$$\quad - a^{n-1}x + a^{n-1}x - a^n$$
$$= x^n - a^n$$

Note that, in the second factor of $x^n - a^n$, the sum of the exponents of the powers of a and of x in each term is $n-1$.

If $G(x) = x^n + a^n$, then $G(-a) = 0$, provided n is odd.

Question. If n is odd, what are two proper factors of $x^n + a^n$?

EXERCISES

1. Factor the following in the universe of real numbers
    (a) $x^6 - a^6$
    (b) $x^2 - 24x - 52$
    (c) $(x-y)^2 - 17(x-y) + 52$
    (d) $x^4 + x^2 + 4$
2. Factor the following in the universe of real numbers
    (a) $8a^2 - 33a + 27$
    (b) $8a^2 + 6a - 27$
    (c) $a^8 - b^8$
    (d) $a^2bc - adc^2 + a^2b^2 - c^2d^2 - bcd^2 + ab^2d$

9.06 CASTING OUT $b-1$'s

It is an interesting fact (known for at least seventeen centuries) that the remainder obtained by dividing a number, say, 769, by 9 is the same as the remainder obtained by dividing the sum of its digits* by 9, that is,

$$769 = 85(9) + 4$$
$$7 + 6 + 9 = 22 = 2(9) + 4$$

These equations may also be written in modular form, (see Section 1.18)

$$769 \equiv 4 \pmod 9$$
$$7 + 6 + 9 \equiv 4 \pmod 9$$

where the first statement is read, "769 is congruent to 4, modulo 9." The principle described here is known as the "casting out nines" principle. However it is only a special case (in base ten) of a more general theorem holding for numerals in any base. Since the proof is no more difficult for numerals in any natural number base $b > 1$ than it is in base 10, we shall use base b. The proof for base ten may be obtained by replacing b by ten in every instance.

Let $P(x)$ represent the general polynomial, $a_k x^k + a_{k-1} x^{k-1} + \ldots +$

---

*We wish to employ the phrase, "the sum of the digits of a number" as a convenient abbreviation for the more proper expression, "the sum of the numbers corresponding to the digits of the decimal numeral naming the number".

$a_1x + a_0$, where the a_i are any integers. It is sometimes convenient to be able to write a polynomial in abbreviated form. Accordingly we wish to introduce the summation symbol, Σ, by the following definition:

$$\sum_{j=0}^{k} a_j x^j = a_0 + a_1 x + a_2 x^2 + \ldots a_{k-1} x^{k-1} + a_k x^k$$

$$\therefore P(x) = \sum_{j=0}^{k} a_j x^j$$

Then any number N can be expressed in base b, when k and $a_i, i = 0, 1, 2, \ldots, k$, are suitably chosen.

(1) $\qquad N = P(b) = \sum_{j=0}^{k} a_j b^j = a_0 + a_1 b + \ldots + a_{k-1} b^{k-1} + a_k b^k$

where $0 \leqslant a_i < b$ for all a_i (recall that $b^0 = 1$ by definition). The sum of the digits in the numeral may be expressed as

(2) $\qquad n = P(1) = \sum_{j=0}^{k} a_j = a_0 + a_1 + \ldots + a_k$

We employ the division algorithm to obtain the following:

(3) $\qquad N = (b-1)Q + R$ where $0 \leqslant R < b-1$

and

(4) $\qquad n = (b-1)q + r$ where $0 \leqslant r < b-1$

For example, if b is ten and $N = 18367$, we have

$$N = 18367 = 2040(9) + 7$$

and

$$n = 1 + 8 + 3 + 6 + 7 = 25 = 2(9) + 7$$

Thus $R = r = 7$. We assert that this equality of R and r is not an accident:

Theorem. $R = r$.
Proof. From (1) and (2) and the fact that $x^n - a^n = (x-a)(x^{n-1} + \ldots + a^{n-1})$ we have

(5) $N - n = \sum_{j=0}^{k} a_j(b^j - 1) = a_1(b-1) + a_2(b^2 - 1) + \ldots + a_k(b^k - 1)$

$$= \sum_{j=0}^{k} a_j(b-1)(b^{j-1} + b^{j-2} + \ldots + b + 1)$$

$$= (b-1) \sum_{j=0}^{k} a_j(b^{j-1} + b^{j-2} + \ldots + b + 1)$$

$$= (b-1)M$$

where

$$M = \sum_{j=0}^{k} a_j(b^{j-1} + b^{j-2} + \ldots + b + 1)$$

From (3) and (4) we obtain

(6) $$N - n = (b-1)(Q - q) + R - r$$

From (5) and (6) it follows that

$$(b-1)M = (b-1)(Q - q) + (R - r)$$

Hence $(b-1)$ divides $(R - r)$, that is, $R - r = A(b-1)$ for some integer A. We have

(7) $$0 \leq R < b - 1, \text{ from (3)}$$

(8) $$-(b-1) < -r \leq 0, \text{ from (4)}$$

from which we obtain, by addition,

(9) $$-(b-1) < R - r < b - 1$$

Question. How do you justify lines (8) and (9)?

Line (9) may be rewritten as

$$|R - r| < b - 1$$

Since $R - r = A(b-1)$ we must conclude that the only possible value for A is zero and thus that $R = r$.

Question. How do you justify the conclusion that $A = 0$?

We wish to give, here, an alternate proof of this theorem. This second proof employs the concept of congruence modulo $(b-1)$ and requires the demonstration of two elementary lemmas which are stated in the following *Question*.

Question. Can you prove that, if $a \equiv b \pmod{K}$ and $c \equiv d \pmod{K}$, then (1) $a + c \equiv b + d \pmod{K}$? (2) $ac \equiv bd \pmod{K}$?

In this proof we shall use the notations employed in the previous proof, for example, $P(x) = \sum_{j=0}^{k} a_j x^j$.

Since
$$b = 1 + (b - 1), \text{ we may also write}$$
$$b \equiv 1 \pmod{b - 1}$$

Accordingly, we also have
$$b^2 \equiv 1 \pmod{b - 1} \text{ Why?}$$
$$b^3 \equiv 1 \pmod{b - 1}$$
$$\cdots\cdots\cdots\cdots\cdots$$
$$b^n \equiv 1 \pmod{b - 1}, \text{ for any natural number } n.$$

Hence
$$a_k b^k \equiv a_k \pmod{b - 1} \text{ Why?}$$
$$a_{k-1} b^{k-1} \equiv a_{k-1} \pmod{b - 1}$$
$$\cdots\cdots\cdots\cdots\cdots$$
$$a_1 b \equiv a_1 \pmod{b - 1}$$
$$a_0 \equiv a_0 \pmod{b - 1}$$

Therefore
$$\sum_{j=0}^{k} a_j b^j \equiv \sum_{j=0}^{k} a_j \pmod{b - 1}$$

that is
$$P(b) \equiv P(1) \pmod{b - 1}$$

or
$$N \equiv n \pmod{b - 1}$$

This is equivalent to line (5) of the first proof. The final result follows as in that proof.

Let us return to our example where b is ten. We had
$$N = 18367 = 9(2040) + 7$$
and
$$n = 1 + 8 + 3 + 6 + 7 = 25 = 9(2) + 7$$

and we observed that the remainders in both cases are the same. There are two points that should be noted here. In obtaining the remainder on division of n by 9 we could have reapplied the theorem and obtained the remainder as $2 + 5 = 7$ directly. If we are interested only in the remainder on division of N by 9, we may group the digits whose sum is 9 and "cast them out," leaving 7 as the remainder, that is,

$$\cancel{1} \quad \cancel{8} \quad \cancel{3} \quad \cancel{6} \quad 7$$
$$1 + 8 = 9 \qquad 3 + 6 = 9$$

212   More Algebra

Hence we can tell very quickly, for example, that 9 is a factor of 1,935,847,692.

It is undoubtedly true that the practical value of "casting out nines" is relatively small in view of the increasing use of automatic computational devices. However it is surely of interest from the theoretical point of view. One example in addition will suffice:

$$80357 = 9A + 5 \equiv 5 \pmod{9}$$
$$4936 = 9B + 4 \equiv 4 \pmod{9}$$
$$14358 = 9C + 3 \equiv 3 \pmod{9}$$
$$2761 = 9D + 7 \equiv 7 \pmod{9}$$

The sum of the four numbers is 102412 which may be expressed as $9E + 1 \equiv 1 \pmod{9}$. We have a considerable check on our addition when we note that

$$5 + 4 + 3 + 7 = 19 \equiv 1 \pmod{9}$$

This check is certainly not fool-proof since a transposition or interchange of digits will not be detected by this procedure nor will an error of 9 in addition. However one's ability to add numbers must be unusually poor if errors of the magnitude of 9 are present.

EXERCISES

1. (a) Is 4 a factor of $43203_{(\text{five})}$?
   (b) Check by converting to base ten.
2. (a) What is the remainder when $360542_{(\text{seven})}$ is divided by 6?
   (b) Check by converting to base ten.
3. Can you devise a proof, similar to the second proof of the "casting out $(b - 1)$'s" theorem, for a "casting out $(b + 1)$'s" theorem? What is the statement of the latter theorem? What form does it assume when b is ten?

9.07 RATIONAL ZEROS OF POLYNOMIALS

Suppose that we are interested in finding the rational zeros of the polynomial,

$$P(x) = a_n x^n + a_{n-1} x^{n-1} + \ldots + a_1 x + a_0$$

where the coefficients are rational numbers and $a_n \neq 0$. We note that the zeros of $P(x)$ are the same as the zeros of $KP(x)$ where K is any nonzero integer. In particular we may choose K to be the least common denominator of the rational numbers $a_n, a_{n-1}, \ldots, a_1, a_0$, so that $KP(x)$ is a polynomial with integral coefficients. Thus, for example, the zeros of $\frac{2}{3}x^3 - \frac{1}{4}x^2 + \frac{1}{2}x - \frac{5}{6}$ are the same as the zeros of $12(\frac{2}{3}x^3 - \frac{1}{4}x^2 + \frac{1}{2}x - \frac{5}{6})$ $= 8x^3 - 3x^2 + 6x - 10$.

We shall therefore assume in what follows that the $a_i, i = 0, 1, 2, \ldots, n$ are integers. We shall suppose that the rational number $\frac{p}{q}$ is in its lowest terms, that is, with p and q relatively prime, and that $\frac{p}{q}$ is a zero of $P(x)$.

$$\therefore P\left(\frac{p}{q}\right) = a_n\left(\frac{p}{q}\right)^n + a_{n-1}\left(\frac{p}{q}\right)^{n-1} + \ldots + a_1\left(\frac{p}{q}\right) + a_0 = 0$$

$$\therefore a_n p^n + a_{n-1} p^{n-1} q + a_{n-2} p^{n-2} q^2 + \ldots + a_1 p q^{n-1} + a_0 q^n = 0$$

Since
$$a_n p^n + a_{n-1} p^{n-1} q + \ldots + a_1 p q^{n-1} = -a_0 q^n$$

we know that p must divide $a_0 q^n$. Hence p must divide a_0.

Questions. (1) If a, p, and q are integers and if p and q are relatively prime, can you show that if p divides aq, then p divides a? (*Hint:* You may wish to employ the unique factorization of natural numbers, discussed in Section 1.14.) Similarly, if p divides aq^n, does p necessarily divide a?
(2) If we are given that r divides st, where r, s, t are integers, and r does not divide t, can you say whether or not it is necessary that r divide s?

Similarly
$$-a_n p^n = a_{n-1} p^{n-1} q + a_{n-2} p^{n-2} q^2 + \ldots + a_1 p q^{n-1} + a_0 q^n$$

and an identical argument leads to the conclusion that q must divide a_n. Hence if $\frac{p}{q}$ is to be a zero of $P(x)$ where

$$P(x) = a_n x^n + a_{n-1} x^{n-1} + \ldots + a_1 x + a_0$$

then p must be a factor of a_0 and q a factor of a_n. Hence by examining the factors of a_0 and a_n we are able to list all the possible rational roots of the equation $P(x) = 0$. These numbers may then be checked by synthetic substitution to determine whether or not they are zeros of $P(x)$. For example, consider the cubic equation, $P(x) = 0$, where

$$P(x) = 4x^3 + 16x^2 - 23x - 15$$

214 More Algebra

Since $a_n = 4$ and $a_0 = -15$, then p must be a factor of 15 and q a factor of 4, if $\frac{p}{q}$ is to be a root of the equation. Hence the possible rational numbers which might be roots are the following:

$$\pm 1, \pm 3, \pm 5, \pm 15, \pm\frac{1}{2}, \pm\frac{3}{2}, \pm\frac{5}{2}, \pm\frac{15}{2}, \pm\frac{1}{4}, \pm\frac{3}{4}, \pm\frac{5}{4}, \pm\frac{15}{4}.$$

Let us employ synthetic substitution. For example we might test -3, as follows:

$$\begin{array}{r|rrrr}
-3 & 4 & 16 & -23 & -15 \\
 & & -12 & -12 & 105 \\
\hline
 & 4 & 4 & -35 & 90
\end{array}$$

Therefore $P(-3) = 90$ and hence -3 is not a root of $P(x) = 0$. Eventually we might test $-\frac{1}{2}$

$$\begin{array}{r|rrrr}
-\frac{1}{2} & 4 & 16 & -23 & -15 \\
 & & -2 & -7 & 15 \\
\hline
 & 4 & 14 & -30 & 0
\end{array}$$

Hence

$$\begin{aligned}
4x^3 + 16x^2 - 23x - 15 &= [x - (-\tfrac{1}{2})][4x^2 + 14x - 30] \\
&= (x + \tfrac{1}{2})(2)(2x^2 + 7x - 15) \\
&= (2x + 1)(2x - 3)(x + 5)
\end{aligned}$$

Accordingly the solution set of the cubic equation

$$4x^3 + 16x^2 - 23x - 15 = 0$$

is

$$\{-\tfrac{1}{2}, \tfrac{3}{2}, -5\}$$

EXERCISES

1. Factor
   (a) $x^5 - a^5$
   (b) $x^7 + b^7$
2. (a) What is the set of possible rational roots of the equation
   $$8x^3 + 14x^2 + 17x + 15 = 0?$$
   (b) What is the set of actual rational roots of the equation in (a)?
3. Find the solution sets for the following sentences in the universe of real numbers:
   (a) $6x^3 - 17x^2 + 6x + 8 = 0$
   (b) $5x^3 - 3x^2 + 3x + 2 = 0$

9.08 SIMULTANEOUS INEQUALITIES

We have noted in Chapter 4, Section 4.07, Exercise 5, that a line in a plane separates that plane into three disjoint sets, namely two half-planes and the line itself. If we make use of the techniques of coordinate geometry we may be much more specific in this regard. Let us consider the equation $2x - 3y + 1 = 0$. It will be convenient to think of $2x - 3y + 1$ as an example of a function of two variables x and y, and to represent it by $f(x,y)$. This situation is quite similar to that considered in Section 9.02 except that in this case the function f maps the ordered pair (x,y) into the real number $f(x,y) = 2x - 3y + 1$. The function f may be thought of as the set of ordered triples, $\{(x,y,z) | z = f(x,y) = 2x - 3y + 1\}$. If we consider a point with coordinates $(2,1)$ (see footnote on p. 101, Section 4.09) lying to the right of the point $(1,1)$, (which lies on $f(x,y) = 0$), we note that $f(2,1) > 0$; similarly, if we consider the point $(1,0)$ lying below $(1,1)$ we find that $f(1,0) > 0$. In

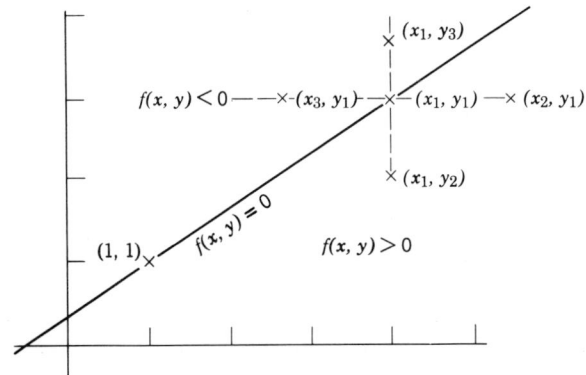

general if we think of (x_1, y_1) as a point lying on the line in question, we know $2x_1 - 3y_1 + 1 = 0$; hence $f(x_1, y_1) = 0$. Let us hold y_1 constant and allow x_1 to increase to a new value x_2. Then it is easily seen that $f(x_2, y_1) > 0$. Similarly if we allow x_1 to decrease to x_3, then we find that $f(x_3, y_1) < 0$. On the other hand, if we hold x_1 constant and let y_1 decrease to y_2, then $f(x_1, y_2) > 0$ and, also, if y_1 increases to y_3, then $f(x_1, y_3) < 0$.

We may conclude then that $2x - 3y + 1 > 0$ for any point (x, y) located "below" or "to the right of" the line and, similarly, $2x - 3y + 1 < 0$ for any point (x, y) "above" or "to the left of" this line. Hence the three sets of points into which the plane is separated by the line correspond to the sets of ordered pairs (x, y) for which $2x - 3y + 1 < 0, = 0$, or > 0.

216   More Algebra

We frequently encounter problems which involve two or more of such inequalities. It is often possible to employ the graphs of the inequalities to good advantage as the following example will illustrate:

Jack decides that he can spare a total of 18 hours in preparation for his mathematics and English finals, each of which will be marked on a basis of 100 points. He estimates that he is sure to get at least 50 points in mathematics, plus 5 points for each hour he studies mathematics. He also estimates that in English he is sure of 70 points with an added 2 points for each hour he studies English. In addition he finds it imperative that he consume one thirty cent hamburger each hour while studying mathematics and one ten cent bottle of orange drink each hour while studying English. He has only $3.60 available for these two purposes. How many hours should he study each subject in order to obtain the maximum number of points?

If we let x and y represent the number of hours spent on mathematics and English respectively, then we know that

$$50 + 5x \leq 100$$

and

$$70 + 2y \leq 100$$

from which we obtain

(1) $$0 \leq x \leq 10$$

and

(2) $$0 \leq y \leq 15$$

We know also that

(3) $$x + y \leq 18$$

and

(4) $$30x + 10y \leq 360$$

His estimate of the total points on the two examinations is then $P = 120 + 5x + 2y$ and he wishes to maximize P, subject to the limitations imposed by (1), (2), (3), and (4). Let us graph the lines $x = 0$, $x = 10$, $y = 0$, $y = 15$, $x + y = 18$, and $3x + y = 36$. Then it is clear that any suitable pair of values of x and y must denote a point within or on the boundary of the polygon $OABCDE$. Let us plot the line $P = 120 + 5x + 2y$, for $P = 140$, that is, $5x + 2y = 20$. It passes through $(4,0)$ and $(0,10)$. If we consider a slightly larger value of P,

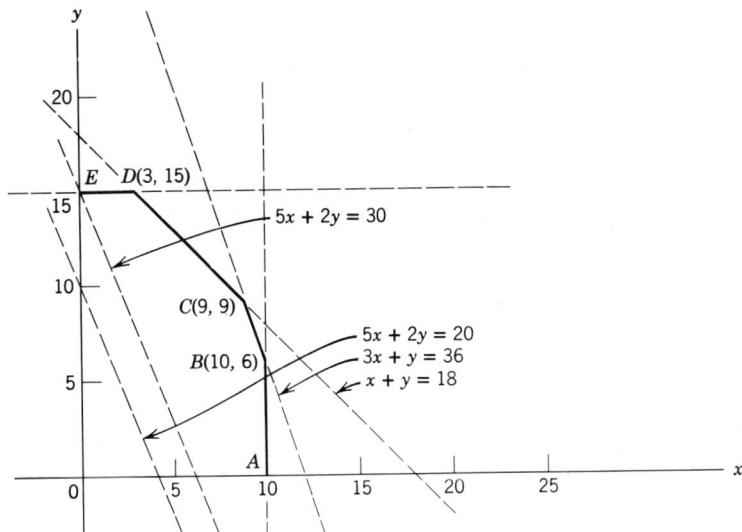

for example, 150, then the line corresponds to the equation $5x + 2y = 30$ and has the same slope as before, this time passing through E. All these lines for various values of P are evidently going to be parallel and we wish to find the line with the greatest value of P. Clearly the line with slope $-\frac{5}{2}$, and passing through $D(3,15)$ will correspond to a larger value of P, namely 165; and the value, 182, of P at $B(10,6)$ is still larger. But we may move the line still further to the right and parallel to the family of lines of slope $-\frac{5}{2}$, until it passes through $C(9,9)$ where the value of P is 183. It is quite evident from the figure that we cannot obtain a larger value of P and also keep a point (x,y) of the line within or on the boundary of the polygon. Lest the reader be left in any doubt we hasten to add that Jack evidently studies 9 hours on each of his two subjects and in the process reduces his entire monetary fund to zero.

Question. What happens to the value of P as the point (x,y) moves

(1) from B to A? Why?

(2) from C to D? Why?

(3) from B to C? Why?

218 More Algebra

It might be of interest to point out that this result is in keeping with a more general theorem,* which may be stated as follows:

A linear function defined over a convex polygon† takes on its maximum (and minimum) value at a corner point of the convex polygon.

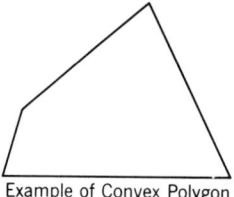
Example of Convex Polygon

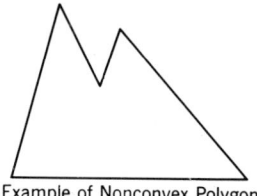
Example of Nonconvex Polygon

EXERCISES

1. (a) Do $\begin{Bmatrix} \text{none} \\ \text{some} \\ \text{all} \end{Bmatrix}$ of the points of the line $4x - y - 7 = 0$ satisfy the inequality $4x - y + 2 < 0$?

   (b) Do $\begin{Bmatrix} \text{none} \\ \text{some} \\ \text{all} \end{Bmatrix}$ of the points of the line $2x - 3y + 5 = 0$ satisfy the inequality $x + 4y - 3 > 0$?

   (c) Do $\begin{Bmatrix} \text{none} \\ \text{some} \\ \text{all} \end{Bmatrix}$ of the points of the line $x - y + 5 = 0$ satisfy the inequality $2|x| + y - 1 > 0$?

2. Graph the solution sets of the following simultaneous inequalities:
   (a) $2x + y - 3 > 0$ and $x - y + 7 < 0$
   (b) $|x| + y - 3 > 0$ and $x - |y| + 2 < 0$
   (c) $|x| + y - 3 < 0$, $x + y - 4 > 0$ and $-x + y - 4 > 0$
   (d) $x - |y| + 2 > 0$, $x - 2|y| + 3 < 0$ and $4x - y - 5 < 0$

3. A manufacturer has 60 pounds of a special plastic for making briefcases and small trunks. He has exactly 24 locks, suitable for trunk or briefcase. He has at most 36 hours of machine time available for manufacturing the two products. Each briefcase requires 1 lock, 1 pound of plastic and 2 hours of machine time, yielding a profit of $2 when sold. Each trunk requires 1 lock, 3 pounds of plastic and 1 hour of machine time, yielding a profit of $3. How many briefcases and trunks will maximize his profit?

*For additional information on this topic, the reader is referred to *Linear Programming and the Theory of Games* by Abraham M. Glicksman, John Wiley & Co., 1963, p. 52.

†A convex polygon is a polygon with the property that, given two points A and B in the interior or on the boundary of the polygon, every point of the segment $\overline{AB}$ is a point in the interior or on the boundary of the polygon.

10 *Statistics*

10.01 MEANING OF THE TERM

The word *statistics* is interpreted in a variety of ways by different people but to many persons it conveys a rather narrow concept, exemplified by the contents of the census report, the attendance on each day of a county fair, the lengths and weights of the fish caught on a certain expedition, or the significant dimensions of a particular beauty queen. This picture of statistics as a set of numbers is a far too limited approach, as we hope to demonstrate.

The more modern view takes the position that, whereas statistics *are* numerical facts, statistics *is* a body of methods for making wise decisions in the face of uncertainty. So often the information available is less than we would prefer to have and it is of tremendous importance that the conclusions drawn from such data shall be reliable. It is true that statistics is certainly involved with the collection of data to help decide questions of practical action or questions in scientific research; but statistics also is concerned with the problem of sampling and is very effective in testing hypotheses. "The Scientific Method" is closely related to the latter procedure, depending as it does on (1) observing what happens, (2) formulating hypotheses from "hunches," (3) making predictions arising out of the hypotheses and, (4) verifying these predictions by observing new facts. At this point the complete cycle is ready to be played through once again.

This sequence of steps might be illustrated by a person driving a car who observes the motor heating up unduly, as evidenced by the temperature reading of the water in the radiator. He guesses that the fan belt might be broken and formulates this as his hypothesis. In his particular car the fan belt runs the generator and so he predicts that the ammeter will show a zero or negative charge. Finally he checks the ammeter reading. If it does show a zero or negative charge his confidence in his hypothesis is strengthened. However it does not prove that his hypothesis is correct, since some other malfunctioning might also cause the ammeter to fail to charge.

Another example in the same vein is the following. Suppose that a person finds that an electric light bulb, which functions properly elsewhere, fails to light in a particular socket. He guesses that the fuse for this circuit has burned out. On the basis of this hypothesis he predicts that some other lights or appliances should not be operating. If he finds some not operating his hypothesis is strengthened. However it does not prove his hypothesis true as there might be some other deficiency in the circuit.

It is our purpose to describe a few very elementary phases of statistics, in order that the reader may have some idea of the scope of this rapidly expanding field.

10.02 FREQUENCY DISTRIBUTION

Although in giving our attention at first to some of the computational aspects of statistics there is a danger of implying that statistics is mainly concerned with mechanical computation, it is necessary to establish clearly some very basic notions.

A very fundamental consideration is that of *frequency*, that is, the number of times a particular event* is observed to occur. A listing of frequencies of related events is known as a *frequency distribution*. Let us illustrate this concept by considering the number of boys and girls in families of five children. If we checked 1000 such families we might have recorded the following data:

5 boys	4 boys	3 boys	2 boys	1 boy	5 girls
	1 girl	2 girls	3 girls	4 girls	
35	160	315	310	150	30

This is a situation in which we may also predict what should be expected on the basis of probability. The probabilities that a newborn child will be a boy or will be a girl are almost equal, the probability being slightly greater than $\frac{1}{2}$(about 0.514) in the case of a boy. Hence, by considering the various orders in which boys and girls may be born in families of five children, we may arrive at the probability (or ideal frequency) distribution.

There is only 1 order for 5 boys and equally so for 5 girls; similarly there are 5 possible orderings of 4 boys and 1 girl as well as for 4 girls and 1 boy. For 3 boys and 2 girls or for 3 girls and 2 boys the number of orderings is $\frac{5!}{2!3!} = \frac{120}{12} = 10$ (see *Question* at end of Section 6.09).

*An event is the result of a statistical experiment, which may be simple or compound in nature.

Hence, assuming that the birth of a boy or a girl is equally likely, the perfect distribution in 32 cases is

$$1 \quad 5 \quad 10 \quad 10 \quad 5 \quad 1$$

If we let p represent the probability of a boy being born, then $q = 1 - p$ will represent the probability of a girl being born. The binomial expansion

$$(p + q)^5 = p^5 + 5p^4q + 10p^3q^2 + 10p^2q^3 + 5pq^4 + q^5$$

exhibits the six possibilities and the coefficients represent the above noted ideal frequencies relative to 32. If we calculate the actual predicted probabilities on the basis of $p = 0.514$ and $q = 0.486$ we have
$(0.514 + 0.486)^5 = 0.036 + 0.170 + 0.321 + 0.303 + 0.143 + 0.027$
$= 1.000$

Hence the expected numbers for 1000 families would be

$$36 \quad 170 \quad 321 \quad 303 \quad 143 \quad 27$$

This is an example of a binomial distribution, since only two different events occur (although they may be repeated) and hence only two probabilities are involved and their sum is 1. Such binomial distributions are often denoted by (n, p), where p denotes the probability of one of the two possible events and n denotes the total number of trials: In our case $p = 0.514$ and $n = 5$.

EXERCISE

Suppose a biased coin has probability 0.6 of falling heads (H).
1. (a) What is the probability of the order HHT occurring when the coin is tossed 3 times?
   (b) What is the probability of obtaining two heads and one tail when the coin is tossed 3 times?
   (c) Determine the expected frequencies of the various possibilities for heads and tails, when the experiment in (a) or (b) is carried out 1000 times.
   (d) How is the calculation (c) related to the binomial expansion $(0.6 + 0.4)^3$?

10.03 GRAPHS

We are going to find that data can be arranged in various ways in order to exhibit essential properties. Let us suppose that we have the following weights* of 31 men students in a physical education class.

					202
186	165	203	193	203	170
198	205	202	201	186	186
165	190	173	186	162	190
215	211	195	179	193	203
174	190	177	198	198	195

In order to learn more about how the weights vary, it is convenient to arrange them in order

162	174	186	193	198	203
165	177	186	195	201	203
165	179	190	195	202	205
170	186	190	198	202	211
173	186	190	198	203	215
		193			

Next we might be inclined to graph them on the number line much as we have done with solution sets of sentences.

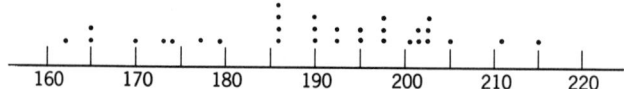

Here each dot indicates an observation and where the dots become most dense we would know that the weights were tending to accumulate. Although a certain amount of information is to be gleaned from such a graph it has the disadvantage of being unable to display satisfactorily several dots at one location. For this reason, we might well consider the possibility of grouping the values in intervals. What shall we choose as end-points of the intervals? If we select integers for this purpose we have the problem of a weight belonging to two intervals if it should happen to coincide with an end-point value. Since all our weights are integers, it turns out that it is very helpful to select, as end-points of intervals, numbers midway between successive integers.

---

*Although we are treating these weights as if they are discrete values, we should recognize that, intrinsically, they are values of a continuous variable, which have merely been approximated by the closest integer.

Hence we might choose the following six intervals with the accompanying frequencies:

$$159.5 - 169.5 : 3 \qquad 189.5 - 199.5 : 10$$
$$169.5 - 179.5 : 5 \qquad 199.5 - 209.5 : 7$$
$$179.5 - 189.5 : 4 \qquad 209.5 - 219.5 : 2$$

Then we may indicate above each interval a rectangle of unit height for each unit in the frequency corresponding to the interval. The resulting graph is known as a *histogram*.

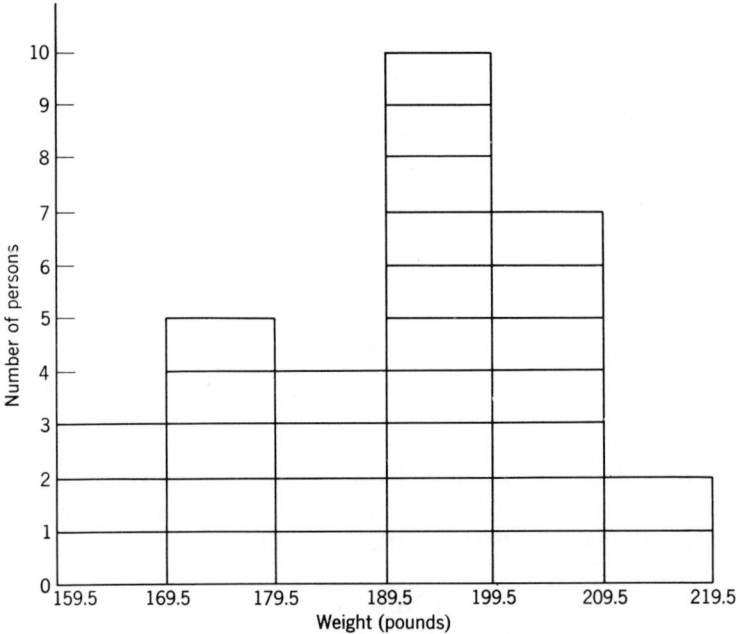

The important characteristic of a histogram is the fact that the area of each rectangle is proportional to the frequency of observations falling in that particular interval. Occasionally we may wish to present more than one histogram on a single graph in which case confusion may arise, especially if the class boundaries coincide. Hence, if we are willing to sacrifice the advantage of area of rectangle being proportional to frequency, we may replace the histogram by a *frequency polygon* or *broken-line graph*, obtained by joining the midpoints of the top segments of the rectangles of the histogram.

The frequency polygon suggests a further step which might be taken, namely that of producing a smooth approximating curve. Although this may be reasonable and desirable when a comparatively large number of data is available, for smaller classes of data the histogram

is more dependable in conveying correct information. Thus the temptation to replace the histogram by a smooth curve should be generally avoided in view of the fact that there is bound to be such considerable latitude in drawing the best smooth fitting curve.

EXERCISE

1. The following are the ages of 31 persons in a class:
   23, 25, 28, 44, 50, 48, 22, 39, 42, 57,
   59, 44, 58, 28, 57, 41, 55, 26, 38, 33,
   40, 22, 33, 42, 21, 28, 43, 31, 35, 23, 45.
   (a) Draw the histogram, grouping the data by 4-year intervals (for example, 20.5–24.5, 24.5–28.5, etc.).
   (b) Draw the broken line graph associated with the histogram in (a).

10.04 THE NORMAL DISTRIBUTION

One of the most important frequency distributions in statistics is the *normal distribution*. Its graph is that of a symmetrical bell-shaped curve. It may be arrived at in the following manner. Suppose 10 coins are tossed and the number of heads (divided by 10*) is recorded. If this procedure were carried out a large number of times, for example, 100, and the relative frequencies plotted, we might obtain a histogram such as the one shown below:

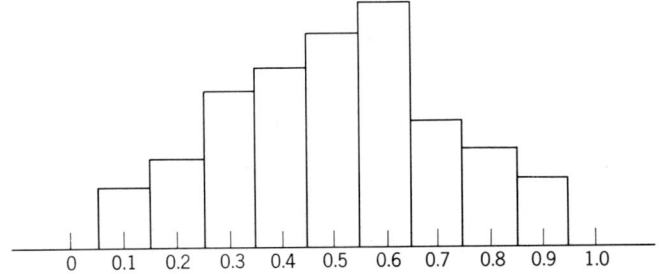

Consider

$$(p + q)^{10} = p^{10} + 10p^9q + 45p^8q^2 + 120p^7q^3 + 210p^6q^4 + 252p^5q^5 + 210p^4q^6 + 120p^3q^7 + 45p^2q^8 + 10pq^9 + p^{10}$$

For a perfect coin the probability, p, of heads equals the probability, q, of tails equals $\frac{1}{2}$ and the relative probabilities are obtained by dividing successive coefficients by $1024 = 2^{10}$, since each term, $p^i q^j$, in the above expansion has $i + j = 10$. Hence by multiplying the relative probabilities by 100 we could obtain the ideal expected values of each number of heads from 0 through 10 in 100 repetitions of the coin-tossing. When the experiment is repeated with 20 and 40 coins, respectively, the histogram begins to assume a more symmetric shape and as the rectangles become steadily narrower the frequency polygon tends more and more closely to the smooth curve known as the *normal curve* (see page 226).

10.05 DESCRIPTIVE MEASURES

There are two devices that can be used to describe and summarize the information contained in a collection of observations. One of these, the frequency distribution, was discussed in Section 10.02. We wish now to say a few words about the second of these, namely, *measures of location*, more commonly called *averages*. They are also known as *measures of central tendency*. We shall find that these numbers, when

---

*This is merely for the purpose of reducing the domain to the interval [0,1]

obtained for the given data, will provide considerable information with regard to where a distribution is located or centered on the scale. We shall describe three of the more familiar types of average.

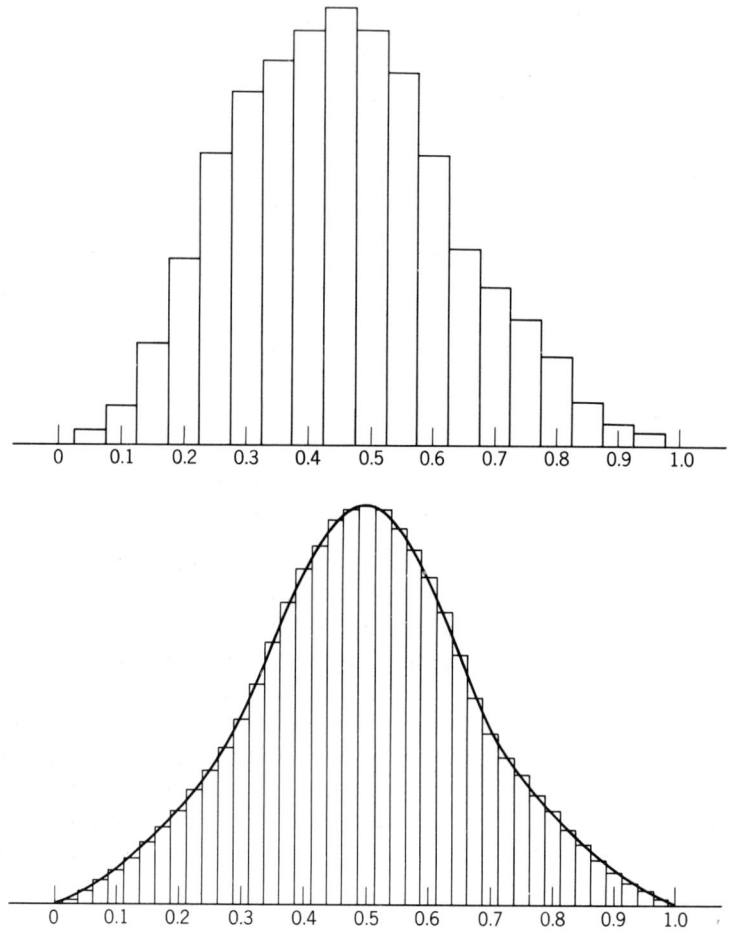

The *mode* is the value that occurs most often and hence indicates where the concentration of items is most dense. In our example of Section 10.03 the modal weight is 186 and it occurs four times. It may be more significant, however, to note that the modal class (class containing most items) is 189.5 − 199.5, which class, incidentally, does not contain the modal item in this example. There may, of course, be more than one mode in a set of data.

Question. Under what circumstances could more than one mode occur?

If we were adding a column of numbers and obtained a variety of answers we might well be inclined to consider, as the sum, the value attained most frequently—especially if there were only one mode of relatively high frequency. Similarly if we were questioning witnesses of a car accident regarding the automobile license number of the hit-and-run driver, the mode of the numbers given by the witnesses would probably be the one we would wish to use. Again, if a storekeeper decides to reduce his stock of items he will undoubtedly choose to continue to sell the item of a particular class which has been the "most popular seller," that is, the modal item of the class.

Another useful average is the *median*, which is the item occurring at the middle of the distribution; that is, as many observations occur above the median as occur below it in the distribution. In our set of 31 data on weights, the median, 193, is the sixteenth item from either end of the ordered set. It should be noted that the median is the observation which has the same number of observations between it and the largest observation as well as between it and the smallest observation, rather than the observation which differs numerically by the same amount from the largest and smallest observations. It is quite possible that there may be some rather unlikely items at one or both ends of a distribution which are not actually characteristic of the quantity being investigated. As a measure of central tendency, the median will be found to be independent of the size of possible "far-out" values at the ends and has a better chance (than the mode may have) of falling in the middle range of values. The median is often used where it is desired to exhibit a typical item. It may be shown that the sum of the absolute values of the differences of the observations from their median is less than from any other number in the distribution. This would be a useful consideration in a situation involving retail stores on a straight road which need to be supplied regularly from a central warehouse. Evidently the warehouse should be located at the median store to minimize the total travel involved in supplying the retailers. The median and the mode both suffer from the disadvantage that there is no way to determine from the modes or medians of separate groups of observations what the mode or median, respectively, would be if all the observations were considered in a single group.

The third average to be considered is the *arithmetic mean*, commonly referred to as the *mean*. This number, $\bar{x}$, is obtained by dividing the sum, $\sum_{i=1}^{n} x_i$, of all the observations $x_1, x_2, \ldots, x_n$, by the number, n, of observations, that is, $\bar{x} = \frac{1}{n} \sum_{i=1}^{n} x_i$.

If we apply this definition in the case of the students' weights, we find that the mean is 190. A little later we shall demonstrate an easier method of computing the mean. One advantage of the mean is that the observations do not have to be ordered in order to obtain it. It is a direct result of the definition that the mean of a set of observations is that number which, when multiplied by the number of observations gives the sum of all the observations. As a consequence of this basic feature we may note one way in which the mean is superior to the mode or median—it allows us to calculate the mean of a combined group, knowing the means and corresponding numbers of observations of the separate groups. Suppose that we have one group of 10 observations, with mean 32.5, another group of 13 observations with mean 27.3 and a third group of 17 observations with mean 25.8. Clearly the sum of all 40 items is $10(32.5) + 13(27.3) + 17(25.8) = 1120$ with a mean of $\frac{1120}{40} = 28.0$. An illustration of this could occur in calculating *Grade Point Average* (GPA). A student's GPA is the ratio of his total accumulated grade points divided by the sum of the "attempted" credits. (1 credit of A grade $= 4$ grade points. B, 3; C, 2; D, 1; E, 0.) Suppose a student has a GPA of 1.90 after having "attempted" 150 credits of work, in which he has 10 credits with E grades. He can graduate with 180 credits of D or better grades, provided his GPA ≥ 2.00. Accordingly he plans to take at least 40 additional credits of work and wonders how well he must do in these courses in order to graduate. The calculations proceed as follows: His present total of grade points is $1.90 \times 150 = 285$. His new total of "attempted" credits is 190, corresponding to which he needs at least 380 grade points. His 40 credits of work must, therefore, produce at least $380 - 285 = 95$ grade points. In other words, for the additional 40 credits of work his GPA must be at least $\frac{95}{40} = 2.38$. Clearly 40 credits with GPA ≥ 2.38 added to 150 credits with GPA 1.90 produce 190 credits with GPA ≥ 2.00.

A very elegant property which may be demonstrated for the mean is that the sum of the squared deviations (differences) of all observations from it is smaller than the sum of the squared deviations from any other number.

As promised earlier let us investigate a method of determining the mean, x, of a distribution $x_1, x_2, \ldots, x_n$, which does not require us to find the sum of all the observations: If we select any number, m (which we may call a trial value), and find the algebraic sum of the differences (positive and negative) between our observations and m, we may calculate

$$\frac{1}{n}\sum_{i=1}^{n}(x_i - m) = \frac{1}{n}\left(\sum_{i=1}^{n} x_i - nm\right)$$
$$= \bar{x} - m$$

Hence
$$\bar{x} = m + \frac{1}{n}\sum_{i=1}^{n}(x_i - m)$$

Question. Can you explain how nm is obtained in the above summation?

The advantage of this procedure lies in the fact that we are free to choose m in such a way that $x_i - m$ for $i = 1, 2, \ldots, n$ will be numerically small and will involve about as many positive as negative numbers, resulting in a relatively small value for $\sum_{i=1}^{n}(x_i - m)$. For example suppose that we wish to obtain the mean of the following set of observations $x_1, \ldots, x_{10}$:

$x_i (i = 1, \ldots, 10)$	$x_i - m$
87352	2
87358	8
87342	−8
87347	−3
87351	1
87342	−8
87345	−5
87356	6
87345	−5
87352	2
	−10

If we choose $m = 87{,}350$, then the algebraic differences $x_i - m$ are given in the second column. Hence

$$x = 87350 + \frac{1}{10}\sum_{i=1}^{10}(x_i - 87350)$$
$$= 87350 + \frac{1}{10}(-10)$$
$$= 87350 - 1$$
$$= 87349$$

Question. Can you use this approach to obtain the mean of the students' weights in Section 10.03?

EXERCISES

1. Determine the mode, median, and mean for the distribution in Exercise 1, Section 10.03.
2. With reference to Exercise 1
   (a) Obtain the sum of the absolute values of the differences of the items from the median.
   (b) Repeat (a) with respect to any item different from the median.
   (c) Obtain the mean by the method of employing a trial value.
   (d) Obtain the sum of the squares of the differences of the items from the mean.
   (e) Repeat (d) with respect to any item different from the mean.
3. If a student has attempted 130 credits with a GPA of 3.2 and then takes 50 credits with a GPA of 2.5, what is his GPA for all 180 credits?
4. For the following sets of observations, tell which of mode, median, or mean is likely to be the most useful and give your reason:
   (a) 10, 20, 30, 40, 50, 60, 68, 69, 69, 70
   (b) 10, 70, 90, 120, 125, 130, 140, 150, 180, 2000, 5000
   (c) 10.1, 11.0, 12.0, 13.0, 14.0, 18.5, 19.0, 20.0, 20.5

10.06 MEASURES OF DISPERSION

When we know one or more of the three averages we are still in ignorance of how the observations lie with respect to the average. For example the two distributions 10.0, 16.0, 20.0, 26.0, 30.0, 30.0, 30.0, 31.0, 40.0, 47.0, 50.0 and 28.5, 28.7, 29.1, 29.4, 29.5, 30.0, 30.0, 30.4, 31.2, 31.3, 31.9 have the same mode, median, mean, and number of observations, as the reader should verify, but differ markedly in their *ranges*, namely, $40.0 = 50.0 - 10.0$ and $3.4 = 31.9 - 28.5$.

Although the range gives us some notion of how the observations may be spread, it tells us nothing about the density of the observations around the center; and, in addition, it has the added disadvantage that it tends to increase as the number of observations increases. Clearly if one continues to add observations to a given set, the range cannot possibly decrease and in practice generally tends to increase. This fact can be verified by writing a set of 40 different numerals, one on each of 40 cards. Select 8 cards at random and note the range of the numbers obtained. Then select another 8 cards and note the range of the combined subset of numbers on the 16 cards and so on, until you have reached the last subset of 8 cards. The behavior of the range should be clearly evident.

We might investigate the *mean* (or *average*) *deviation* in an effort to get closer to an idea of the dispersion of the observations. This measure is the mean of the absolute values of the deviations of observations from the mean, that is,

$$\frac{1}{n}\sum_{i=1}^{n}|x_i - \bar{x}|$$

(If we use actual values instead of absolute values of the deviations, the result, of course, would be zero.)

Question. Can you explain why the above statement in parentheses is true?

For the two distributions given at the beginning of this section we obtain mean deviation values of 8.73 and 0.873, respectively. This indicates considerably greater concentration of observations in the second case than in the first case. In fact, if in the second set of observations the extreme items had been replaced by 10.2 and 50.3, to give the following distribution, 10.2, 28.7, 29.1, 29.4, 29.5, 30.0, 30.0, 30.4, 31.2, 31.3, 50.2 the range would have been 40.0, the same as for the first set and the mean deviation would have been 3.41 which still emphasizes the concentration of observations about the center in the latter case. One disadvantage, similar to that shared by the median and mode, is that from the mean deviations of several groups of observations, it is not possible to find the mean deviation of the combined group of observations.

We come finally to consider a measure which plays a very important role in conveying information concerning distribution of data. This is the *standard deviation*,

$$s = \sqrt{\frac{\sum_{i=1}^{n}(x_i - x)^2}{n-1}}$$

the square of which is known as the *variance*. Occasionally the expression for s may be found with n instead of $n-1$ in the denominator but for many applications of variance the form given is most desirable.

One of the most important uses of the standard deviation is as a verification of the closeness of a given distribution to a normal distribution. Not every symmetrical bell-shaped curve is the graph of a normal distribution. For a normal distribution, about 50% of the observations fall within a distance of two-thirds (actually 0.6745) of the standard deviation from the mean; about two-thirds (68.26%) of the observations differ from the mean by less than the standard deviation; about 95% by less than twice the standard deviation and 99.74% by less than three times the standard deviation. Hence any symmetrical

232 Statistics

bell-shaped distribution with these additional properties is likely to be a close approximation to a normal curve.

EXERCISES

1. (a) Calculate the mean deviation for the data in Exercise 1, Section 10.05.
   (b) Calculate the standard deviation for the data in (a).
   (c) What per cent of all items in the above data differ from the mean
       (i) by less than two-thirds of the standard deviation?
       (ii) by less than the standard deviation?
       (iii) by less than *twice* the standard deviation?
       (iv) by less than *three* times the standard deviation?
2. Repeat the calculations of 1(b) and 1(c) for the following frequency distribution:

x	−30	−28	−26	−24	−22	−20	−18	−16	−14	−12	−10
f	5	8	15	21	35	55	80	110	150	195	241
x	−8	−6	−4	−2	0	2	4	6	8	10	12
f	289	334	369	390	399	392	367	332	291	243	193
x	14	16	18	20	22	24	26	28	30		
f	150	112	78	53	37	23	13	8	3		

3. Suppose $x_1, x_2, \ldots, x_n$ are n observations with mean 10 and standard deviation 3. If a new measurement y_i is obtained from each observation, x_i, by the equation $y = 4x + 2$, what are the mean and variance of $y_1, y_2, \ldots, y_n$?
4. If the mean of observations $x_1, x_2, \ldots, x_n$ is $\bar{x}$, if the standard deviation has value, x', and if $y = ax + b$, what are the mean and standard deviation of $y_1, y_2, \ldots, y_n$, expressed in terms of $\bar{x}, x', a$, and b?
5. (a) What is the effect on the mean of a set of observations $x_1, x_2, \ldots, x_n$, if a constant K is added to each observation?
   (b) What is the effect on variance and standard deviation of the change described in (a)?
6. Suppose U and s^2 are the mean and variance respectively, of a sample of observations $u_1, u_2, \ldots, u_m$, and V and t^2 are the mean and variance, respectively, of a sample of observations $v_1, v_2, \ldots, v_n$. Suppose all these $m + n$ observations are put in one sample.
   (a) Show that the mean of this sample is $\dfrac{mU + nV}{m + n}$.

(b) Show that the variance of this sample is

$$\frac{1}{m+n-1}\left[(m-1)s^2 + (n-1)t^2 + \frac{mn}{m+n}(U-V)^2\right]$$

(*Hint:* Recall that $s^2 = \dfrac{1}{m-1}\sum_{i=1}^{m}(u_i - U)^2$;

$t^2 = \dfrac{1}{n-1}\sum_{i=1}^{n}(v_i - V)^2$ and, wherever possible, deal with u_i and v_i in the expressions $u_i - U$ and $v_i - V$, respectively.)

10.07 SAMPLING

The modern statistician is a student of methods of drawing conclusions about a large number of items (or population, as it is called) on the basis of data that ordinarily is collected from only a sample of the population. Very often it is either impractical or impossible to check the complete population to obtain the desired information. For example, a company which produces a small part of a complicated assembly has to be certain that the number of defective products remains below a certain level, but it is not economically feasible to inspect each individual product. On the other hand, in the case of a product like a fuse, to check it completely would require that it be destroyed in the process. Clearly not every fuse could be so inspected. In such cases the required information is obtained through sampling. By examining enough samples and by determining certain measures for these samples, one is able to infer what the corresponding measures may be for the whole population.

To illustrate this procedure let us imagine a population consisting of a large number of red beads and white beads of the same size. We wish to know the ratio of the number of red beads to the total number of beads, that is, what fraction of the population consists of red beads. Let us suppose that we have an automatic device for allowing exactly 20 of the beads to drop into a box after they are well mixed. Suppose that 13 of the beads in this first drawing were red. From this information we might be willing to guess that probably over half the population consists of red beads. But beyond that we would probably not wish to predict. However let us suppose the process to be repeated fifty times in all, replacing the beads each time before the next drawing. Let us assume that the results are as given in the following table:

Number of red beads	Number of samples
fewer than 7	0
7	1
8	5
9	7
10	9
11	8
12	10
13	5
14	3
15	1
16	0
17	0
18	1
more than 18	0

The result in a single sample depends entirely on chance, but the pattern which emerges in repeated samples is more likely to be characteristic of the population and the effect of chance has been greatly reduced.

In industry, utilization of such a procedure as this to insure uniformity of output is known as *quality control*. The underlying principle of importance in random sampling is the fact that there comes a point beyond which the increase in information from additional observations is not worth the increase in cost.

10.08 HYPOTHESIS TESTING

It would be well for us to note, at the beginning of this section, a clear difference between probability and statistics. They may be thought of as working in opposite directions. Probability proceeds from a known population to derive distributions related to a sample from the population, while statistics proceeds from the observed sample to draw conclusions about unknown features of the population.

Often the necessity exists of choosing between two clearly defined courses of action, where the proper course depends on the value of a certain measure or property associated with a distribution. For example, an anthropologist may believe that he has discovered a primitive tribe in which the ratio of male births to total births is unusually high. He has to choose between publishing his findings or waiting until he has collected more data. The branch of statistics concerned with such a problem as this is known as *hypothesis testing* and is one of the extremely active areas of statistical research.

By a *statistical hypothesis* (or *null hypothesis*, as it is sometimes called) is meant a statement about the way a random variable (or real number assigned to the outcome of an experiment) is distributed. By observing the behavior of such a random variable, it is possible to test the validity of a statistical hypothesis. This might be accomplished in the following way. The hypothesis might state that the random variable in question has a certain distribution. However a dependable sampling procedure, while not capable of disproving the hypothesis, might cast such serious doubt on the hypothesis as to persuade us to abandon it.

For example, a retail merchant has purchased 1000 electric motors from a manufacturer who guarantees that not more than 2% of the motors are improperly wound. The retailer suspects that the per cent of defective motors is higher than 2. He decides, therefore, to disassemble 100 of the motors. If the number of defective motors does not exceed the order of 2, the manufacturer's prediction would appear to be justified. On the other hand, if the number of defective motors in the sample goes considerably beyond 2, then the retailer's suspicion would appear to be well-founded.

In general, then, a decision is to be made depending on whether the null hypothesis, H, is accepted or rejected. This acceptance or rejection of H may depend on the value which is obtained for a particular test statistic T. It is necessary to establish for what values of T the hypothesis H will be rejected and for what values of T it will be accepted. If it is agreed that it will be rejected when $T \geq c$ and accepted when $T < c$, then c is called the *critical value*. In the example of the motors, T is the number of defective motors in the sample of 100 and c is 2.

A closely related problem is concerned with the comparison of two treatments for a particular disease, in an effort to improve the one currently in use. For example, when, in 1954, it was decided to test the effectiveness of the Salk vaccine against polio, 200,745 children were given the vaccine while 201,229 other children did not receive any vaccine. The result of the experiment was such that 33 of the vaccinated group and 115 of the nonvaccinated or *control* group contracted polio. By means of a detailed analysis of these facts statisticians were able to decide that the apparent reduction of polio in the vaccinated group was not due to chance.

In such investigations as the latter example illustrated, the importance of having a group of subjects, the control group, who receive the standard treatment and who are assumed to be as similar as possible to the group which received the special treatment, is clear. Without such a group whose responses may be compared with the responses of the treated group, the experimenter has to fall back on the dubious substitute of comparing with past experience. This is an extremely hazardous practice since, in the polio example, the incidence of polio is much greater in some years than in others. Conclusions based on such considerations are simply not dependable.

It is, of course, highly important that the control group be comparable to the experimental group in its responsiveness to treatment. For instance, in the polio experiment it was most desirable that there be children in the control and experimental groups, of the same age, living in the same area, attending the same school, and so on.

Even with the intention of being most objective, an experimenter with a desire to have the experiment succeed, may unconsciously assign to the control group those subjects more likely to give a poor response. In order to avoid any chance of bias, an acceptable procedure is to have someone, unknown to the experimenter, make a random division of the whole group of subjects into the control group and the experimental group. The degree of success of the experiment is then only known at the end when the identity of the two groups is divulged. It is still essential that the membership of the complete group be as homogeneous as possible. Under such circumstances there is a good chance that the experiment may be accomplished without evidence of bias.

In this concluding chapter we have tried to present a few of the more elementary and fundamental aspects of statistics which are present in the modern approach to this field of mathematics.

EXERCISE

1. A rather simple procedure for comparing the performance of an experimental group and a control group is known as the median test. In this test, the median is determined for the combined groups. If the two groups have been drawn at random from the same population, half of the scores in each group should lie above and half below the common median. Apply this procedure to the following examples:

    (a) The following are the scores on strength of grip of two groups of girls, namely ten with normal hearing and ten who are deaf, respectively:

    16, 12, 17, 18, 15, 21, 16, 22, 18, 16;
    10, 14, 12, 21, 19, 12, 19, 17, 19, 25.

    Is any significant difference indicated in the two groups in this respect?

(b) The following are the sales (in thousands of dollars) of two groups of salesman, with and without training, respectively:

18,8,10,8,16,4,10,6,8,12;
18,4,6,4,6,8,3,4,6,5.

Do the two groups exhibit any significant difference with regard to their ability as salesmen?

Appendix A

Example of a Geometric Sophism (or Fallacious Argument)

Given the quadrilateral $ABCD$ in which $\angle B$ is a right angle, $\angle C$ is smaller than a right angle, and $AB = CD$. Let the perpendicular bisectors of segments $\overline{AD}$ and $\overline{BC}$ be $\overline{EO}$ and $\overline{FO}$ intersecting at O. Draw segments $\overline{AO}, \overline{BO}, \overline{CO}, \overline{DO}$.

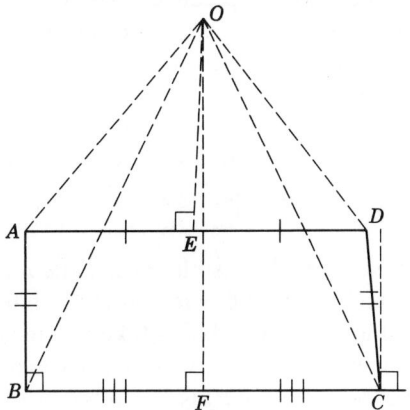

To prove. $\angle FBA \cong \angle FCD$ (that is, a right angle is congruent to an angle which is less than a right angle).

Proof. By construction, $\triangle AEO \cong \triangle DEO$ (SAS); therefore, $AO = DO$. Similarly, $\triangle BFO \cong \triangle CFO$ (SAS); therefore, $BO = CO$ and $\angle FBO \cong \angle FCO$. Since $AB = CD$, it follows that $\triangle ABO \cong \triangle DCO$ (SSS). Therefore $\angle ABO \cong \angle DCO$. Hence $m\angle FBO + m\angle ABO = m\angle FCO + m\angle DCO$. That is, $\angle FBA \cong \angle FCD$.

Question. Can you discover the basic discrepancy which underlies the above fallacy?

Appendix B

Determinants

The idea of a determinant introduced in Section 6.03 may be extended to third and higher orders and is useful in providing solutions (when they exist) for three or more linear equations in this same number of variables. We are going to limit our discussion to third-order determinants but the material will be presented in such a way that the concept may be generalized in an obvious manner to higher orders.

We wish first to define an inversion. When we write 1,2,3, we say that these three natural numbers are in normal order. If we write the numbers in a different order, such as 1,3,2, then we define an *inversion* to exist whenever one number precedes any number smaller than it. For example, in the order 1,3,2, we have one inversion since 3 precedes 2. Similarly, in the order 3,1,2 we find two inversions since 3 precedes 1 and 3 precedes 2.

The determinant,

$$\Delta = \begin{vmatrix} a_1 & b_1 & c_1 \\ a_2 & b_2 & c_2 \\ a_3 & b_3 & c_3 \end{vmatrix}$$

is defined to be the sum of all possible terms, like $a_1 b_2 c_3$, (there are six of these terms) formed in the following way: Each term is the product of three entries, one and only one being taken from any one row or any one column, multiplied by a power of -1. The exponent of the power of -1 associated with the term $a_i b_j c_k$ is the number of inversions in the ordering i,j,k. For example, the product $a_3 b_2 c_1$ will be multiplied by $(-1)^3 = -1$ to give the term $-a_3 b_2 c_1$, since the ordering, 3,2,1, possesses three inversions. Hence $\Delta = a_1 b_2 c_3 - a_1 b_3 c_2 + a_2 b_3 c_1 - a_2 b_1 c_3 + a_3 b_1 c_2 - a_3 b_2 c_1$. There are six different ways in which we may group these six terms, in three pairs, like the following:

$$\Delta = a_1(b_2 c_3 - b_3 c_2) - a_2(b_1 c_3 - b_3 c_1) + a_3(b_1 c_2 - b_2 c_1)$$

$$= a_1 \begin{vmatrix} b_2 & c_2 \\ b_3 & c_3 \end{vmatrix} - a_2 \begin{vmatrix} b_1 & c_1 \\ b_3 & c_3 \end{vmatrix} + a_3 \begin{vmatrix} b_1 & c_1 \\ b_2 & c_2 \end{vmatrix}$$

Appendix B 241

Each of the three second-order determinants in this expression is called a second-order minor and is obtained by eliminating, in the third-order determinant,* the row and column containing a particular entry. In the above expression these latter entries belong to the first column. Let us repeat the grouping, this time using the second row of entries. Then we have

$$\Delta = -a_2(b_1c_3 - b_3c_1) + b_2(a_1c_3 - a_3c_1) - c_2(a_1b_3 - a_3b_1)$$

$$= -a_2 \begin{vmatrix} b_1 & c_1 \\ b_3 & c_3 \end{vmatrix} + b_2 \begin{vmatrix} a_1 & c_1 \\ a_3 & c_3 \end{vmatrix} - c_2 \begin{vmatrix} a_1 & b_1 \\ a_3 & b_3 \end{vmatrix}$$

The reader will have observed the alternating signs which are necessary if the expression is to have the desired form, as well as the fact that each second-order minor is multiplied by the entry common to the eliminated row and column. The situation will be clarified if we make the following definition: If h_i is the entry in the rth row and cth column of the determinant, then the *cofactor*, H_i, of h_i is the product of $(-1)^{r+c}$ and the second-order minor obtained by eliminating the rth row and cth column. For example, referring again to Δ,

$$A_2 = (-1)^{2+1} \begin{vmatrix} b_1 & c_1 \\ b_3 & c_3 \end{vmatrix}; \quad B_3 = (-1)^{3+2} \begin{vmatrix} a_1 & c_1 \\ a_2 & c_2 \end{vmatrix}; \quad C_1 = (-1)^{1+3} \begin{vmatrix} a_2 & b_2 \\ a_3 & b_3 \end{vmatrix}$$

Hence we can rewrite the two groupings, obtained above, as

$$\Delta = a_1A_1 + a_2A_2 + a_3A_3$$
and
$$\Delta = a_2A_2 + b_2B_2 + c_2C_2$$

Question. Can you obtain the other four expressions, like the two above, and verify that each is equal to Δ?

---

*Strictly speaking, *since the determinant is a number*, we eliminate the row and column in the array or *matrix* (see Exercise 5, Section 3.09) illustrated at the right and then consider the determinant associated with the remaining array. $\begin{pmatrix} a_1 & b_1 & c_1 \\ a_2 & b_2 & c_2 \\ a_3 & b_3 & c_3 \end{pmatrix}$

By way of illustration, we shall calculate $\begin{vmatrix} 1 & 0 & 0 \\ 0 & 2 & 3 \\ 4 & 3 & 5 \end{vmatrix}$, "expanding" along three different rows:

$$\begin{vmatrix} 1 & 0 & 0 \\ 0 & 2 & 3 \\ 4 & 3 & 5 \end{vmatrix} = 1\begin{vmatrix} 2 & 3 \\ 3 & 5 \end{vmatrix} - 0\begin{vmatrix} 0 & 3 \\ 4 & 5 \end{vmatrix} + 0\begin{vmatrix} 0 & 2 \\ 4 & 3 \end{vmatrix} = 10 - 9 = 1 \text{ (first row)}$$

$$= -0\begin{vmatrix} 0 & 0 \\ 3 & 5 \end{vmatrix} + 2\begin{vmatrix} 1 & 0 \\ 4 & 5 \end{vmatrix} - 3\begin{vmatrix} 1 & 0 \\ 4 & 3 \end{vmatrix} = 10 - 9 = 1 \text{ (second row)}$$

$$= 4\begin{vmatrix} 0 & 0 \\ 2 & 3 \end{vmatrix} - 3\begin{vmatrix} 1 & 0 \\ 0 & 3 \end{vmatrix} + 5\begin{vmatrix} 1 & 0 \\ 0 & 2 \end{vmatrix} = -9 + 10 = 1 \text{ (third row)}$$

The answer to the above *Question* establishes the fact that, at least for third-order determinants, the value of the determinant is given by the sum, in *any* row or in *any* column, of the products of entry and corresponding cofactor. This result holds true for determinants of *any* order. Although any determinant may be computed on the basis of this principle alone, there are certain properties of determinants which we shall not discuss here which make possible much speedier and more efficient computation. One of these properties is illustrated in Exercise 6 below.

EXERCISES

1. Compare the determinants

   (a) $\begin{vmatrix} a_1 & b_1 \\ a_2 & b_2 \end{vmatrix}$ and $\begin{vmatrix} a_1 & a_2 \\ b_1 & b_2 \end{vmatrix}$

   (b) $\begin{vmatrix} a_1 & b_1 & c_1 \\ a_2 & b_2 & c_2 \\ a_3 & b_3 & c_3 \end{vmatrix}$ and $\begin{vmatrix} a_1 & a_2 & a_3 \\ b_1 & b_2 & b_3 \\ c_1 & c_2 & c_3 \end{vmatrix}$

2. What is the value of the determinant

   (a) $\begin{vmatrix} a & b \\ a & b \end{vmatrix}$?

   (b) $\begin{vmatrix} a & b & c \\ a & b & c \\ d & e & f \end{vmatrix}$?

Appendix B   243

3. How does the determinant $\begin{vmatrix} a_1 & b_1 & c_1 \\ a_2 & b_2 & c_2 \\ a_3 & b_3 & c_3 \end{vmatrix}$ compare with the determinant

$\begin{vmatrix} c_1 & b_1 & a_1 \\ c_2 & b_2 & a_2 \\ c_3 & b_3 & a_3 \end{vmatrix}$?

4. Compare the determinant $\begin{vmatrix} a_1+b_1 & c_1 & d_1 \\ a_2+b_2 & c_2 & d_2 \\ a_3+b_3 & c_3 & d_3 \end{vmatrix}$ with $\begin{vmatrix} a_1 & c_1 & d_1 \\ a_2 & c_2 & d_2 \\ a_3 & c_3 & d_3 \end{vmatrix} + \begin{vmatrix} b_1 & c_1 & d_1 \\ b_2 & c_2 & d_2 \\ b_3 & c_3 & d_3 \end{vmatrix}$.

5. If $\begin{vmatrix} a_1 & b_1 & c_1 \\ a_2 & b_2 & c_2 \\ a_3 & b_3 & c_3 \end{vmatrix} = \Delta$, what does $\begin{vmatrix} a_1 & Kb_1 & c_1 \\ a_2 & Kb_2 & c_2 \\ a_3 & Kb_3 & c_3 \end{vmatrix}$ equal, where $K \neq 0$?

6. If $\begin{vmatrix} a_1 & b_1 & c_1 \\ a_2 & b_2 & c_2 \\ a_3 & b_3 & c_3 \end{vmatrix} = \Delta$, what does $\begin{vmatrix} a_1+Kb_1 & b_1 & c_1 \\ a_2+Kb_2 & b_2 & c_2 \\ a_3+Kb_3 & b_3 & c_3 \end{vmatrix}$ equal, where $K \neq 0$?

7. Since $a_1A_1 + a_2A_2 + a_3A_3 = \begin{vmatrix} a_1 & b_1 & c_1 \\ a_2 & b_2 & c_2 \\ a_3 & b_3 & c_3 \end{vmatrix}$, what is the value of

(a) $a_1B_1 + a_2B_2 + a_3B_3$?
(b) $a_1A_2 + b_1B_2 + c_1C_2$?

(Note that A_i, B_i, C_i are the cofactors, respectively, of a_i, b_i, c_i.)

8. Establish Cramer's Rule for three linear equations in three variables, that is, if $\Delta \neq 0$, the solution of the following three equations
$$a_1x + b_1y + c_1z = d_1$$
$$a_2x + b_2y + c_2z = d_2$$
$$a_3x + b_3y + c_3z = d_3$$

is $x = \dfrac{\begin{vmatrix} d_1 & b_1 & c_1 \\ d_2 & b_2 & c_2 \\ d_3 & b_3 & c_3 \end{vmatrix}}{\Delta}$, $y = \dfrac{\begin{vmatrix} a_1 & d_1 & c_1 \\ a_2 & d_2 & c_2 \\ a_3 & d_3 & c_3 \end{vmatrix}}{\Delta}$, $z = \dfrac{\begin{vmatrix} a_1 & b_1 & d_1 \\ a_2 & b_2 & d_2 \\ a_3 & b_3 & d_3 \end{vmatrix}}{\Delta}$,

where $\Delta = \begin{vmatrix} a_1 & b_1 & c_1 \\ a_2 & b_2 & c_2 \\ a_3 & b_3 & c_3 \end{vmatrix}$.

(*Hint:* To solve for x, multiply both sides of the given equations by the cofactor A_1, A_2, A_3 respectively and add.)

Appendix C

Some Elementary Facts about Matrices

In Exercise 5, Section 3.09 we defined the addition and multiplication of "two-by-two" matrices and in Exercise 8 of Appendix B we stated Cramer's Rule for three linear equations in three variables. In this section we should like to present sufficient material on the behavior of matrices that we might be able to demonstrate a matrix approach to Cramer's Rule. There will inevitably be a good many *Questions*.

As a point of departure we are going to define two matrices to be equal if and only if corresponding elements of each matrix are equal. If we represent our two matrices A and B by (a_{ij}) and (b_{ij}), respectively, where we have indicated only the element in the ith row and jth column in the usual double subscript notation, $i = 1, 2, \ldots, m$ and $j = 1, 2, \ldots, n$, then $A = B \iff a_{ij} = b_{ij}$, for all admissible values of i and j.

Next we define the result of multiplying a matrix by a number (often referred to as a scalar; hence the name, scalar multiplication, applied to this operation) to be the matrix in which each individual element is multiplied by the scalar, that is, $K(a_{ij}) = (Ka_{ij})$. For example,

$$3 \begin{pmatrix} -1 & 2 \\ 0 & 1 \\ 2 & -3 \end{pmatrix} = \begin{pmatrix} -3 & 6 \\ 0 & 3 \\ 6 & -9 \end{pmatrix}$$

We wish to add two matrices, having the same number of rows and the same number of columns (but not necessarily square), by creating a "sum" matrix, each of whose elements is the sum of corresponding elements of the individual matrices, that is, $A + B = (a_{ij}) + (b_{ij}) = (a_{ij} + b_{ij})$ which means that $(a_{ij}) + (b_{ij}) = (c_{ij})$ where $c_{ij} = a_{ij} + b_{ij}$. For example,

$$\begin{pmatrix} 2 & -3 \\ 0 & 1 \\ -4 & 2 \end{pmatrix} + \begin{pmatrix} -1 & 5 \\ 3 & -3 \\ -2 & 6 \end{pmatrix} = \begin{pmatrix} 1 & 2 \\ 3 & -2 \\ -6 & 8 \end{pmatrix}$$

Questions. 1. How would you demonstrate that addition of matrices is commutative and associative?
2. If $b_{ij} = 0$ for all i and j, what can be said about $A + B$?
3. If $b_{ij} = -a_{ij}$, for each i and j, what can be said about $A + B$?

The procedure for multiplying two matrices is more complicated than that for addition and involves multiplying elements in a row of A by corresponding elements in a column of B and adding the products in order to form the product AB. For this to be possible it is necessary that the left multiplying matrix have exactly as many columns as there are rows in the matrix on the right. In other words, if A has m rows and n columns (in this case we often refer to A as an "m by n" matrix) and B is a "p by q" matrix, then we must have $n = p$ if we are to be able to obtain the matrix AB. When this is true we say that A is compatible with B. To be specific,

$$AB = (a_{i1}b_{1j} + a_{i2}b_{2j} + a_{i3}b_{3j} + \ldots + a_{in}b_{nj}) = \left(\sum_{k=1}^{n} a_{ik}b_{kj}\right)$$

where we have shown in parentheses only the element in the ith row and jth column position in the product matrix. For example,

$$\begin{pmatrix} 2 & -3 \\ 0 & 1 \\ -4 & 2 \end{pmatrix} \times \begin{pmatrix} -1 & 3 & -2 & 4 \\ 5 & -3 & 6 & -1 \end{pmatrix} = \begin{pmatrix} -17 & 15 & -22 & 11 \\ 5 & -3 & 6 & -1 \\ 14 & -18 & 20 & -18 \end{pmatrix}$$

since $2(-1) + (-3)(5) = -17$, $2(3) + (-3)(-3) = 15$, $0(-1) + 1(5) = 5$, etc.

Questions. 1. Do you believe that multiplication of matrices is associative?
2. Can you demonstrate that multiplication of matrices is *not* commutative by showing that

$$\begin{pmatrix} 1 & -2 \\ 3 & -1 \end{pmatrix}\begin{pmatrix} 2 & 4 \\ -5 & 3 \end{pmatrix} \neq \begin{pmatrix} 2 & 4 \\ -5 & 3 \end{pmatrix}\begin{pmatrix} 1 & -2 \\ 3 & -1 \end{pmatrix}?$$

3. What is the special nature of $\begin{pmatrix} 1 & 0 \\ 0 & 1 \end{pmatrix}$ as illustrated in the product $\begin{pmatrix} -4 & 5 \\ 1 & 2 \\ -3 & 0 \end{pmatrix}\begin{pmatrix} 1 & 0 \\ 0 & 1 \end{pmatrix}$? or of $\begin{pmatrix} 1 & 0 & 0 \\ 0 & 1 & 0 \\ 0 & 0 & 1 \end{pmatrix}$ in the product

$$\begin{pmatrix} 1 & 0 & 0 \\ 0 & 1 & 0 \\ 0 & 0 & 1 \end{pmatrix}\begin{pmatrix} -4 & 5 \\ 1 & 2 \\ -3 & 0 \end{pmatrix}?$$

In the case where A is a square matrix (n rows and n columns) we would like to consider the question of the existence of a matrix B such that $AB = I$, where I is a square matrix with 1's on the main diagonal (from upper left to lower right) and 0's in every other position. In other words what we would like to obtain is a multiplicative inverse A^{-1} of the matrix A. Let us form the following products, where A_{ij} is the cofactor of a_{ij} and $|a_{ij}|$ is the determinant of the matrix (a_{ij}):

If $b_{ij} = \dfrac{A_{ji}}{|a_{ij}|}$, then

$$(a_{ij}) \times (b_{ij}) = (a_{ij}) \times \left(\dfrac{A_{ji}}{|a_{ij}|}\right)$$

$$= \left(\dfrac{a_{i1}A_{j1}}{|a_{ij}|} + \dfrac{a_{i2}A_{j2}}{|a_{ij}|} + \ldots + \dfrac{a_{in}A_{jn}}{|a_{ij}|}\right)$$

If $j = i$, the expression in the parentheses is equal to 1 since $\sum_{k=1}^{n} a_{ik}A_{ik} = |a_{ij}|$ and if $j \neq i$ this element is 0 (see Exercise 7, Appendix B). Hence we have on the right side of the equation the matrix

$$\begin{pmatrix} 1 & 0 & 0 & 0 & . & . & . & 0 \\ 0 & 1 & 0 & 0 & . & . & . & 0 \\ 0 & 0 & 1 & 0 & . & . & . & 0 \\ 0 & 0 & 0 & 1 & . & . & . & . \\ . & . & . & . & & & & . \\ . & . & . & . & & & & . \\ . & . & . & . & & & & 0 \\ 0 & 0 & 0 & . & . & . & 0 & 1 \end{pmatrix}$$

The same result is obtained for $\left(\dfrac{A_{ji}}{|a_{ij}|}\right)(a_{ij})$.

Therefore we have obtained a multiplicative inverse of A when A is square and $|A| \neq 0$. It may be shown that if $|A| = 0$, then no multiplicative inverse exists for A. Let us illustrate with the following example:

If A is $\begin{pmatrix} 4 & -2 & 0 \\ 0 & -3 & 2 \\ 3 & 2 & -1 \end{pmatrix}$, then

$$A_{11} = \begin{vmatrix} -3 & 2 \\ 2 & -1 \end{vmatrix} = -1; A_{12} = -\begin{vmatrix} 0 & 2 \\ 3 & -1 \end{vmatrix} = 6; A_{13} = \begin{vmatrix} 0 & -3 \\ 3 & 2 \end{vmatrix} = 9$$

$$A_{21} = -\begin{vmatrix} -2 & 0 \\ 2 & -1 \end{vmatrix} = -2; A_{22} = \begin{vmatrix} 4 & 0 \\ 3 & -1 \end{vmatrix} = -4; A_{23} = -\begin{vmatrix} 4 & -2 \\ 3 & 2 \end{vmatrix} = -14$$

$$A_{31} = \begin{vmatrix} -2 & 0 \\ -3 & 2 \end{vmatrix} = -4; A_{32} = -\begin{vmatrix} 4 & 0 \\ 0 & 2 \end{vmatrix} = -8; A_{33} = \begin{vmatrix} 4 & -2 \\ 0 & -3 \end{vmatrix} = -12$$

$$\begin{vmatrix} 4 & -2 & 0 \\ 0 & -3 & 2 \\ 3 & 2 & -1 \end{vmatrix} = 4(-1) + (-2)6 = -16$$

$$\therefore A^{-1} = -\frac{1}{16} \begin{pmatrix} -1 & -2 & -4 \\ 6 & -4 & -8 \\ 9 & -14 & -12 \end{pmatrix}$$

Questions. 1. Is it true, in the above example, that $AA^{-1} = A^{-1}A = I = \begin{pmatrix} 1 & 0 & 0 \\ 0 & 1 & 0 \\ 0 & 0 & 1 \end{pmatrix}$?

2. Is it true that the multiplicative inverse of $\begin{pmatrix} 4 & 3 \\ -2 & 5 \end{pmatrix}$ is

$$\begin{pmatrix} \frac{5}{14} & \frac{3}{14} \\ \frac{2}{14} & \frac{4}{14} \end{pmatrix} \quad \text{or} \quad \frac{1}{14}\begin{pmatrix} 5 & 3 \\ 2 & 4 \end{pmatrix}?$$

We have seen in Section 6.03 how an augmented matrix, such as $\begin{pmatrix} 1 & -1 & 2 & -9 \\ 2 & -3 & -1 & -5 \\ 3 & 2 & -1 & 4 \end{pmatrix}$ can describe the essential characteristics of a system of linear equations, viz.

$$x - y + 2z = -9$$
$$2x - 3y - z = -5$$
$$3x + 2y - z = 4$$

We can go further and represent the system of equations by

$$AX = B$$

where $A = \begin{pmatrix} 1 & -1 & 2 \\ 2 & -3 & -1 \\ 3 & 2 & -1 \end{pmatrix}$; $X = \begin{pmatrix} x \\ y \\ z \end{pmatrix}$; $B = \begin{pmatrix} -9 \\ -5 \\ 4 \end{pmatrix}$

Here the matrix on each side of the equation $AX = B$ is a 3 by 1 matrix and the three statements of equality of corresponding elements provide the original three equations. Incidentally the matrix equation $AX = B$ can also be employed in this manner when A is rectangular, that is, when the number of variables is not equal to the number of equations and hence the number of rows of A is not equal to the number of its columns.

In order to be able to apply the above theory in what follows we shall necessarily consider only a system of equations in which the number of variables is equal to the number of equations. In particular we shall deal with the equations

$$a_{11}x_1 + a_{12}x_2 + a_{13}x_3 = b_1$$
$$a_{21}x_1 + a_{22}x_2 + a_{23}x_3 = b_2$$
$$a_{31}x_1 + a_{32}x_2 + a_{33}x_3 = b_3$$

which are represented by the matrix equation $AX = B$ where

$$A = \begin{pmatrix} a_{11} & a_{12} & a_{13} \\ a_{21} & a_{22} & a_{23} \\ a_{31} & a_{32} & a_{33} \end{pmatrix}; \quad X = \begin{pmatrix} x_1 \\ x_2 \\ x_3 \end{pmatrix}; \quad B = \begin{pmatrix} b_1 \\ b_2 \\ b_3 \end{pmatrix}$$

In addition to having A a square matrix we shall require that $|A| \neq 0$ in order that A^{-1} shall exist. If we multiply both sides of the matrix equation $AX = B$ by A^{-1} we shall obtain $A^{-1}AX = A^{-1}B$, that is, $IX = A^{-1}B$ or $X = A^{-1}B$, from which we can read off the solution for x_1, x_2, and x_3. (For example, if $A^{-1}B = \begin{pmatrix} 5 \\ -3 \\ 7 \end{pmatrix}$ then $\begin{pmatrix} x_1 \\ x_2 \\ x_3 \end{pmatrix} = \begin{pmatrix} 5 \\ -3 \\ 7 \end{pmatrix}$ and hence $x_1 = 5$, $x_2 = -3$, and $x_3 = 7$.)

We would like to show that the solution $X = A^{-1}B$ has the form of Cramer's Rule referred to in Exercise 8 in Appendix B. We know that

$$A^{-1} = \frac{1}{|A|} \begin{pmatrix} A_{11} & A_{21} & A_{31} \\ A_{12} & A_{22} & A_{32} \\ A_{13} & A_{23} & A_{33} \end{pmatrix}$$

$$\therefore A^{-1}B = \frac{1}{|A|} \begin{pmatrix} A_{11}b_1 + A_{21}b_2 + A_{31}b_3 \\ A_{12}b_1 + A_{22}b_2 + A_{32}b_3 \\ A_{13}b_1 + A_{23}b_2 + A_{33}b_3 \end{pmatrix}$$

Now
$$A_{11}b_1 + A_{21}b_2 + A_{31}b_3 = \begin{vmatrix} b_1 & a_{12} & a_{13} \\ b_2 & a_{22} & a_{23} \\ b_3 & a_{32} & a_{33} \end{vmatrix},$$

$$A_{12}b_1 + A_{22}b_2 + A_{32}b_3 = \begin{vmatrix} a_{11} & b_1 & a_{13} \\ a_{21} & b_2 & a_{23} \\ a_{31} & b_3 & a_{33} \end{vmatrix},$$

and
$$A_{13}b_1 + A_{23}b_2 + A_{33}b_3 = \begin{vmatrix} a_{11} & a_{12} & b_1 \\ a_{21} & a_{22} & b_2 \\ a_{31} & a_{32} & b_3 \end{vmatrix}.$$

Hence $X = A^{-1}B$ has the form

$$\begin{pmatrix} x_1 \\ x_2 \\ x_3 \end{pmatrix} = \frac{1}{|A|} \begin{pmatrix} \begin{vmatrix} b_1 & a_{12} & a_{13} \\ b_2 & a_{22} & a_{23} \\ b_3 & a_{32} & a_{33} \end{vmatrix} \\ \begin{vmatrix} a_{11} & b_1 & a_{13} \\ a_{21} & b_2 & a_{23} \\ a_{31} & b_3 & a_{33} \end{vmatrix} \\ \begin{vmatrix} a_{11} & a_{12} & b_1 \\ a_{21} & a_{22} & b_2 \\ a_{31} & a_{32} & b_3 \end{vmatrix} \end{pmatrix}$$

from which

$$x_1 = \frac{\begin{vmatrix} b_1 & a_{12} & a_{13} \\ b_2 & a_{22} & a_{23} \\ b_3 & a_{32} & a_{33} \end{vmatrix}}{\begin{vmatrix} a_{11} & a_{12} & a_{13} \\ a_{21} & a_{22} & a_{23} \\ a_{31} & a_{32} & a_{33} \end{vmatrix}}; \quad x_2 = \frac{\begin{vmatrix} a_{11} & b_1 & a_{13} \\ a_{21} & b_2 & a_{23} \\ a_{31} & b_3 & a_{33} \end{vmatrix}}{\begin{vmatrix} a_{11} & a_{12} & a_{13} \\ a_{21} & a_{22} & a_{23} \\ a_{31} & a_{32} & a_{33} \end{vmatrix}}; \quad x_3 = \frac{\begin{vmatrix} a_{11} & a_{12} & b_1 \\ a_{21} & a_{22} & b_2 \\ a_{31} & a_{32} & b_3 \end{vmatrix}}{\begin{vmatrix} a_{11} & a_{12} & a_{13} \\ a_{21} & a_{22} & a_{23} \\ a_{31} & a_{32} & a_{33} \end{vmatrix}}$$

which is Cramer's Rule.

Appendix D

Proof of the Binomial Theorem for Positive Integral Exponents

In establishing the Binomial Theorem we wish to prove that $P(n)$ is true for any natural number n, where $P(n)$ represents:

$$(a + x)^n = a^n + na^{n-1}x + \frac{n(n-1)}{1 \cdot 2}a^{n-2}x^2 + \ldots$$
$$+ \frac{n(n-1) \ldots (n-r+2)}{1 \cdot 2 \cdot 3 \ldots (r-1)}a^{n-r+1}x^{r-1} + \frac{n(n-1) \ldots (n-r+1)}{1 \cdot 2 \cdot 3 \ldots r}a^{n-r}x^r$$
$$+ \ldots + nax^{n-1} + x^n$$

The coefficients of the terms $a^{n-r}x^r, r = 0, 1, 2, \ldots, n$ in the expression on the right provide the numbers in the $n + 1$st row of Pascal's Triangle. The proof will employ the Principle of Mathematical Induction. Let S be the set of natural numbers n for which $P(n)$ is true. Since $(a + x)^1 = a + x$, $P(1)$ is true and hence $1 \in S$. Assume $k \in S$; that is, $P(k)$ is true; hence

$$(a + x)^k = a^k + ka^{k-1}x + \frac{k(k-1)}{1 \cdot 2}a^{k-2}x^2 + \ldots$$
$$+ \frac{k(k-1) \ldots (k-r+2)}{1 \cdot 2 \cdot 3 \ldots (r-1)}a^{k-r+1}x^{r-1}$$
$$+ \frac{k(k-1) \ldots (k-r+1)}{1 \cdot 2 \cdot 3 \ldots r}a^{k-r}x^r + \ldots + kax^{k-1} + x^k$$

We wish to show

$$(a + x)^{k+1} = a^{k+1} + (k+1)a^k x + \frac{(k+1)(k)}{1 \cdot 2}a^{k-1}x^2 + \ldots$$
$$+ \frac{(k+1)k(k-1) \ldots (k+1-r+1)}{1 \cdot 2 \cdot 3 \ldots r}a^{k+1-r}x^r + \ldots + (k+1)ax^k + x^{k+1}$$

Appendix D   251

We know that

$$(a + x)^{k+1} = (a + x)(a + x)^k$$
$$= (a + x)\left[a^k + ka^{k-1}x + \frac{k(k-1)}{1 \cdot 2}a^{k-2}x^2 + \ldots\right.$$
$$+ \frac{k(k-1)\ldots(k-r+2)}{1 \cdot 2 \cdot 3 \ldots (r-1)}a^{k-r+1}x^{r-1}$$
$$+ \frac{k(k-1)\ldots(k-r+1)}{1 \cdot 2 \cdot 3 \ldots r}a^{k-r}x^r + \ldots + kax^{k-1} + x^k \bigg]$$
$$= a^{k+1} + ka^kx + \frac{k(k-1)}{1 \cdot 2}a^{k-1}x^2 + \ldots$$
$$+ \frac{k(k-1)\ldots(k-r+2)}{1 \cdot 2 \cdot 3 \ldots (r-1)}a^{k-r+2}x^{r-1}$$
$$+ \frac{k(k-1)\ldots(k-r+1)}{1 \cdot 2 \cdot 3 \ldots r}a^{k-r+1}x^r + \ldots + ka^2x^{k-1} + ax^k$$
$$+ a^kx + ka^{k-1}x^2 + \frac{k(k-1)}{1 \cdot 2}a^{k-2}x^3 + \ldots$$
$$+ \frac{k(k-1)\ldots(k-r+2)}{1 \cdot 2 \cdot 3 \ldots (r-1)}a^{k-r+1}x^r$$
$$+ \frac{k(k-1)\ldots(k-r+1)}{1 \cdot 2 \cdot 3 \ldots r}a^{k-r}x^{r+1} + \ldots + kax^k + x^{k+1}$$
$$= a^{k+1} + (k+1)a^kx + \frac{ka^{k-1}x^2}{1 \cdot 2}(2 + k - 1) + \ldots$$
$$+ \frac{k(k-1)\ldots(k-r+2)}{1 \cdot 2 \cdot 3 \ldots (r-1)r}a^{k-r+1}x^r(r + k - r + 1)$$
$$+ \ldots + (k+1)ax^k + x^{k+1}$$

Hence $P(k + 1)$ is true, $k + 1 \in S$, and S contains all the natural numbers. For example, $(a + x)^6 = a^6 + 6a^5x$

$$+ \frac{6 \cdot 5}{1 \cdot 2}a^4x^2 + \frac{6 \cdot 5 \cdot 4}{1 \cdot 2 \cdot 3}a^3x^3 + \frac{6 \cdot 5 \cdot 4 \cdot 3}{1 \cdot 2 \cdot 3 \cdot 4}a^2x^4 + \frac{6 \cdot 5 \cdot 4 \cdot 3 \cdot 2}{1 \cdot 2 \cdot 3 \cdot 4 \cdot 5}ax^5$$
$$+ \frac{6 \cdot 5 \cdot 4 \cdot 3 \cdot 2 \cdot 1}{1 \cdot 2 \cdot 3 \cdot 4 \cdot 5 \cdot 6}x^6$$

$$= a^6 + 6a^5x + 15a^4x^2 + 20a^3x^3 + 15a^2x^4 + 6ax^5 + x^6.$$

If Pascal's Triangle is continued for two more rows in Section 6.08 it will be seen to be in agreement with the above results.

Glossary

∴ therefore
↝ corresponds to
↔ corresponds to (in a 1 : 1 correspondence)
=> implies
<=> is equivalent to; or is defined to be
∃ there exists
∋ such that
| such that, as used in set-builder notation
= equals; $a = b$ means that a and b are names for the same object
≠ is unequal to
∈ belongs to, is a member of
∉ does not belong to, is not a member of
∅ empty or null set; a set that contains no elements
Equal sets: sets that contain exactly the same elements
1 : 1 (one-to-one) correspondence: there is a one-to-one correspondence between the elements of a set A and the elements of a set B if the elements of the two sets can be paired (not necessarily uniquely) so that to each element of A there corresponds exactly one element of B and each element of B is the correspondent or image of exactly one element of A
Equivalent sets: two sets whose elements can be put in 1 : 1 correspondence with each other
⊆ is contained in, is a subset of
⊈ is not contained in, is not a subset of
Universal set: the set of elements we deal with in a given situation
Set-builder notation: a pair of braces enclosing a literal symbol followed by | and the condition(s) that characterize the set
∪ Union: $A \cup B = \{x | x \in A \ \ or \ \ x \in B\}$
∩ Intersection: $A \cap B = \{x | x \in A \ \ and \ \ x \in B\}$
Disjoint sets: sets whose intersection is the empty set
Venn diagram: a diagram in which the elements of a set are represented as points within a closed boundary, often a circle or rectangle
Ordered pair: an object (a, b) which has the property that $(a, b) = (c, d)$ => $a = c$ and $b = d$
Binary operation: a procedure for assigning to an ordered pair of two elements a third element, for example, $(a, b) \stackrel{*}{\rightsquigarrow} a * b$

Glossary

Commutative: a binary operation $*$ on a set is commutative if $a*b = b*a$, for every two elements a and b of the set

Associative: a binary operation $*$ on a set is associative if $(a*b)*c = a*(b*c)$, for every three elements a, b, c of the set

Distributive: a binary operation $*$ is distributive with respect to a binary operation $\#$, both on a given set, if $a*(b \# c) = (a*b) \# (a*c)$ for every three elements a, b, c of the set

Difference set: difference of sets A and $B = A - B = \{x | x \in A \text{ and } x \notin B\}$

Function or mapping: a rule according to which each element of one set is made to correspond to a particular element of another set

Numeral: a name for a number

Cartesian product: Cartesian product of sets A and $B = A \times B = \{(a,b) | a \in A \text{ and } b \in B\}$

Additive identity: element 0 such that $0 + a = a + 0 = a$

Multiplicative identity: element 1 such that $1.a = a.1 = a$

Additive inverse of an element a: element $-a$ such that $(-a) + a = a + (-a) = 0$

Multiplicative inverse of an element a: element a^{-1} such that $a^{-1}.a = a.a^{-1} = 1$

Factor: one of two or more elements being multiplied

Product: the result of multiplying two or more factors

Positive: a number is positive if it is the coordinate of a point on the number line lying on that side of the point corresponding to 0, which contains the point corresponding to 1

Order: $a > b \Longleftrightarrow \exists \; c \text{ positive} \ni a = b + c$

Law of trichotomy for order: for any two real numbers b, c either (1) $b > c$, (2) $c > b$, or (3) $b = c$

Subtraction: $a - b = c \Longleftrightarrow \exists \; c \ni a = b + c$

Division: $a \div b = c \Longleftrightarrow \exists \; c \ni a = bc$

Prime number: a number which has exactly two factors, itself and 1

Greatest common divisor: the largest number that is a factor of each of a set of numbers

Least common multiple: the smallest number that has as a factor each of a set of numbers

Congruence and modular system: $a \equiv b \pmod{m}$ (read "a is congruent to b modulo m") $\Longleftrightarrow a - b$ is a multiple of m.

Isomorphism: a 1:1 correspondence between elements of two mathematical systems that preserves corresponding operations

Inductive set: S is inductive if $k + 1 \in S$ whenever $k \in S$

Principle of mathematical induction: If (1) S is inductive and (2) $1 \in S$, all the natural numbers belong to S.

N set of natural numbers
W set of whole numbers
I set of integers
R' set of rational numbers
R set of real numbers
C set of complex numbers
$\wedge$ conjunction; $p \wedge q$ means "p and q"

∨   disjunction; $p \vee q$ means "p or q"
$\bar{p}$ negation of p
→   conditional; $p \rightarrow q$ means "if p, then q"
↔   biconditional; $p \leftrightarrow q$ means "p if and only if q"
Contrapositive of $p \rightarrow q$: $\bar{q} \rightarrow \bar{p}$
Fallacy: an invalid argument
Numerical sentence: statement involving numbers only — may be true or false
Open sentence: statement involving at least one variable
Solution set: set of elements, which, when used to replace the variable(s) in an open sentence, make it a true numerical sentence
Absolute value: $|b| = b$ if $b \geq 0$
                      $= -b$ if $b < 0$
Relation: a subset of the Cartesian product of two sets
Equivalence relation: a relation R which is

    (1) reflexive: $a \text{ R } a$
    (2) symmetric: $a \text{ R } b \Rightarrow b \text{ R } a$
    (3) transitive: $a \text{ R } b$ and $b \text{ R } c \Rightarrow a \text{ R } c$

Equivalence class: a subset consisting of all elements of a set which are equivalent to one another under an equivalence relation R
Real part of complex number: the real number a in the complex number $a + bi$
Imaginary part of complex number: the real number b in the complex number $a + bi$
Conjugate of $a + bi$: $\overline{a + bi} = a - bi$
AB distance between points A and B
ABC B is a point between points A and C; that is, A, B, C are three points on a line and $AB + BC = AC$
$\overleftrightarrow{AB}$ line through A and B
$\overline{AB}$ segment; set of points on $\overleftrightarrow{AB}$ between A and B and including A and B. Hence $\overline{AB} = \{A, B\} \cup \{D | D \in \overleftrightarrow{AB} \text{ and } ADB\}$
$\overrightarrow{AB}$ ray; set of points on $\overleftrightarrow{AB}$ on B side of A, including A. Hence $\overrightarrow{AB} = \overline{AB} \cup \{E | E \text{ is on } \overleftrightarrow{AB} \text{ and } ABE\}$
$\angle ABC$ angle: $\overrightarrow{BA} \cup \overrightarrow{BC}$
$\triangle ABC$ triangle: $\overline{AB} \cup \overline{BC} \cup \overline{CA}$

Abscissa: the signed measure of the directed displacement of the point from the y-axis in a direction parallel to the x-axis
Ordinate: the signed measure of the directed displacement of the point from the x-axis in a direction parallel to the y-axis
Slope of a line: for two points on a line, which is not parallel to the y-axis, the difference between their ordinates divided by the *corresponding* difference between their abscissas
Locus: a set of points

256   Glossary

Family of loci: a set of loci, all members of which share some common property

Precision: the characteristic of a measure that is concerned directly with the magnitude of the error, that is, with the size of the smallest unit employed in obtaining the measure

Accuracy: the characteristic of a measure that depends on the relative error, that is, the ratio of the error divided by the measure

Significant digits: digits in a measure that are justified by the accuracy with which the measure was made

Graph of a set: a pictorial representation of the elements of the set

Equivalent sentences: sentences having the same solution set relative to the same universe

Closed interval $[a,b]$: $\{x | x \in R \text{ and } a \leq x \leq b\}$

Open interval (a,b): $\{x | x \in R \text{ and } a < x < b\}$

Matrix: a rectangular array of elements, generally obtained from a field

Determinant: a particularly defined number associated with a square matrix of numbers

Discriminant of the quadratic equation, $ax^2 + bx + c = 0$: the expression $b^2 - 4ac$

Arithmetic progression: a sequence of terms in which each successive term is formed by adding a constant quantity to the preceding term

Geometric progression: a sequence of terms in which each successive term is formed by multiplying the preceding term by a constant quantity

Permutation: arrangement

Combination: selection without arranging

Ratio of a to b: $a:b = a \div b = \dfrac{a}{b}$

Countable or denumerable: capable of a 1:1 correspondence with the natural numbers

Principal qth root of b: $\sqrt[q]{b} =$ (1) that real number t such that $t^q = b$, when q is an odd natural number, $=$ (2) that non-negative real number t such that $t^q = b$, when q is an even natural number

Per cent: K per cent $= K\% = \dfrac{K}{100}$

Congruent figures ($\cong$): generally, figures of the same shape and size

Parallel lines: coplanar lines that do not intersect

Similar figures ($\approx$): generally, figures of the same shape

Division algorithm: given two natural numbers N and D, there exist non-negative integers Q and R such that $N = Q \cdot D + R$ and $0 \leq R < D$

Domain: the set of elements for which a correspondence is established with elements of a second (or "image") set

Range: the set of (image) elements to which elements of a domain correspond

Polynomial over the real numbers: an expression like $a_n x^n + a_{n-1} x^{n-1} + \cdots + a_1 x + a_0$, in which the coefficients $a_i, i = 0, 1, \ldots, n$ are real numbers and the exponents are whole numbers

Degree of a polynomial: the exponent of the variable in the term containing the highest power of the variable

Remainder theorem (factor theorem): $P(x) = (ax + b) Q(x) + P\left(-\dfrac{b}{a}\right)$

Frequency: the number of times a particular event is observed to occur

Frequency distribution: a listing of frequencies of related events

Histogram: a graphing of a frequency distribution by means of vertical rectangles

Frequency polygon: a broken-line graph obtained by joining the midpoints of the top segments of the rectangles of a histogram

Mode: the item that occurs most often in a distribution

Median: the item that has in a distribution as many items larger than it is as it has smaller

Arithmetic mean: $\bar{x} = \dfrac{1}{n}\sum_{i=1}^{n} x_i$, the result of dividing the sum of the items in a distribution by the number of items

Mean deviation: $\dfrac{1}{n}\sum_{i=1}^{n} |x_i - \bar{x}|$

Variance: $s^2 = \dfrac{1}{n-1}\sum_{i=1}^{n}(x_i - \bar{x})^2$

Standard deviation: $s =$ the square root of the variance

Answers to Selected Odd-Numbered Exercises

CHAPTER 1

Section 1.01
1. (a) Valid (b) Invalid—a matter of individual opinion (c) Valid (d) Valid
3. (a) True; false; true (b) True; false; true

Section 1.02
1. (a) Correct (b) Incorrect (c) Incorrect (d) Incorrect (e) Correct (f) Incorrect
3. (a) One: $\varnothing$ itself (b) Two: $\{1\}, \varnothing$ (c) Four: $\{1,2\},\{1\},\{2\},\varnothing$ (d) Eight (e) Sixteen (f) 2^n

Section 1.03
1. (a) True (b) False (c) False
3. No
5. Only if $C = D$ (which includes case $C = D = \varnothing$)
7. (a) (i) B (ii) A (b)

(i) 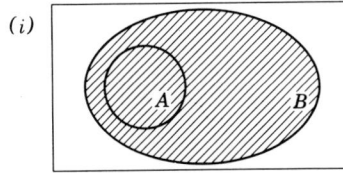   (ii)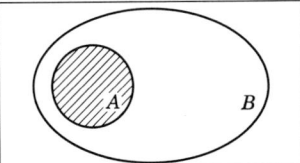

9. 1: $A \cap B \cap C$ 2: $(A \cap B) - C$
   3: $(B \cap C) - A$ 4: $(A \cap C) - B$
   5: $A - (B \cup C)$ 6: $B - (A \cup C)$
   7: $C - (A \cup B)$ 8: $U - (A \cup B \cup C)$

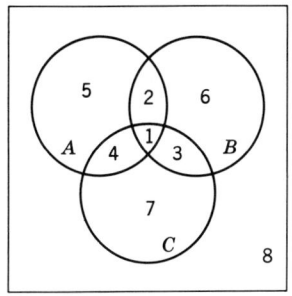

Answers to Exercises

Section 1.04
3. (a) $(a,b) \overset{Q}{\leadsto} a + (b + b)$
   $(a,b) \overset{L}{\leadsto} a$
   $(a,b) \overset{\#}{\leadsto} (a + a) + (b + b)$
   (b) The operations Q, L, and, $\#$ all represent many-to-one correspondences.

Section 1.06
1. (a) (i) Yes (ii) Yes (b) (i) The set AXB is equivalent to the set BXA.
   (ii) The set $(AXB)XC$ is equivalent to the set $AX(BXC)$.
3. $a = 1, b = 2, c = 3$

Section 1.07
1. $b^3 \times b^2 = b^5;\ b^7 \times b^{10} = b^{17}$
3. 3 a's and 3 b's; 20 a's and 30 b's; n a's and n b's.
   Hence $(ab)^n = a^n b^n;\ (ab^2)^5 = a^5 b^{10};\ (a^3 b^5)^7 = a^{21} b^{35}$.

Section 1.08
1. (c) $7(69 + 11) = 7(80)$ (d) $15(20 + 3) = 300 + 45$ (e) $27(63 + 37) = 27(100)$
   (f) $75 \times (40 + 2) = 3000 + 150$
3. (a) $(n+4)(n+1)$ (b) $(n+2)^2$ (c) $(2n+1)(n+3)$

Section 1.11
5. 0

Section 1.13
1. (a) Yes, since $(2m)(2n) = 4mn = 2(2mn)$. (b) Yes, since $(2m + 1)(2n + 1) = 4mn + 2m + 2n + 1 = 2(2mn + m + n) + 1$.
3. $m + (m+1) + (m+2) = 3m + 3 = 3(m+1)$.

Section 1.14
$3 \times 2^{10};\ 5 \times 2^8;\ 2^3 \times 3^5$

Section 1.15
1. 6 3. 1

Section 1.16
1. $2^4 \times 3^4 \times 5 = 6480$

Section 1.17
3. Note the units' digit in the numeral.
5. Note whether the number represented by the units' digit is divisible by 2; note whether the number represented by the units' digit is divisible by 5; note whether the number represented by the tens' and units' digits is divisible by 4; note whether the number represented by the tens' and units' digits is divisible by 25.
7. 107
9. $110110_{(two)}$
11. Note whether the units' digit is divisible by 2; no; note whether the units' digit is divisible by 4.
13. $222021_{(three)}$
15. (a) $110000_{(two)}$ (b) $110111_{(two)}$ (c) $111_{(two)}$ (d) $111_{(two)}$ (e) $1310_{(five)}$
    (f) $313123_{(five)}$ (g) $2334_{(five)}$ (h) $142_{(five)}$
17. $0.10110_{(two)}$

Answers to Exercises 261

CHAPTER 2

Section 2.01

1.

p	q	r	p ∧ q	p ∨ r	q ∨ r	(p ∧ q) ∨ r	(p ∨ r) ∧ (q ∨ r)
T	T	T	T	T	T	T	T
T	T	F	T	T	T	T	T
T	F	T	F	T	T	T	T
T	F	F	F	T	F	F	F
F	T	T	F	T	T	T	T
F	T	F	F	F	T	F	F
F	F	T	F	T	T	T	T
F	F	F	F	F	F	F	F

3. (a) $p \wedge \bar{q}$ (b) $\bar{p} \wedge \bar{q}$ (c) $\bar{p} \vee \bar{q}$ (d) $\overline{(p \vee q)}$ (e) $\bar{p} \wedge \bar{q}$ (f) $\overline{(\bar{p} \wedge \bar{q})}$

5. (a) If Mary got an E in English then John got an A in math and if John got an A in math then Mary got an E in English.
   (b) John got an A in math and Mary did not get an E in English.
   (c) If John did not get an A in math and Mary did not get an E in English then John got an A in math or Mary got an E in English.
   (d) John got an A in math or if Mary did not get an E in English then John did not get an A in math.
   (e) It is not true that John got an A in math and Mary got an E in English.
   (f) If John got an A in math then Mary did not get an E in English.
   (g) It is not true that John got an A in math or Mary got an E in English.
   (h) John did not get an A in math if and only if Mary got an E in English.
   (i) If John did or did not get an A in math then Mary got an E in English.

7. (a)

p	q	p → q	p ↔ q	(p → q) ∨ (p ↔ q)
T	T	T	T	T
T	F	F	F	F
F	T	T	F	T
F	F	T	T	T

(b)

p	q	r	q ∨ r	p → (q ∨ r)	p ∧ r	(p ∧ r) → $\bar{q}$	[p → (q ∨ r)] ∧ [(p ∧ r) → $\bar{q}$]
T	T	T	T	T	T	F	F
T	T	F	T	T	F	T	T
T	F	T	T	T	T	T	T
T	F	F	F	F	F	T	F
F	T	T	T	T	F	T	T
F	T	F	T	T	F	T	T
F	F	T	T	T	F	T	T
F	F	F	F	T	F	T	T

9. $\overline{(p \leftrightarrow q)}$

11. Are you telling the truth if and only if door *A* leads to freedom?

Section 2.02

1. (a) 20 (b) 30 (c) 38

3. (a) (i) $(A - B) \cap (B \cap \bar{A}) = \emptyset$ (ii) $(\bar{A} \cap \bar{B}) \cap (A \cup B) = \emptyset$ (iii) $A \cap B \subseteq A$
   (iv) $(B - A) \subseteq \bar{A}$.

Section 2.03

1.

p	q	(a) $p \vee q$	(b) $\bar{p} \wedge \bar{q}$	$p \wedge q$	(c) $(p \wedge q) \leftrightarrow q$	$\bar{p} \vee q$	(d) $(\bar{p} \vee q) \leftrightarrow q$
T	T	T	F	T	T	T	T
T	F	T	F	F	F	F	T

3. (a), (d), and (e) are logically true.
5. (a) $(p \wedge q) \vee (\bar{p} \wedge \bar{q}) \iff [(p \wedge q) \vee \bar{p}] \wedge [(p \wedge q) \vee \bar{q}]$
   $\iff [(p \vee \bar{p}) \wedge (q \vee \bar{p})] \wedge [(p \vee \bar{q}) \wedge (q \vee \bar{q})]$
   $\iff (q \vee \bar{p}) \wedge (p \vee \bar{q})$
   (b) The truth sets corresponding to each of the equivalent propositions in (a) are equal sets.

Section 2.04

1. (a) Valid (b) Invalid (c) Valid (d) Invalid
3. $t \Rightarrow \bar{s}$
9. T F T T F
11. 3, 3, 25

CHAPTER 3

Section 3.02

1. (a) 6 (b) 6 (c) -12 (d) -6
3. (a) -2 (b) 3 (c) 2 (d) -3

Section 3.03

1. (a) -2 (b) -200 (c) 8 (d) 0 (e) -8 (f) -80
3. (a) $|a+b| = |a| + |b|$ whenever $a \geq 0$ and $b \geq 0$ or whenever $a \leq 0$ and $b \leq 0$.
   $|a| - |b| = |a + b|$ whenever $a \geq 0$ and $b \leq 0$ or whenever $a \leq 0$ and $b \geq 0$ and, in each case, provided $|a| \geq |b|$
   $|a| - |b| = |a + b| = |a| + |b|$ whenever $b = 0$
   (b) $|a| + |b|$ is greater than the other two expressions whenever $a > 0$ and $b < 0$ or whenever $a < 0$ and $b > 0$.
   $|a| - |b|$ is smaller than the other two expressions whenever $a > 0$ and $b > 0$ or whenever $a < 0$ and $b < 0$, or whenever $|b| > |a|$
   (c) $|a| - |b| \leq |a + b| \leq |a| + |b|$
5. $a = 1, b = 2, c = 3; a = -1, b = -2, c = -3; a = -n, b = n, c = 0$ for any integer n.

Section 3.04

1. (a) No (b) Yes (c) No (d) No

Section 3.05

1. (a) $\dfrac{a^2}{ab + b^2}$ (b) $\dfrac{a+b}{a-b}$ (c) $a + b$ (d) $\dfrac{a^2 - a^3 - b^2 + b^3}{(1-b)(1-a)}$
5. $24 < n < 40$

Section 3.07

1. $x^{12} - 4ax^9 + 6a^2x^6 - 4a^3x^3 + a^4 - b - 2c = 0$
3. No

Section 3.09

1. (a) $5 + 3i$ (b) $6 + 3i$ (c) $(-13) + 41i$ (d) $10 + 11i$
   (e) $\left(-\dfrac{7}{29}\right) + \left(\dfrac{-26}{29}\right)i$ (f) $\dfrac{21}{65} + \left(\dfrac{12}{65}\right)i$ (g) $(-3) + \left(-\dfrac{3}{2}\right)i$ (h) $(-3) + i$
   (i) $2 + i$ or $(-2) + (-1)i$

CHAPTER 4

Section 4.07
1. (a) True (b) False (c) True (d) True
3. RQS and PQS; or RSQ and PSQ
5. (a) (The side of $\overleftrightarrow{BC}$ containing A) $\cap$ (The side of $\overleftrightarrow{BA}$ containing C)
   (b) Interior of $\angle BAC$ $\cap$ Interior of $\angle ABC$; or Interior of $\angle BAC$ $\cap$ Interior of $\angle BCA$; or Interior of $\angle ABC$ $\cap$ Interior of $\angle BCA$.
7. No. The union of the two angles contains many points which do not belong to the triangle itself.

Section 4.09
1. $x = -8$
3. $x = -3$
5. $2x - 3y = 0$
7. (a) $\dfrac{y_2 - y_1}{x_2 - x_1}$ (b) $\dfrac{y - y_1}{x - x_1} = \dfrac{y_2 - y_1}{x_2 - x_1}$
9. (c) $y - 1 = 3(x - 2)$ (d) $y - y_1 = m(x - x_1)$ (e) $y = mx + b$ (f) $y = m(x - a)$
11. (a) The lines are all parallel to the y-axis.
    (b) The lines all have slope 3 and hence are parallel to each other.
    (c) The lines all pass through the point $(2,4)$.
    (d) The lines all have x-intercept -3, that is, they all pass through the point $(-3,0)$.

CHAPTER 5

Section 5.02
1. (a) (1) 5.2 yd (2) 5.2 yd (b) (1) 0.68 ft (2) 23.5 ft (c) (1) same precision (2) 0.235 in.
3. (a) $(3\tfrac{7}{10} \pm \tfrac{1}{20})$ cm (b) $\tfrac{1}{20}$ cm
5. (a) $2\tfrac{9}{32}$ in., $2\tfrac{11}{32}$ in. (b) $\tfrac{1}{32}$ in.
7. $13\tfrac{9}{64}$ sq in.; $11\tfrac{25}{64}$ sq in.
9. The piston head.
11. No. Consider $x = 3\tfrac{5}{8}$ in., $y = 147\tfrac{1}{4}$ in.

Section 5.03
1. (a) (526500, 527500); 500 (b) (5265, 5275); 5 (c) (52650, 52750); 50 (d) (52.65, 52.75); 0.05 (e) (0.52695, 0.52705); 0.00005 (f) (526.95, 527.05); 0.05
3. (a) 0.00038000; 0.00038000 (b) 3.800×10^5; 3.80×10^3 (c) No; 0.3800 and 3.800×10^5 have same accuracy.
5. (a) 3.2 (b) 3.20
7. (a) $420\bar{0}$ ft (b) $23,\bar{0}00$ mi (c) $48,\bar{0}00,000$ people

Section 5.04
1. (a) 731.8 (b) 1.0 (c) 4780 (d) 1758.03 (e) 415,000

Section 5.05
1. (a) 4880 (b) 151.6 (c) 0.366
3. (a) 4.4 (b) 1.14 (c) 0.392×10^6
5. 255,000
7. $25\bar{0}$ cu ft

Section 5.06
1. (a) 112.94 (b) 112.94

CHAPTER 6

Section 6.02

1. (a) $\{x \mid x \neq 5\}$
   (b) $\{x \mid x > 1\}$
   (c) R
   (d) $\{0, 2\}$
   (e) $\emptyset$

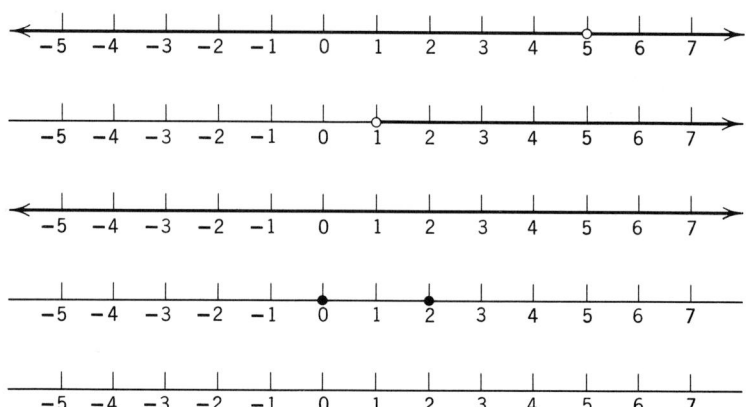

3. (a) $\{-3, 0, 3\}$
   (b) $\{0\}$
   (c) $\{x \mid x < 0\}$
   (d) $\{x \mid 0 < x < 3\} \cup \{x \mid -3 < x < 0\}$
   (e) $\emptyset$
   (f) $\{x \mid -4 \leq x \leq 3\}$

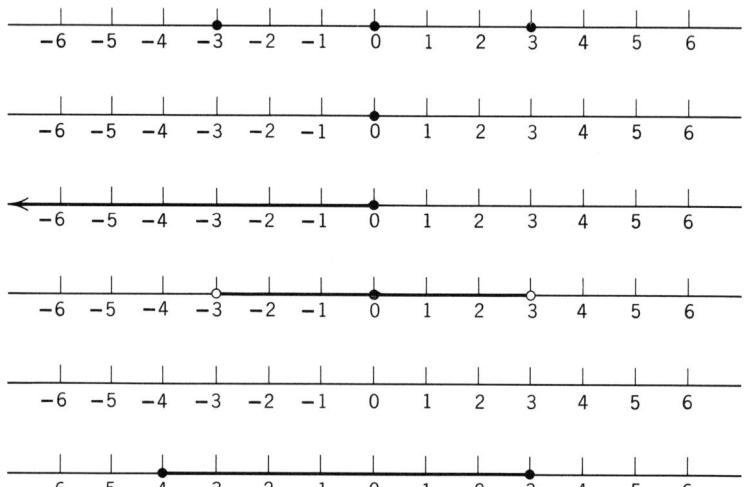

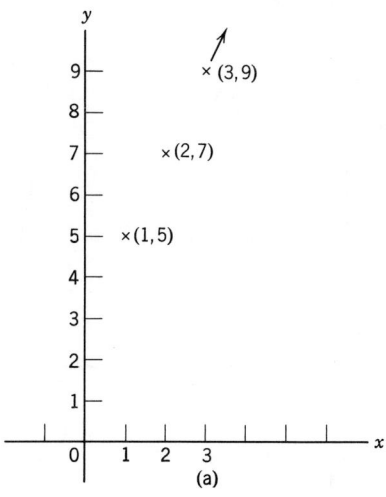

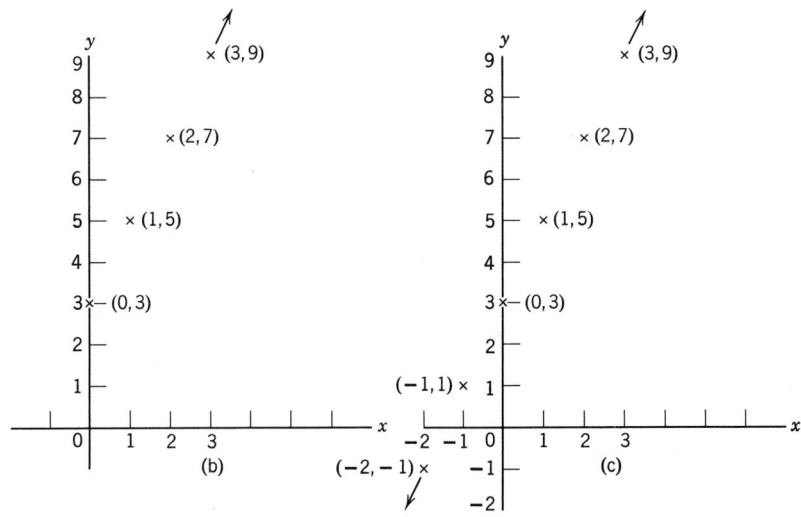

7. More than 23 minutes and at most 27 minutes.

Section 6.03

1. (a) $\{(1,1,2)\}$ (b) $\{(\frac{1}{11}, \frac{31}{55}, \frac{2}{5})\}$ (c) $\varnothing$ (d) $\left\{\left(\frac{-k+7}{5}, \frac{3k-1}{5}, k\right)\right\}$ (e) $\varnothing$
3. 24 miles 5. 12 7. $1.04 9. $29\frac{1}{6}$ mph 11. 207
13. It is not possible to average 40 mph since the downhill trip would have to be accomplished in zero time, i.e., at an infinitely great speed.

Section 6.04
1.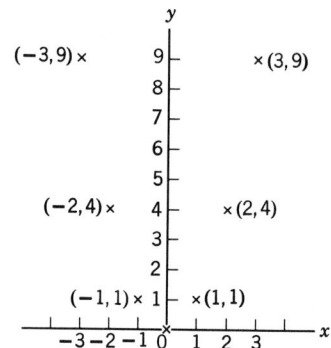

3. (a) $K = 5$ or 8 or 9 (b) $M = 7$ or 8 or 13
5. The fourth equation was obtained from the third equation by the inadmissible procedure of "dividing by zero."
7. If $x^2 + px + q = (x + a)(x + b)$, then $x^2 - px + q = (x - a)(x - b)$.
9. If $b_1 = dk_1$ and $b_2 = dk_2$, then $b_1 + b_2 = d(k_1 + k_2)$ and $b_1 - b_2 = d(k_1 - k_2)$.
11. *Hint:* $r_1^2 + r_2^2 = (r_1 + r_2)^2 - 2(r_1 r_2)$.
13. *Hint:* Consider $5(r_1 + r_2)$ and $25(r_1 r_2)$.

Section 6.06
1. $\{-1, 8\}$ 3. $\{0\}$ 5. $\{0\}$ 7. $\{2, 3\}$ 9. $\varnothing$ 11. $\{\frac{4}{3}\}$ 13. $\{20\}$
15. $\varnothing$ 17. $\{\frac{1}{2}, \frac{5}{2}\}$ 19. $\{\frac{65}{16}\}$

Section 6.07
1. (a) 0 (b) -43 3. 6 years   7. None

Section 6.08
1. (a) $x^5 + 10x^4y + 40x^3y^2 + 80x^2y^3 + 80xy^4 + 32y^5$.
   (b) $64a^6 - 192a^5b + 240a^4b^2 - 160a^3b^3 + 60a^2b^4 - 12ab^5 + b^6$.
   (c) 1.0510100501

Section 6.09
1. (a) 720 (b) 924 (c) n (d) $\dfrac{n}{n-2}$ (e) $\dfrac{10101}{100}$

3. (a) $\dfrac{(n+1)!}{(n+1-r-1)!} = \dfrac{(n+1)[n!]}{(n-r)!}$
   (b) One of the $n + 1$ objects can be selected in $n + 1$ ways. Each time set the selected object aside temporarily. Arrange the remaining n objects, r at a time, in all possible ways (namely $P_{n,r}$). Then place the selected object at, say, the right-hand end of each permutation. This will produce $(n + 1)P_{n,r}$ permutations of the desired type. You should verify that none is missing.

5. (a) $6!$ (b) $\dfrac{6!}{2!}$
7. (a) $4(5)^3$ (b) 96
9. 420
11. (a) 120 (b) 60 (c) 24 (d) 6 (e) 18

Section 6.10
1. 99   3. 84   5. $(5!)C_{16,4}C_{5,1} = 1{,}092{,}000; 218{,}400$
7. $2^{10} - 1; 2^{10} - 11$

Section 6.11
1. $\frac{1}{6}, \frac{1}{3}, \frac{1}{2}$ 3. $\frac{1}{3}$ 5. $\frac{3}{17}$ 7. $\frac{1}{4}$ 9. $\frac{37}{60}, \frac{23}{60}$ 11. $\frac{3}{8}$

CHAPTER 7

Section 7.01
1. (a) $\frac{8}{5}$ (b) $\frac{9}{2}$ 3. 2   5. 36, 42   7. 16

Section 7.03
1. (a) Yes   (b) Yes   (c) Yes   (d) Yes   (e) Yes   (f) Yes

Section 7.04
1. (a) $1.87\dot{4}\dot{9}$ (b) $1.1\dot{9}$ (c) $3.\dot{1}4285\dot{7}$ (d) $3.12\dot{1}$
3. Products of powers of 2 and 5; products of powers of 2; products of powers of 2 and 3.
5. Yes
7. $0.1\dot{0}11\dot{0}_{(two)} = \frac{10101_{(two)}}{11110_{(two)}} = \frac{21}{30} = \frac{7}{10}$

Section 7.05
1. Both numbers are irrational.

Section 7.06
1. $\frac{3}{8\sqrt{2}}; \frac{23}{11\sqrt{3}}$ 3. $(\sqrt{3}+1)(16\sqrt{3}+28) = 76 + 44\sqrt{3} = (2\sqrt{3}+4)(6\sqrt{3}+10)$

Section 7.07
1. $3\frac{1}{3}$ gal   3. He lost 50 cents.

CHAPTER 8

Section 8.01
1. Yes
3. $\angle AOC \cong \angle BOD$ when either (1) A and B are on opposite sides of O and C and D are on opposite sides of O or (2) A and B are on the same side of O and C and D are on the same side of O. $\angle AOC \not\cong \angle BOD$ when only one of (1) holds together with only one of (2).
5. Yes

Section 8.02
1. Two; Four
3. $\overleftrightarrow{ON}$ and $\overleftrightarrow{RS}$ are perpendicular.
5. Three noncollinear points are always coplanar. In the case of four points any three noncollinear ones are coplanar but the fourth point may not be in that plane.

Section 8.06
1. Let $\overline{AB}$ be the given line segment and $\overrightarrow{AC}$ any ray passing through A and not lying in $\overleftrightarrow{AB}$. Choose points D_1, D_2, D_3, D_4 and D_5 on $\overrightarrow{AC}$ so that $\overline{AD_1} \cong \overline{D_1D_2} \cong \overline{D_2D_3} \cong \overline{D_3D_4} \cong \overline{D_4D_5}$. Let the lines through D_i, $i = 1,2,3,4$, which are parallel to $\overline{BD_5}$ meet $\overline{AB}$ at E_i, $i = 1,2,3,4$, respectively. Why must points E_i exist? Show $\overline{AE_1} \cong \overline{E_1E_2} \cong \overline{E_2E_3} \cong \overline{E_3E_4} \cong \overline{E_4B}$.
3. These three areas are equal.

CHAPTER 9

Section 9.02
1. $f(4y+2) = 3(4y+2)+2 = 12y+8 = 4(3y+2) = 4f(y)$.
3. $f(y+a) - f(y-a) = \dfrac{1}{y+a} - \dfrac{1}{y-a} = \dfrac{-2a}{y^2-a^2} = \dfrac{2a}{a^2-y^2}$.

5. (a) $f(y+2) \cdot f(y) = \dfrac{y+1}{y+3} \cdot \dfrac{y-1}{y+1} = \dfrac{\frac{y-1}{2}}{\frac{y+3}{2}} = \dfrac{\frac{y+1}{2}-1}{\frac{y+1}{2}+1} = f\left(\dfrac{y+1}{2}\right)$.

Domain $= \{x \in R \mid x \neq -1\}$.

(b) $f(y+1) \cdot f(y-4) = \dfrac{y+4}{y-1} \cdot \dfrac{y-1}{y-6} = \dfrac{\frac{y+4}{2}}{\frac{y-6}{2}} = \dfrac{\left(\frac{y}{2}-1\right)+3}{\left(\frac{y}{2}-1\right)-2} = f\left(\dfrac{y}{2}-1\right)$

Domain $= \{x \in R \mid x \neq 2\}$.

(c) $f(y+3) \cdot f(y) = \dfrac{y+1}{y+4} \cdot \dfrac{y-2}{y+1} = \dfrac{\frac{y-2}{2}}{\frac{y+4}{2}} = \dfrac{\frac{y+2}{2}-2}{\frac{y+2}{2}+1} = f\left(\dfrac{y+2}{2}\right)$.

Domain $= \{x \in R \mid x \neq -1\}$.

Section 9.03
1. $n_1 + n_2$
3. (a) 5, 56, 45, 0, 21, 35, 0, 45, 80, 0. (b) $(x-2)(x+4)(2x-3)$.

Section 9.04
1. (a) No (b) $f(x)$ cannot equal zero for any $x > 3$.
3. (a) $4x^4 - 3x^3 - 7x^2 - 4x - 9 = (x-3)(4x^3 + 9x^2 + 20x + 56) + 159$
   (b) $4x^4 - 3x^3 - 7x^2 - 4x - 9 = (x+2)(4x_3 - 11x^2 + 15x - 34) + 59$

Section 9.05
1. (a) $(x-a)(x+a)(x^2 + ax + a^2)(x^2 - ax + a^2)$ (b) $(x-26)(x+2)$
   (c) $(x-y-3)(x-y-14)$ (d) $(x^2 + \sqrt{3}x + 2)(x^2 - \sqrt{3}x + 2)$

Section 9.06
1. (a) Yes

3. *Hint*: Obtain $b^n \equiv (-1)^n \pmod{b+1}$ and $\sum_{j=0}^{k} a_j b^j \equiv \sum_{j=0}^{k} a_j(-1)^j \pmod{b+1}$. When the number N is represented as a numeral in base b, let n' be the sum of the digits with alternately positive and negative signs, beginning with the units' digit as positive. Then the remainder obtained when N is divided by $b+1$ is equal to the remainder when n' is divided by $b+1$.

In the decimal system the remainder when N is divided by 11 equals the remainder when the sum of the digits with alternating sign is divided by 11. For example, 11 is a factor of 9,371,648.

Section 9.07
1. (a) $(x-a)(x^4 + ax^3 + a^2x^2 + a^3x + a^4)$
   (b) $(x+b)(x^6 - bx^5 + b^2x^4 - b^3x^3 + b^4x^2 - b^5x + b^6)$

3. (a) $\left\{-\frac{1}{2}, \frac{4}{3}, 2\right\}$ (b) $\left\{-\frac{2}{5}\right\}$

Section 9.08

1. (a) None (b) Some (c) All
3. Maximum profit of $66 with 6 briefcases and 18 trunks.

CHAPTER 10

Section 10.02

1. (a) 0.144 (b) 0.432 (c) 3 heads 216 times; 2 heads and 1 tail 432 times; 2 tails and 1 head 288 times; 3 tails 64 times. (d) the answers to (c) are the four terms in the expansion of $1000(0.6 + 0.4)^3$.

Section 10.03

1. (a)

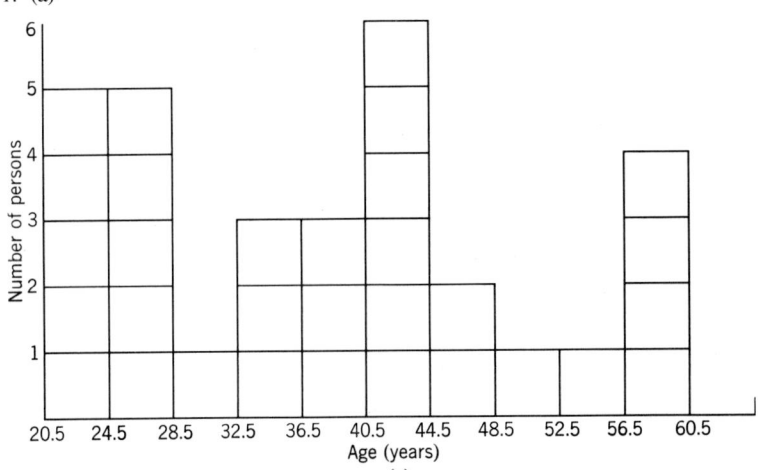

(a)

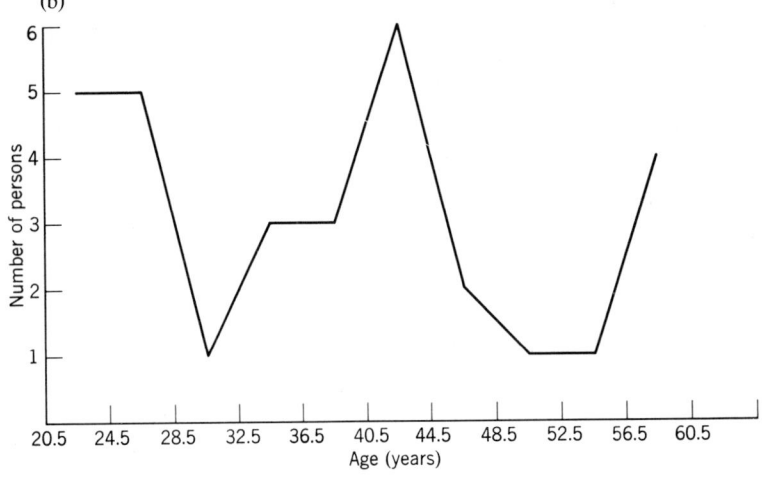

(b)

270   Answers to Exercises

Section 10.05
1. Mode: 28; median: 39; mean: 38.1
3. 3.00

Section 10.06
1. (a) 10.0 (b) 11.9 (c) (i) 45.2 (ii) 54.8 (iii) 100 (iv) 100
3. Mean 42; variance 144
5. (a) The mean is increased by K.
   (b) Variance and standard deviation remain unchanged.

Section 10.08
1. (a) No (b) Yes

Appendix B

1. (a) $\begin{vmatrix} a_1 & b_1 \\ a_2 & b_2 \end{vmatrix} = a_1 b_2 - a_2 b_1 = \begin{vmatrix} a_1 & a_2 \\ b_1 & b_2 \end{vmatrix}$

   (b) $\begin{vmatrix} a_1 & b_1 & c_1 \\ a_2 & b_2 & c_2 \\ a_3 & b_3 & c_3 \end{vmatrix} = a_1 b_2 c_3 - a_1 b_3 c_2 + a_2 b_3 c_1 - a_2 b_1 c_3 + a_3 b_1 c_2 - a_3 b_2 c_1$
   $= \begin{vmatrix} a_1 & a_2 & a_3 \\ b_1 & b_2 & b_3 \\ c_1 & c_2 & c_3 \end{vmatrix}$

3. $\begin{vmatrix} c_1 & b_1 & a_1 \\ c_2 & b_2 & a_2 \\ c_3 & b_3 & a_3 \end{vmatrix} = c_1 b_2 a_3 - c_1 b_3 a_2 + c_2 b_3 a_1 - c_2 b_1 a_3 + c_3 b_1 a_2 - c_3 b_2 a_1$
   $= -(a_1 b_2 c_3 - a_1 b_3 c_2 + a_2 b_3 c_1 - a_2 b_1 c_3 + a_3 b_1 c_2 - a_3 b_2 c_1)$
   $= -\begin{vmatrix} a_1 & b_1 & c_1 \\ a_2 & b_2 & c_2 \\ a_3 & b_3 & c_3 \end{vmatrix}$

5. $\begin{vmatrix} a_1 & Kb_1 & c_1 \\ a_2 & Kb_2 & c_2 \\ a_3 & Kb_3 & c_3 \end{vmatrix} = -Kb_1 \begin{vmatrix} a_2 & c_2 \\ a_3 & c_3 \end{vmatrix} + Kb_2 \begin{vmatrix} a_1 & c_1 \\ a_3 & c_3 \end{vmatrix} - Kb_3 \begin{vmatrix} a_1 & c_1 \\ a_2 & c_2 \end{vmatrix}$
   $= K\left[-b_1 \begin{vmatrix} a_2 & c_2 \\ a_3 & c_3 \end{vmatrix} + b_2 \begin{vmatrix} a_1 & c_1 \\ a_3 & c_3 \end{vmatrix} - b_3 \begin{vmatrix} a_1 & c_1 \\ a_2 & c_2 \end{vmatrix} \right]$
   $= K \cdot \Delta$

7. (a) $a_1 B_1 + a_2 B_2 + a_3 B_3 = \begin{vmatrix} a_1 & a_1 & c_1 \\ a_2 & a_2 & c_2 \\ a_3 & a_3 & c_3 \end{vmatrix} = 0$

   (b) $a_1 A_2 + b_1 B_2 + c_1 C_2 = \begin{vmatrix} a_1 & b_1 & c_1 \\ a_1 & b_1 & c_1 \\ a_3 & b_3 & c_3 \end{vmatrix} = 0$

Answers to Questions

CHAPTER 1

Section 1.01
Are all equal sets equivalent?

Yes. Because the sets are equal, corresponding elements are the same; the 1 : 1 correspondence between identical elements, although trivial, is sufficient to establish that the sets are equivalent.

Are any two equivalent sets necessarily equal?

No. The 1 : 1 correspondence between elements guarantees nothing with regard to equality of elements.

Section 1.03
What set is equal to $\bar{\bar{A}}$, by which we mean $\overline{(\bar{A})}$?

Set A. The complement of $\bar{A}$ is the set of elements of U which do not belong to $\bar{A}$, hence must comprise set A.

Can you express $A \cap B$ in set-builder notation?

$$A \cap B = \{x \mid x \in A \text{ and } x \in B\}.$$

Can you prove that the operation of intersection of sets is commutative?

If $x \in A \cap B$, then $x \in A$ and $x \in B$. Hence $x \in B$ and $x \in A$ and therefore $x \in B \cap A$. Accordingly, $A \cap B \subseteq B \cap A$. By an exactly similar argument it may be shown that $B \cap A \subseteq A \cap B$. Hence $A \cap B = B \cap A$.

Section 1.04
Do you think addition of natural numbers is commutative?

The answer should be "yes," for it has been shown that the union of two sets is commutative. Hence, if $A \cap B = \emptyset$, $a + b = n(A) + n(B) = n(A \cup B) = n(B \cup A) = n(B) + n(A) = b + a$.

If (a,b) and (c,d) are two ordered pairs such that $(a,b) = (c,d)$, can you show that $a = c$ and $b = d$?

We may write $(a,b) = \{\{a\},\{a,b\}\}$ and $(c,d) = \{\{c\},\{c,d\}\}$. Hence $\{\{a\},\{a,b\}\} = \{\{c\},\{c,d\}\}$. Then either $\{a\} = \{c\}$ or $\{c,d\}$. If $\{a\} = \{c,d\}$, then $c = d$. However, in general, $c \neq d$ and therefore $\{a\} \neq \{c,d\}$. Hence $\{a\} = \{c\}$ and $a = c$. Also we must have $\{a,b\} = \{c,d\}$ which has $b = d$ as a consequence.

In the special case in which $c = d$, $\{c,d\} = \{c\}$ and $\{\{c\},\{c,d\}\} = \{\{c\},\{c\}\} = \{\{c\}\}$. Hence $\{\{a\},\{a,b\}\} = \{\{c\}\}$. Therefore $\{a\} = \{a,b\}$ and it must be true that $b = a$. Then we have $\{\{a\},\{a,b\}\} = \{\{a\},\{a\}\} = \{\{a\}\} = \{\{c\}\}$, whence $\{a\} = \{c\}$ and $a = c$. Therefore $a = b = c = d$.

Can you show that addition of natural numbers is associative?

We wish to show, for three natural numbers a,b,c, that $(a + b) + c = a + (b + c)$. Hence, if $a = n(A)$, $b = n(B)$, $c = n(C)$, where $A \cap B = \emptyset$, $B \cap C = \emptyset$, $(A \cup B) \cap$

272   Answers to Questions

$C = \emptyset$, $A \cap (B \cup C) = \emptyset$, we wish to show $n((A \cup B) \cup C) = n(A \cup (B \cup C))$. Therefore we should show that $(A \cup B) \cup C$ is equivalent to $A \cup (B \cup C)$. It will certainly suffice if we show $(A \cup B) \cup C = A \cup (B \cup C)$. We will demonstrate that $(A \cup B) \cup C \subseteq A \cup (B \cup C)$. If $x \in (A \cup B) \cup C$, then either (1) $x \in C$ or (2) $x \in A \cup B$. If (1) $x \in C$, then $x \in B \cup C$ and $x \in A \cup (B \cup C)$. If (2) $x \in A \cup B$, then either (a) $x \in A$ and, as a result, $x \in A \cup (B \cup C)$ or (b) $x \in B$, from which it follows that $x \in B \cup C$ and also $x \in A \cup (B \cup C)$. Hence $(A \cup B) \cup C \subseteq A \cup (B \cup C)$. A corresponding argument establishes that $A \cup (B \cup C) \subseteq (A \cup B) \cup C$ and our original goal is achieved. (It might be noted in passing that the two conditions, $A \cap B = \emptyset$ and $(A \cup B) \cap C = \emptyset$ are sufficient to guarantee the four conditions assumed in the second sentence of this paragraph.)

Section 1.06

Can you show that $1 \times b = b$?

Let $1 = n(\{a\})$ and $b = n(\{m_1, m_2, \ldots, m_b\})$
Then $1 \times b = n(\{a\} \times \{m_1, m_2, \ldots, m_b\})$
$= n(\{(a, m_1), (a, m_2), \ldots, (a, m_b)\})$

The sets $\{m_1, m_2, \ldots, m_b\}$ and $\{(a, m_1), (a, m_2), \ldots, (a, m_b)\}$ are equivalent, for a 1:1 correspondence is easily seen to exist between them by letting $m_i \leftrightarrow (a, m_i)$. Hence $n(\{(a, m_1), (a, m_2), \ldots, (a, m_b)\}) = b$.

Is the set of natural numbers closed under multiplication?

Each factor in a product of two numbers can be represented as the number associated with a particular set. The Cartesian product of the two sets exists by definition and has a unique natural number associated with it. Hence the result of multiplying two natural numbers is again a natural number.

Section 1.08

Can you prove that $(A \times B) \cap (D \times B) = \emptyset$, whenever $A \cap D = \emptyset$?

Let $A = \{a_1, a_2, \ldots, a_m\}$, $B = \{b_1, b_2, \ldots, b_n\}$, $D = \{d_1, d_2, \ldots, d_q\}$. Then $A \times B = \{(a_i, b_j) | a_i \in A$ and $b_j \in B\}$, and $D \times B = \{(d_k, b_j) | d_k \in D$ and $b_j \in B\}$. No a_i is equal to any d_k since $A \cap D = \emptyset$. Therefore no (a_i, b_j) is equal to any (d_k, b_j).

Section 1.09

Can you show that 0 is a unique number?

If $0'$ is another number that does the work of 0, then we must have $0 = 0' + 0 = 0'$. Hence $0 = 0'$ and 0 is therefore unique.

Do all previously described properties hold for W as well as for N?

Yes.

Section 1.11

What can you say about commutativity and associativity of subtraction?

Neither of these properties holds in subtraction, as is illustrated by (1) $9 - 3 \neq 3 - 9$, (2) $(9 - 3) - 2 \neq 9 - (3 - 2)$.

How would you prove that $ab \neq ac \iff a(b - c) \neq 0$?

Since $ac = ac + 0$, $ab \neq ac \iff ab \neq ac + 0$
$\iff ab - ac \neq 0$
$\iff a(b - c) \neq 0$

We show that $ab - ac = a(b - c)$ as follows:

$b - c = d \iff \exists d \in W \ni b = c + d$
$\therefore ab = a(c + d)$
$= ac + ad$

Hence $ad = ab - ac$ and therefore $a(b - c) = ab - ac$.

Answers to Questions 273

Section 1.13

What is the status of division from the point of view of commutativity and associativity?

Neither of the foregoing properties holds for division, as the following illustrations demonstrate:

(1) $9 \div 3 \neq 3 \div 9$

(2) $(16 \div 4) \div 2 \neq 16 \div (4 \div 2)$

Is the set of odd numbers closed under addition?

No. A single counterexample, such as $1 + 3 = 4$, suffices as proof. Since $(2m + 1) + (2n + 1) = 2m + 2n + 2 = 2(m + n + 1)$, it is also true that the sum of *any* two odd numbers is an even number.

Section 1.15

Can you explain why the preceding sentence is true?

The GCD of two numbers will, itself, be expressible as a product of a unique set of factors. Each such factor is a common factor of both given numbers, hence occurs no more often in both numbers than in the GCD. If this were not so, the factor would have to occur in a higher power as a factor of the GCD, thereby producing a larger GCD. In the example $(2^2 \cdot 3^5 \cdot 5^3, 2^4 \cdot 3^3 \cdot 5^2)$ the factor 2 occurs twice in the first number and four times in the second and must appear as 2^2 in the GCD. Similarly 3 must have exponent 3 and 5 exponent 2 in the GCD.

Section 1.17

Can you complete the following sequence of binary numerals for the first sixteen natural numbers?

1, 10, 11, 100, 101, 110, 111, 1000, 1001, 1010, 1011, 1100, 1101, 1110, 1111, 10000.

Why does this procedure give the desired result?

If we expand the telescoped form, we obtain $2[2(2\{2[2(1) + 0] + 1\} + 0) + 1] + 1$ which by repeated applications of the distributive principle may be expressed as $1(2)^5 + 0(2)^4 + 1(2)^3 + 0(2)^2 + 1(2) + 1$. This number is exactly that represented by the numeral $101011_{(two)}$.

1. *Why is the above procedure correct in changing a numeral from decimal to binary form?*

Since $43 = 2(21) + 1 = 2(2[10] + 1) + 1$
$= 2(2[2\{5\} + 0] + 1) + 1$
$= 2(2[2\{2(2) + 1\} + 0] + 1) + 1$
$= 2(2[2\{2(2[1] + 0) + 1\} + 0] + 1) + 1$
$= 1(2)^5 + 0(2)^4 + 1(2)^3 + 0(2)^2 + 1(2) + 1$

2. *How can you change a numeral from octal (base eight) to binary form?*

You can change the numeral to base ten form and then transform to base two.

How can this be done without changing back to base ten?

This can be accomplished by replacing each digit in the octal numeral by its representation in base two; for example,

$6574_{(eight)} = 6(8)^3 + 5(8)^2 + 7(8) + 4$
$= (4 + 2 + 0)(2^3)^3 + (4 + 0 + 1)(2^3)^2 + (4 + 2 + 1)(2^3) + (4 + 0 + 0)$
$= (2^2 + 2 + 0)(2^9) + (2^2 + 0 + 1)(2^6) + (2^2 + 2 + 1)(2^3) + (2^2 + 0 + 0)$
$= 1(2^{11}) + 1(2^{10}) + 0(2)^9 + 1(2^8) + 0(2^7) + 1(2^6) + 1(2^5) + 1(2^4) + 1(2^3)$
$\quad + 1(2^2) + 0(2) + 0$
$= 110101111100_{(two)}$

Note that $110_{(two)} = 6_{(eight)}$; $101_{(two)} = 5_{(eight)}$; $111_{(two)} = 7_{(eight)}$; $100_{(two)} = 4_{(eight)}$.

274   *Answers to Questions*

Can you change a numeral from binary to octal?

Here we reverse the procedure by grouping the digits in the binary representation in threes from the right; for example $110101111100_{(two)} = $ 110 101 111 100$_{(two)}$

$$= [1(2^{11}) + 1(2^{10}) + 0(2^9)] +$$
$$[1(2^8) + 0(2^7) + 1(2^6)] + [1(2^5)$$
$$+ 1(2^4) + 1(2^3)] + [1(2^2)$$
$$+ 0(2) + 0]$$
$$= [1(2^2) + 1(2) + 0](2^9) + [1(2^2)$$
$$+ 0(2) + 1](2^6) +$$
$$[1(2^2) + 1(2) + 1](2^3)$$
$$+ [1(2^2) + 0(2) + 0]$$
$$= 6(2^3)^3 + 5(2^3)^2 + 7(2^3) + 4$$
$$= 6(8^3) + 5(8^2) + 7(8) + 4$$
$$= 6574_{(eight)}$$

1. *Can you complete the following sequence of CPC numerals for the first sixteen natural numbers?*

   1, 11, 10, 110, 111, 101, 100, 1100, 1101, 1111, 1110, 1010, 1011, 1001, 1000, 11000.

2. *Can you devise rules (two are needed) for writing the CPC numeral for the number larger by one than a given number?*

   If the number of 1's in the numeral is even, replace the right-hand digit by its opposite (we will think of 0 as the opposite of 1 and 1 as the opposite of 0). If the number of 1's in the numeral is odd, replace the digit to the immediate left of the right-most 1 by its opposite.

3. *Can you add such numbers?*

   Yes. However, considerable care must be exercised to produce an answer in which the signs associated with the 1's alternate. It is helpful to place a plus or dash above each 1 according to whether the sign is positive or negative respectively. It is also a help to keep a tally, at the right, of the -1's and any extra $+1$'s obtained in the sum. The following examples illustrate the procedure, but for an explanation the reader is referred to the article given in the footnote. It should be noted that dual forms also exist for the examples illustrated on the next page, in which the (+) and (−) signs are interchanged.

```
     +                    +                       +
     1                   1 0                     1 0 0
     +                    +                       +
     1                   1 0                     1 0 0
   -----                -------                 ---------
    +− +                + − +                   +  −  +
    1 1 = 1 0 (−)       1 0 1 = 1 0 0 (−)       1 0 0 1 = 1 0 0 0 (−)
    = 1 1               = 1 0 1                 = 1 0 0 1
```

```
     +−              +−              +−
     1 1             1 1 0           1 1 0 0
      −               −               −
      1               1               1
     ───             ───             ─────
      +               +               +
      1              1 0             1 0 0
  =   1          =   1 0         =   1 0 0


    + − +          +−  +−
    1 0 1 0 1      1 1 0 1 1
    +−+−           + − +
    1 1 1 1 0      1 0 1 0 1
    ─────────      ─────────
    + − −+         + −−+
    1 0 1 0 1 1 (−) 1 0 1 1 1 0 (−)
    +−+ −+         +−+−+
  = 1 1 1 0 1 1  = 1 1 1 1 1 0
  = 1 1 1 0 1 1  = 1 1 1 1 1 0


       + +                −
    +−+−+            +−+−
    1 1 1 1 1         1 1 1 1
    +−+−+            +−  +−
    1 1 1 1 1         1 1 0 1 1
    ─────────        ─────────
    +  − −           + −+
    1 0 1 0 1 0 (−−−) 1 0 1 1 0 (+)
    +−+ −            +   −
  = 1 1 1 0 1 0 (−−) = 1 0 0 1 0
    +−+−+
  = 1 1 1 1 1 0 (−) = 1 0 0 1 0
    +−+−+−
  = 1 1 1 1 1 1
  = 1 1 1 1 1 1
```

Section 1.18

Can you show that the remaining items in the two tables given are correct?

Because $2m + (2n + 1) = 2(m + n) + 1$, the sum of an even number and an odd number is an odd number; hence $0 \oplus 1 = 1$ and $1 \oplus 0 = 1$. As far as multiplication is concerned, we have $2m \times 2n = 2(2mn)$, hence $0 \otimes 0 = 0$; $2m \times (2n + 1) = 2[m(2n + 1)]$, hence $0 \otimes 1 = 0$ and $1 \otimes 0 = 0$; $(2m + 1) \times (2n + 1) = 4mn + 2m + 2n + 1 = 2(2mn + m + n) + 1$, hence $1 \otimes 1 = 1$.

1. *Can you verify the correctness of the remaining items in the tables under the latter interpretation?*

Current will not flow when two open switches are in parallel; hence $0 \oplus 0 = 0$; likewise, when two open switches are in series, giving $0 \otimes 0 = 0$. Current will certainly flow with two closed switches in series; hence $1 \otimes 1 = 1$.

2. *Are the two operations $\oplus$ and $\otimes$, discussed in this section, commutative and associative?*

   (a) *When related to even and odd numbers.*

   Both operations must be both commutative and associative because they are defined as the ordinary addition and multiplication of even and odd numbers, which operations are already known to be commutative and associative.

   (b) *When related to switches.*

   Commutativity is ensured for both operations by observing that each of the tables is symmetric with respect to the main diagonal (from upper left to lower right). In order to demonstrate associativity, we must check the following:

$$0 \oplus (0 \oplus 0) = 0 = (0 \oplus 0) \oplus 0; \quad 0 \otimes (0 \otimes 0) = 0 = (0 \otimes 0) \otimes 0$$
$$1 \oplus (0 \oplus 0) = 1 = (1 \oplus 0) \oplus 0; \quad 1 \otimes (0 \otimes 0) = 0 = (1 \otimes 0) \otimes 0$$
$$0 \oplus (1 \oplus 0) = 1 = (0 \oplus 1) \oplus 0; \quad 0 \otimes (1 \otimes 0) = 0 = (0 \otimes 1) \otimes 0$$
$$0 \oplus (0 \oplus 1) = 1 = (0 \oplus 0) \oplus 1; \quad 0 \otimes (0 \otimes 1) = 0 = (0 \otimes 0) \otimes 1$$
$$1 \oplus (1 \oplus 0) = 1 = (1 \oplus 1) \oplus 0; \quad 1 \otimes (1 \otimes 0) = 0 = (1 \otimes 1) \otimes 0$$
$$1 \oplus (0 \oplus 1) = 1 = (1 \oplus 0) \oplus 1; \quad 1 \otimes (0 \otimes 1) = 0 = (1 \otimes 0) \otimes 1$$
$$0 \oplus (1 \oplus 1) = 1 = (0 \oplus 1) \oplus 1; \quad 0 \otimes (1 \otimes 1) = 0 = (0 \otimes 1) \otimes 1$$
$$1 \oplus (1 \oplus 1) = 1 = (1 \oplus 1) \oplus 1; \quad 1 \otimes (1 \otimes 1) = 1 = (1 \otimes 1) \otimes 1$$

3. *Is the $\otimes$ operation distributive with respect to the $\oplus$ operation?*

   (a) *When related to even and odd numbers.*

   The answer is yes, for the ordinary multiplication of numbers is distributive with respect to addition, and it is in terms of these operations that $\otimes$ and $\oplus$ are defined.

   (b) *When related to switches.*

   Here it is necessary to check the following:

$$0 \otimes (0 \oplus 0) = 0 = (0 \otimes 0) \oplus (0 \otimes 0)$$
$$1 \otimes (0 \oplus 0) = 0 = (1 \otimes 0) \oplus (1 \otimes 0)$$
$$0 \otimes (1 \oplus 0) = 0 = (0 \otimes 1) \oplus (0 \otimes 0)$$
$$0 \otimes (0 \oplus 1) = 0 = (0 \otimes 0) \oplus (0 \otimes 1)$$
$$1 \otimes (1 \oplus 0) = 1 = (1 \otimes 1) \oplus (1 \otimes 0)$$
$$1 \otimes (0 \oplus 1) = 1 = (1 \otimes 0) \oplus (1 \otimes 1)$$
$$0 \otimes (1 \oplus 1) = 0 = (0 \otimes 1) \oplus (0 \otimes 1)$$
$$1 \otimes (1 \oplus 1) = 1 = (1 \otimes 1) \oplus (1 \otimes 1)$$

Hence $\otimes$ is distributive with respect to $\oplus$.

4. *Is the $\oplus$ operation distributive with respect to the $\otimes$ operation?*

   (a) *When related to even and odd numbers.*

   The answer is *no* and one counterexample will suffice:

$$1 \oplus (1 \otimes 0) = 1 \oplus 0 = 1; \quad (1 \oplus 1) \otimes (1 \oplus 0) = 0 \otimes 1 = 0$$

(b) *When related to switches.*
Here we must verify the following:

$$0 \oplus (0 \otimes 0) = 0 = (0 \oplus 0) \otimes (0 \oplus 0)$$
$$1 \oplus (0 \otimes 0) = 1 = (1 \oplus 0) \otimes (1 \oplus 0)$$
$$0 \oplus (1 \otimes 0) = 0 = (0 \oplus 1) \otimes (0 \oplus 0)$$
$$0 \oplus (0 \otimes 1) = 0 = (0 \oplus 0) \otimes (0 \oplus 1)$$
$$1 \oplus (1 \otimes 0) = 1 = (1 \oplus 1) \otimes (1 \oplus 0)$$
$$1 \oplus (0 \otimes 1) = 1 = (1 \oplus 0) \otimes (1 \oplus 1)$$
$$0 \oplus (1 \otimes 1) = 1 = (0 \oplus 1) \otimes (0 \oplus 1)$$
$$1 \oplus (1 \otimes 1) = 1 = (1 \oplus 1) \otimes (1 \oplus 1)$$

Hence $\oplus$ is distributive with respect to $\otimes$

5. *Can you diagram the circuits in the various cases involved in 2(b), 3(b), and 4(b)?*
In order to conserve space we illustrate only the first diagram in each group.

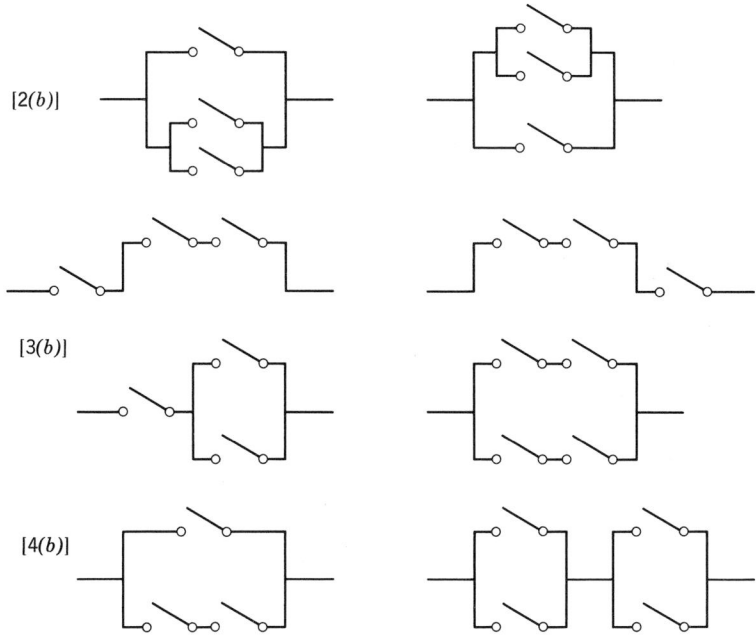

1. *Do you think the two operations $*$ and $\#$ are commutative and associative?*
Symmetry of the two tables with respect to the main diagonal indicates that both operations are commutative.
Both operations are associative but it requires checking sixty-four relations of each of the following types to demonstrate the facts conclusively:

$$A * (B * C) = B = (A * B) * C \qquad A \# (B \# C) = B = (A \# B) \# C$$

278   Answers to Questions

2. *Do you think each operation is distributive with respect to the other?*
By examining the sixty-four relations such as

$$A \# (B * C) = A = (A \# B) * (A \# C)$$

it can be shown that the # operation is distributive with respect to the * operation.

However, since $A * (B \# C) = C$, whereas $(A * B) \# (A * C) = D$, we know that the * operation is *not* distributive with respect to the # operation.

Next you will find partly completed addition and multiplication tables for the number system modulo four.

(1) *Can you complete these tables?*

+	0	1	2	3		×	0	1	2	3
0	0	1	2	3		0	0	0	0	0
1	1	2	3	0		1	0	1	2	3
2	2	3	0	1		2	0	2	0	2
3	3	0	1	2		3	0	3	2	1

(2). *Can you establish an isomorphic correspondence between the set $\{A,B,C,D\}$ (as described on page 30) and the set $\{0,1,2,3\}$ with the operations + and × defined on it, as completed in the preceding question?*

If we let $D \leftrightarrow 0$, $A \leftrightarrow 1$, $B \leftrightarrow 2$, $C \leftrightarrow 3$ and #, ×, and *,+ be corresponding pairs of operations, the two tables for the set $\{A,B,C,D\}$ will be exact replicas of the tables for the set $\{0,1,2,3\}$. Hence the 1 : 1 correspondence establishes the desired isomorphism.

Section 1.19
Can you verify the statement made concerning $P(n)$ for $n = 1, 2, 3, 4, 5,$ and 40?

n	1	2	3	4	5	40
$P(n)$	43	47	53	61	71	$(41)^2$

CHAPTER 2

Section 2.01

1. *What statement is a correct alternative expression for the first illustrative proposition in the second sentence above?*
   $2 + 2 \neq 5$ and Los Angeles is not the capital of the United States.

2. *Can you obtain, in terms of $\bar{p}$ and $\bar{q}$, a proposition which is equivalent to $\overline{(p \wedge q)}$?*
   $\bar{p} \vee \bar{q}$. Check the following table:

p	q	$\overline{p \wedge q}$	$\bar{p} \vee \bar{q}$
T	T	F	F
T	F	T	T
F	T	T	T
F	F	T	T

Answers to Questions   279

Are $(p \wedge q) \vee r$ and $p \wedge (q \vee r)$ equivalent propositions?

p	q	r	$p \wedge q$	$q \vee r$	$(p \wedge q) \vee r$	$p \wedge (q \vee r)$
T	T	T	T	T	T	T
T	T	F	T	T	T	T
T	F	T	F	T	T	T
T	F	F	F	F	F	F
F	T	T	F	T	T	F
F	T	F	F	T	F	F
F	F	T	F	T	T	F
F	F	F	F	F	F	F

Hence the given propositions are *not* equivalent.

Can you construct a proposition to fit the following truth table?

$(p \wedge q \wedge \bar{r}) \vee (p \wedge \bar{q} \wedge r) \vee (\bar{p} \wedge q \wedge r) \vee (\bar{p} \wedge q \wedge \bar{r}) \vee (\bar{p} \wedge \bar{q} \wedge r)$ or $\overline{[(p \wedge q \wedge r) \vee (p \wedge \bar{q} \wedge \bar{r}) \vee (\bar{p} \wedge \bar{q} \wedge \bar{r})]}$ which may also be written as $\overline{(p \wedge q \wedge r)} \wedge \overline{(p \wedge \bar{q} \wedge \bar{r})} \wedge \overline{(\bar{p} \wedge \bar{q} \wedge \bar{r})}$ or $(\bar{p} \vee \bar{q} \vee \bar{r}) \wedge (\bar{p} \vee q \vee r) \wedge (p \vee q \vee r)$.

1. *Is the proposition $q \rightarrow p$ equivalent to $p \rightarrow q$?*
   No. Compare their truth tables below.
2. *Is the proposition $p \rightarrow q$ equivalent to $\bar{p} \vee q$?*
   Yes. Observe that they have the same truth table.

p	q	$p \rightarrow q$	$q \rightarrow p$	$\bar{p} \vee q$
T	T	T	T	T
T	F	F	T	F
F	T	T	F	T
F	F	T	T	T

Can you give another combination of propositions to which $p \leftrightarrow q$ is equivalent?
$(\bar{p} \vee q) \wedge (p \vee \bar{q})$.

p	q	$\bar{p} \vee q$	$p \vee \bar{q}$	$(\bar{p} \vee q) \wedge (p \vee \bar{q})$	$p \leftrightarrow q$
T	T	T	T	T	T
T	F	F	T	F	F
F	T	T	F	F	F
F	F	T	T	T	T

Section 2.02

1. *Can you show by comparing Venn diagrams that the truth set for $\overline{(p \wedge \bar{q})}$ is the same as $\bar{P} \cup Q$?*

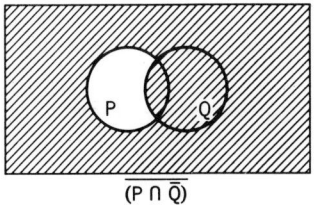
$\overline{(P \cap \bar{Q})}$

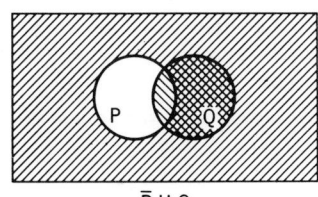
$\bar{P} \cup Q$

280   Answers to Questions

2. *What is the Venn diagram for the truth set of* $\bar{p} \wedge q$?

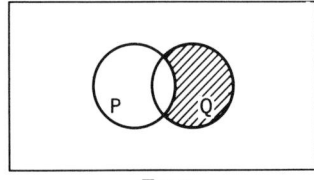

$\bar{P} \cap Q$

1. *Does this Venn diagram also represent the truth set of the proposition* $(p \to q) \wedge (q \to p)$?   Yes.
   Of the proposition $(\bar{p} \vee q) \wedge (p \vee \bar{q})$?   Yes.
   Of $\overline{(p \wedge \bar{q})} \wedge \overline{(\bar{p} \wedge q)}$?   Yes.
   Of $\overline{(p \wedge \bar{q}) \vee (\bar{p} \wedge q)}$?   Yes.
2. *Does this Venn diagram also represent* $(P \cap Q) \cup (\bar{P} \cap \bar{Q})$?
   Yes.

Section 2.03

What is the truth set of a logically true proposition?
   The universal set.

Of a logically false proposition?
   The empty set.

1. *Can you demonstrate that* $\overline{(P \cup Q)} = \bar{P} \cap \bar{Q}$?

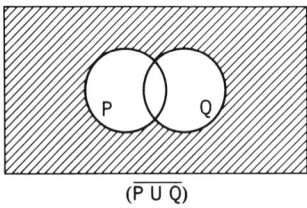
$\overline{(P \cup Q)}$

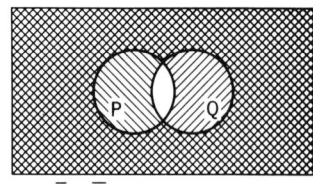
$\bar{P} \cap \bar{Q}$ (Double-thatched part)

2. *What are the two definitions given for p is equivalent to q?*
   (a) *p* and *q* have the same truth tables
   (b) $p \iff q$; that is, the biconditional of *p* and *q* is logically true.
3. *Can you show that these two definitions are completely consistent; that is, can each one be derived from the other?*

   Yes. If *p* and *q* have the same truth tables, then, by definition, the biconditional $p \leftrightarrow q$ will be true in each row of its truth table. Similarly, if the biconditional of *p* and *q* is logically true it is impossible, by definition, for *p* and *q* to have different truth tables.

Section 2.04

Can you demonstrate that the argument (often referred to as modus tollens) exhibited at the right is valid?

$\bar{q}$
$p \Rightarrow q$
———
$\therefore \bar{p}$

p	$\bar{p}$	q	$\bar{q}$	$p \to q$	$\bar{q} \wedge (p \to q)$	$(\bar{q} \wedge (p \to q)) \to \bar{p}$
T	F	T	F	T	F	T
T	F	F	T	F	F	T
F	T	T	F	T	F	T
F	T	F	T	T	T	T

Can you demonstrate that the argument at the right also represents a fallacy?

$$p \Rightarrow q$$
$$\bar{p}$$
$$\therefore \bar{q}$$

p	$\bar{p}$	q	$\bar{q}$	$p \to q$	$\bar{p} \wedge (p \to q)$	$(\bar{p} \wedge (p \to q)) \to \bar{q}$
T	F	T	F	T	F	T
T	F	F	T	F	F	T
F	T	T	F	T	T	F
F	T	F	T	T	T	T

Can you show that the proposition $(p \to q) \wedge (q \to r)$ implies $p \to r$?

p	q	r	$p \to r$	$p \to q$	$q \to r$	$(p \to q) \wedge (q \to r)$	$((p \to q) \wedge (q \to r)) \to (p \to r)$
T	T	T	T	T	T	T	T
T	T	F	F	T	F	F	T
T	F	T	T	F	T	F	T
T	F	F	F	F	T	F	T
F	T	T	T	T	T	T	T
F	T	F	T	T	F	F	T
F	F	T	T	T	T	T	T
F	F	F	T	T	T	T	T

CHAPTER 3

Section 3.02

1. *Can you show that the additive inverse of b is unique?*

   If we assume that b' does the work of $(-b)$, then $b + b' = b' + b = 0$. Hence $(-b) = (-b) + 0 = (-b) + (b + b') = [(-b) + b] + b' = 0 + b' = b'$.

2. *What is the additive inverse of $(-b)$?*

   Since $b + (-b) = (-b) + b = 0$, we observe that b is doing the work of an additive inverse of $(-b)$. In view of the result that the additive inverse of any integer is unique, it follows that b is the additive inverse of $(-b)$.

In the definition of order for integers, why have we specified that $c \in N$?

We wish our definition of $a > b$ to be consistent with the interpretation in terms of numbers represented on the number line; that is, we want the number a to lie to the right of the number b on the line. Hence we want a positive displacement to be combined with the directed displacement b to give the directed displacement a.

Answers to Questions

Section 3.03

1. *Do you believe addition of integers is commutative?*

   When $c \geq 0$ and $d \geq 0$ and $c < 0$ and $d < 0$, we use lines (1) and (6), respectively, of the definition of addition; the statement follows from the corresponding result for whole numbers. When $c \geq 0, d < 0$, and $|c| \geq |d|$, then, by definition,

   $$c + d = |c| - |d|, \quad \text{by line (2)}$$
   $$d + c = |c| - |d|, \quad \text{by line (4)}$$
   $$\text{Hence } c + d = d + c.$$

2. *Do you believe addition of integers is associative?*

   This rather lengthy demonstration requires the consideration of eighteen individual cases. We illustrate the general approach by considering one of the nontrivial cases.

   Let us suppose that $a \geq 0, b < 0, c \geq 0, |b| \geq c, a \geq |b + c|$

   $$\therefore a + (b + c) = a + [-(|b| - c)] \left.\begin{array}{l} \\ = a - (|b| - c) \\ = a - p \end{array}\right\} \text{by definition of addition of integers}$$

   where $|b| - c = p \geq 0 \iff |b| = c + p$.

   When we consider $(a + b) + c$ we must treat two cases: (1) $a \geq |b|$
   (2) $a < |b|$

   (1) $(a + b) + c = (a - |b|) + c$
   $\qquad\qquad\quad = r_1 + c$

   where $a - |b| = r_1 \geq 0 \iff a = |b| + r_1$.

   Now we wish to show that $a - p = r_1 + c$. We know that

   $$a = |b| + r_1$$
   $$= (c + p) + r_1$$
   $$= c + (p + r_1) \quad \text{since } c, p, \text{ and } r_1 \text{ are all } \geq 0$$
   $$= c + (r_1 + p)$$
   $$= (c + r_1) + p$$
   $$\therefore a - p = c + r_1 \text{ by definition of subtraction}$$
   $$= r_1 + c.$$

   (2) $(a + b) + c = -(|b| - a) + c$ since $|b| > a$
   $\qquad\qquad\quad = -r_2 + c$

   where $|b| - a = r_2 \geq 0 \iff |b| = a + r_2$.

   First of all we wish to show that $c \geq r_2$. Let us suppose that $c < r_2$. We know that $p \leq a$. Since $c, r_2, p,$ and a are all ≥ 0, we may add corresponding sides of the inequalities to obtain $c + p < a + r_2$. However, this contradicts the fact that $|b| = a + r_2$ and $|b| = c + p$. Hence $c \geq r_2$ and $c + (-r_2) = c - r_2 = q \geq 0 \iff c = r_2 + q$. Now we wish to show that $a - p = q$. We have $a + r_2 = c + p$. Hence $(a + r_2) + q = (c + p) + q$.

Since $a, r_2, q, c,$ and p are ≥ 0, it is true that

and
$$a + (r_2 + q) = c + (p + q)$$

Hence
$$a + c = (p + q) + c \text{ since } c = r_2 + q$$

Therefore
$$a = [(p + q) + c] - c = p + q \text{ (see Section 1.12)}$$

$$a - p = q$$
$$= c - r_2$$
$$= -r_2 + c$$

3. *Does 0 continue to act as the additive identity?*
If $a \geq 0$ and $b = 0$, then $a + b = |a| + |0| = a$. If $a < 0$ and $b = 0$, $a + b = |0| - |a| = a$. *And uniquely?*
Yes. The proof given earlier is also valid here.
1. *Do you believe that the multiplication of integers is commutative?*
If $b \geq 0$ and $c \geq 0$ or $b < 0$ and $c < 0$, then $b \times c = |b| \times |c| = |c| \times |b| = c \times b$. If $b \geq 0$ and $c < 0$ or $b < 0$ and $c \geq 0$, then $b \times c = -(|b| \times |c|) = -(|c| \times |b|) = c \times b$.
2. *Do you believe that the multiplication of integers is associative?*
There are eight individual cases that need demonstration. We give one proof by way of illustrating the procedure.

If $a \geq 0, b \geq 0, c < 0$, then $(a \times b) \times c = -(|a \times b| \times |c|)$
$$= -[(|a| \times |b|) \times |c|]$$
$$= -[|a| \times (|b| \times |c|)]$$
$$= -(|a| \times (|b| \times c|)$$
$$= a \times (b \times c)$$

Since the reasoning in some of the steps is rather involved, in this question and in the following one we did not ask the reader to produce solutions.
3. *Do you believe the multiplication of integers is distributive with respect to addition?*
For a complete demonstration twelve cases must be considered. We illustrate two such cases.
   (1) If $a \geq 0, b < 0, c < 0$, then

$$a \times (b + c) = a \times [-(|b| + |c|)]$$
$$= -[|a| \times (|b| + |c|)]$$
$$= -[(|a| \times |b|) + (|a| \times |c|)]$$
$$= -[(|ab| + |ac|)]$$
$$= ab + ac$$

   (2) If $a \geq 0, b < 0, c \geq 0, |b| > c$, then

$$a \times (b + c) = a \times [-(|b| - |c|)]$$
$$= -[|a| \times (|b| - |c|)]$$
$$= -[(|a| \times |b|) - (|a| \times |c|)]$$
$$= -(|ab| - |ac|)$$
$$= ab + ac$$

284 Answers to Questions

4. *Does 1 continue to act as a multiplicative identity?*
$$b \times 1 = \begin{cases} |b| \times |1| & \text{if } b \geq 0 \\ -(|b| \times |1|) & \text{if } b < 0 \end{cases}$$
$$= \begin{cases} |b| & \text{if } b \geq 0 \\ -|b| & \text{if } b < 0 \end{cases}$$
$$= b$$

And uniquely?
   Yes. Proof used with natural numbers continues to apply.

5. *Does 0 continue to multiply in the usual way?*
   Yes. $b \times 0 = 0 \times b = \begin{cases} |0| \times |b| & \text{if } b \geq 0 \\ -(|0| \times |b|) & \text{if } b < 0 \end{cases}$
   $= 0$

Proof of uniqueness of 0 is the same as that used in Section 1.09.

Section 3.04

In which of the following examples of a relation R is R an equivalence relation?
1. $R =$ *is the square of.* No, since none of the requirements is satisfied.
2. $R =$ *is the same age as.* Yes. All three requirements are satisfied.
3. $R =$ *is a friend of.* No. Transitivity fails.

Consider the set of all the cities in the United States. If a R b <=> a and b are cities in the same state, what are the equivalence classes with respect to this relation?
The equivalence classes are the sets of cities belonging to the individual states.

Section 3.05

Can you show that $(bx)d = (bd)x$?

$(bx)d = b(xd)$ (associativity of multiplication)
$\quad\quad= b(dx)$ (commutativity of multiplication)
$\quad\quad= (bd)x$ (associativity of multiplication)

1. *Can you show that the addition of rational numbers is commutative and associative?*

$$\frac{a}{b} + \frac{c}{d} = \frac{ad + bc}{bd} \quad \text{(definition)}$$
$$= \frac{cb + da}{db} \quad \text{(commutativity of addition and multiplication of integers)}$$
$$= \frac{c}{d} + \frac{a}{b} \quad \text{(definition)}$$

$$\left(\frac{a}{b} + \frac{c}{d}\right) + \frac{f}{g} = \frac{ad + bc}{bd} + \frac{f}{g}$$
$$= \frac{(ad + bc)g + (bd)f}{bdg}$$
$$= \frac{adg + (bcg + bdf)}{bdg}$$
$$= \frac{a(dg) + b(cg + df)}{b(dg)}$$
$$= \frac{a}{b} + \frac{cg + df}{dg}$$
$$= \frac{a}{b} + \left(\frac{c}{d} + \frac{f}{g}\right)$$

2. *Can you verify that* $0 + \frac{a}{b} = \frac{a}{b}$?

$$0 + \frac{a}{b} = \frac{0}{1} + \frac{a}{b}$$
$$= \frac{0(b) + 1(a)}{1(b)}$$
$$= \frac{0 + a}{b}$$
$$= \frac{a}{b}$$

1. *Can you prove that the multiplication of rational numbers is commutative, associative, and distributive with respect to addition?* **Yes**.

$$\frac{a}{b} \times \frac{c}{d} = \frac{a \times c}{b \times d} \qquad \left(\frac{a}{b} \times \frac{c}{d}\right) \times \frac{f}{g} = \frac{a \times c}{b \times c} \times \frac{f}{g}$$

$$= \frac{c \times a}{d \times b} \qquad\qquad\qquad = \frac{(a \times c) \times f}{(b \times d) \times g}$$

$$= \frac{c}{d} \times \frac{a}{d} \qquad\qquad\qquad = \frac{a \times (c \times f)}{b \times (d \times g)}$$

$$\frac{a}{b}\left(\frac{c}{d} + \frac{f}{g}\right) = \frac{a}{b}\left(\frac{cg + df}{dg}\right) \qquad = \frac{a}{b} \times \frac{c \times f}{d \times g}$$

$$= \frac{a(cg + df)}{b(dg)} \qquad\qquad = \frac{a}{b} \times \left(\frac{c}{d} \times \frac{f}{g}\right)$$

$$= \frac{acg + adf}{bdg}$$

$$= \frac{acg}{bdg} + \frac{adf}{bdg}$$

$$= \frac{ac}{bd} + \frac{af}{bg}$$

$$= \left(\frac{a}{b} \times \frac{c}{d}\right) + \left(\frac{a}{b} \times \frac{f}{g}\right)$$

2. *Can you show that* $1 \times \frac{a}{b} = \frac{a}{b}$?

$$1 \times \frac{a}{b} = \frac{1}{1} \times \frac{a}{b}$$
$$= \frac{1 \times a}{1 \times b}$$
$$= \frac{a}{b}$$

286   Answers to Questions

3. *Can you show that* $0 \times \frac{a}{b} = 0$?

$$0 \times \frac{a}{b} = \frac{0}{1} \times \frac{a}{b}$$
$$= \frac{0 \times a}{1 \times b}$$
$$= \frac{0}{b}$$
$$= 0$$

Can you show why $\frac{b}{c} + \frac{d}{c} = \frac{b+d}{c}$?

$$\frac{b}{c} + \frac{d}{c} = \frac{bc + dc}{c \times c}$$
$$= \frac{(b+d)c}{c \times c}$$
$$= \frac{b+d}{c} \times \frac{c}{c}$$
$$= \frac{b+d}{c}$$

When b and d have a common factor f, specifically $b = b_1 f$ and $d = d_1 f$, how would you establish the result $\frac{a}{b} + \frac{c}{d} = \frac{ad_1 + cb_1}{b_1 d_1 f}$?

$$\frac{a}{b} + \frac{c}{d} = \frac{a}{b_1 f} + \frac{c}{d_1 f}$$
$$= \frac{a}{b_1 f} \times \frac{d_1}{d_1} + \frac{c}{d_1 f} \times \frac{b_1}{b_1}$$
$$= \frac{ad_1}{b_1 d_1 f} + \frac{cb_1}{b_1 d_1 f}$$
$$= \frac{ad_1 + cb_1}{b_1 d_1 f}, \text{ by the result of the preceding question.}$$

1. *Can you show that the multiplicative inverse of b is unique?*

Let b' be a number which does the work of $\frac{1}{b}$. Hence

$$\frac{1}{b} = 1 \times \frac{1}{b}$$
$$= (b' \times b) \times \frac{1}{b}$$
$$= b' \times (b \times \frac{1}{b})$$
$$= b' \times 1$$
$$= b'$$

2. Can you show that b is the reciprocal of $\frac{1}{b}$?

Since $b \times \frac{1}{b} = 1$, then, by definition, b is the multiplicative inverse of $\frac{1}{b}$, and therefore b is the reciprocal of $\frac{1}{b}$.

3. What is the reciprocal of $\frac{a}{b}$ when $a \neq 0$ and $b \neq 0$?

$$\frac{b}{a} \times \frac{a}{b} = \frac{b \times a}{a \times b}$$
$$= \frac{a}{a} \times \frac{b}{b}$$
$$= 1$$

Therefore $\frac{b}{a}$ is the multiplicative inverse, or reciprocal, of $\frac{a}{b}$.

4. How can it best be demonstrated that $\dfrac{\frac{a}{b}}{\frac{c}{d}} = \dfrac{ad}{bc}$?

$$\dfrac{\frac{a}{b}}{\frac{c}{d}} = \dfrac{\frac{a}{b}}{\frac{c}{d}} \times \dfrac{\frac{d}{c}}{\frac{d}{c}} = \dfrac{\frac{a}{b} \times \frac{d}{c}}{\frac{c}{d} \times \frac{d}{c}} = \dfrac{\frac{ad}{bc}}{1} = \dfrac{ad}{bc}$$

or

$$\dfrac{\frac{a}{b}}{\frac{c}{d}} = \dfrac{\frac{a}{b}}{\frac{c}{d}} \times \dfrac{\frac{bd}{bd}}{\frac{bd}{bd}} = \dfrac{\frac{a}{b} \times \frac{bd}{1}}{\frac{c}{d} \times \frac{bd}{1}} = \dfrac{ad \times \frac{b}{b}}{bc \times \frac{d}{d}} = \dfrac{ad}{bc}$$

1. Can you show that the additive inverse of $\frac{a}{b}$ is unique?

Let $\frac{c}{d}$ be a rational number such that $\frac{c}{d} + \frac{a}{b} = 0$.
Then
$$\frac{c}{d} = \frac{c}{d} + 0$$
$$= \frac{c}{d} + \left[\frac{a}{b} + \left(-\frac{a}{b}\right)\right]$$
$$= \left(\frac{c}{d} + \frac{a}{b}\right) + \left(-\frac{a}{b}\right)$$
$$= 0 + \left(-\frac{a}{b}\right)$$
$$= -\frac{a}{b}$$

Hence the additive inverse of $\frac{a}{b}$ is unique.

Answers to Questions

2. *Can you use the information in Question 1 to show that* $-\left(\frac{a}{b}\right) = (-1)\left(\frac{a}{b}\right)$?

$$\frac{a}{b} + (-1)\frac{a}{b} = 1 \cdot \frac{a}{b} + (-1)\frac{a}{b}$$
$$= [1 + (-1)]\left(\frac{a}{b}\right)$$
$$= 0\left(\frac{a}{b}\right)$$
$$= 0$$

Therefore $(-1)\frac{a}{b} = -\left(\frac{a}{b}\right)$ since $(-1)\frac{a}{b}$ is doing the work of the additive inverse and the latter has been shown to be unique.

3. *Can you show that* $\frac{-a}{b} = \frac{a}{-b} = (-a)\frac{1}{b} = a\left(\frac{1}{-b}\right) = -\left(\frac{a}{b}\right)$?

$$-\left(\frac{a}{b}\right) = (-1)\frac{a}{b}$$
$$= \left(\frac{-1}{1}\right)\left(\frac{a}{b}\right) = \frac{(-1)(a)}{1(b)} = \frac{-a}{b}$$
$$= \left(\frac{-1}{1}\right)\left(\frac{-1}{-1}\right)\left(\frac{a}{b}\right) = \frac{1(a)}{(-1)(b)} = \frac{a}{-b}$$

$$\frac{-a}{b} = \frac{(-a)1}{1 \cdot b} = \left(\frac{-a}{1}\right)\left(\frac{1}{b}\right) = (-a)\left(\frac{1}{b}\right)$$

$$\frac{a}{-b} = \frac{a \cdot 1}{1(-b)} = \left(\frac{a}{1}\right)\left(\frac{1}{-b}\right) = a\left(\frac{1}{-b}\right)$$

4. (a) *Can you define subtraction of rational numbers in keeping with the definitions given in Sections 1.11 and 3.02?*

$$\frac{a}{b} - \frac{c}{d} = \frac{f}{g} \iff \frac{c}{d} + \frac{f}{g} = \frac{a}{b}$$

(b) *Can you show that* $\frac{a}{b} - \frac{c}{d} = \frac{a}{b} + \left(-\frac{c}{d}\right)$, *where* a, b, c, d, *are integers,* $b, d \neq 0$?

$$\frac{a}{b} + \left(-\frac{c}{d}\right) = \left(\frac{c}{d} + \frac{f}{g}\right) + \left(-\frac{c}{d}\right) = \left(\frac{f}{g} + \frac{c}{d}\right) + \left(-\frac{c}{d}\right)$$
$$= \frac{f}{g} + \left[\frac{c}{d} + \left(-\frac{c}{d}\right)\right]$$
$$= \frac{f}{g} + 0$$
$$= \frac{f}{g}$$
$$= \frac{a}{b} - \frac{c}{d}$$

(c) *Is multiplication of rational numbers distributive with respect to subtraction?*
We wish to show that $\frac{a}{b}\left(\frac{c}{d} - \frac{f}{g}\right) = \frac{a}{b}\left(\frac{c}{d}\right) - \frac{a}{b}\left(\frac{f}{g}\right)$.

Recall that

$$\frac{c}{d} - \frac{f}{g} = \frac{h}{k} \iff \frac{c}{d} = \frac{f}{g} + \frac{h}{k}$$

Therefore

$$\frac{a}{b}\left(\frac{c}{d}\right) = \frac{a}{b}\left(\frac{f}{g} + \frac{h}{k}\right)$$
$$= \frac{a}{b}\left(\frac{f}{g}\right) + \frac{a}{b}\left(\frac{h}{k}\right)$$

Hence

$$\frac{a}{b}\left(\frac{c}{d} - \frac{f}{g}\right) = \frac{a}{b}\left(\frac{h}{k}\right)$$
$$= \frac{a}{b}\left(\frac{c}{d}\right) - \frac{a}{b}\left(\frac{f}{g}\right)$$

by the definition of subtraction.

Would we be justified in making this statement if a, b, c, d were any rational numbers, with $a \neq c$?

If the coefficients were rational numbers instead of integers, we could proceed equally well to obtain the solution set; let the equation be

$$\frac{a_1}{b_1}x + \frac{c_1}{d_1} = \frac{a_2}{b_2}x + \frac{c_2}{d_2},$$

where $b_1, d_1, b_2, d_2, \neq 0$, and $\dfrac{a_1}{b_1} \neq \dfrac{a_2}{b_2}$

By use of the additive inverse and the associative property of addition we obtain

$$\frac{a_1}{b_1}x - \frac{a_2}{b_2}x = \frac{c_2}{d_2} - \frac{c_1}{d_1}$$

Hence

$$\left(\frac{a_1}{b_1} - \frac{a_2}{b_2}\right)x = \frac{c_2}{d_2} - \frac{c_1}{d_1}$$

$$\frac{a_1 b_2 - a_2 b_1}{b_1 b_2}x = \frac{c_2 d_1 - c_1 d_2}{d_2 d_1}$$

Therefore

$$x = \frac{c_2 d_1 - c_1 d_2}{d_2 d_1} \times \frac{b_1 b_2}{a_1 b_2 - a_2 b_1},$$

provided $a_1 b_2 - a_2 b_1 \neq 0$, and the solution set is

$$\left\{\left(\frac{b_1 b_2}{d_1 d_2}\right)\left(\frac{c_2 d_1 - c_1 d_2}{a_1 b_2 - a_2 b_1}\right)\right\}$$

Verification:

$$RS = \left(\frac{a_2}{b_2}\right)\left(\frac{b_1 b_2}{d_1 d_2}\right)\left(\frac{c_2 d_1 - c_1 d_2}{a_1 b_2 - a_2 b_1}\right) + \frac{c_2}{d_2}$$

$$= \left(\frac{a_2 b_1}{d_1 d_2}\right)\left(\frac{c_2 d_1 - c_1 d_2}{a_1 b_2 - a_2 b_1}\right) + \left(\frac{c_2}{d_2}\right)\left(\frac{d_1}{d_1}\right)\left(\frac{a_1 b_2 - a_2 b_1}{a_1 b_2 - a_2 b_1}\right)$$

$$= \frac{a_1 b_2 c_2 d_1 - a_2 b_1 c_1 d_2}{d_1 d_2 (a_1 b_2 - a_2 b_1)}$$

$$LS = \left(\frac{a_1}{b_1}\right)\left(\frac{b_1 b_2}{d_1 d_2}\right)\left(\frac{c_2 d_1 - c_1 d_2}{a_1 b_2 - a_2 b_1}\right) + \frac{c_1}{d_1}$$

$$= \left(\frac{a_1 b_2}{d_1 d_2}\right)\left(\frac{c_2 d_1 - c_1 d_2}{a_1 b_2 - a_2 b_1}\right) + \left(\frac{c_1}{d_1}\right)\left(\frac{d_2}{d_2}\right)\left(\frac{a_1 b_2 - a_2 b_1}{a_1 b_2 - a_2 b_1}\right)$$

$$= \frac{a_1 b_2 c_2 d_1 - a_2 b_1 c_1 d_2}{d_1 d_2 (a_1 b_2 - a_2 b_1)}$$

$\therefore$ LS = RS

Alternatively we may multiply both sides of the equation by the least common multiple of the denominators of the coefficients, thereby obtaining an equation with integral coefficients. That the new equation so obtained is equivalent (has the same solution set) to the original equation is demonstrated in Section 6.06.

1. *If $b > 0$, can you show that $\frac{1}{b} > 0$? Similarly, if $b < 0$, can you show that $\frac{1}{b} < 0$?*

   Given that $b > 0$, we know that either (1) $\frac{1}{b} < 0$, (2) $\frac{1}{b} = 0$ or (3) $\frac{1}{b} > 0$.

   Suppose (1) $\frac{1}{b} < 0$. Then $b\left(\frac{1}{b}\right) < 0$. However $b\left(\frac{1}{b}\right) = 1 > 0$. Therefore $\frac{1}{b} \not< 0$.

   Suppose (2) $\frac{1}{b} = 0$. Then $b\left(\frac{1}{b}\right) = 0$. Again we have a contradiction. Therefore $\frac{1}{b} \neq 0$.

   Hence (3) $\frac{1}{b} > 0$. A similar proof establishes the second result.

2. *If $a > b$, can you show that $ac > bc$, if $c > 0$, and $ac < bc$, if $c < 0$, where a, $b, c \in I$? Where $a, b, c \in R'$, the set of rational numbers?*

   $$a > b \iff \exists\, d \in N \ni a = b + d$$

   Therefore, if $c > 0$, $ac = (b + d)c = bc + dc$ and $dc > 0$. Hence $ac > bc$. If $c < 0$, then $-c > 0$ and, by the preceding result, $a(-c) > b(-c)$. Hence, by adding $ac + bc$ to both sides of the inequality we obtain $bc > ac$.

   If a, b, and c are rational numbers the proof is similar. Let

   $$a = \frac{a_1}{a_2}, \quad b = \frac{b_1}{b_2}, \quad c = \frac{c_1}{c_2}$$

Then

$$\frac{a_1}{a_2} > \frac{b_1}{b_2} \iff \exists\, \frac{f}{g} > 0 \ni \frac{a_1}{a_2} = \frac{b_1}{b_2} + \frac{f}{g}$$

Hence, if $\frac{c_1}{c_2} > 0$,

$$\left(\frac{a_1}{a_2}\right)\left(\frac{c_1}{c_2}\right) = \left(\frac{b_1}{b_2}\right)\left(\frac{c_1}{c_2}\right) + \left(\frac{f}{g}\right)\left(\frac{c_1}{c_2}\right)$$

Since $\left(\dfrac{f}{g}\right)\left(\dfrac{c_1}{c_2}\right) > 0$, therefore $\left(\dfrac{a_1}{a_2}\right)\left(\dfrac{c_1}{c_2}\right) > \left(\dfrac{b_1}{b_2}\right)\left(\dfrac{c_1}{c_2}\right)$. This proof is easily adapted to the case in which $\dfrac{c_1}{c_2} < 0$.

3. *If $x \neq 0$ can you show that $x^2 > 0$?*
   Since $x \neq 0$ then either (1) $x > 0$ or (2) $x < 0$. If (1) $x > 0$, then $x \cdot x > x \cdot 0$; that is, $x^2 > 0$. If (2) $x < 0$, then $-x > 0$ and $(-x)(-x) > 0$; that is, $x^2 > 0$.

4. *If a, b, c, d are all positive integers, is it true that*

$$\frac{a}{b} > \frac{c}{d} \iff ad > bc$$

If $\dfrac{a}{b} > \dfrac{c}{d}$, then $(bd)\left(\dfrac{a}{b}\right) > (bd)\left(\dfrac{c}{d}\right)$; that is, $ad > bc$. If $ad > bc$, then $\dfrac{1}{bd} > 0$ since $\dfrac{1}{b} > 0$ and $\dfrac{1}{d} > 0$. Therefore $\dfrac{1}{bd}(ad) > \dfrac{1}{bd}(bc)$, and $\dfrac{a}{b} > \dfrac{c}{d}$.

Section 3.07

If $a \neq 0$, what is the solution set for the open sentence $ax + b = 0$? Is it unique?

It must be verified that $ax + b = 0$ is a true sentence when x is replaced by $-\dfrac{b}{a}$.

Then LS $= a\left(-\dfrac{b}{a}\right) + b$
$= -b + b$
$= 0 =$ RS

To show that this solution is unique, let x' be *any* solution. Then $ax' + b = 0$. Hence $(ax' + b) + (-b) = -b$
Therefore

$$ax' = -b,$$

$$\frac{1}{a}(ax') = \frac{1}{a}(-b)$$

and

$$x' = \frac{-b}{a} = -\frac{b}{a}$$

Hence the unique solution set is $\left\{-\dfrac{b}{a}\right\}$.

1. *Can you show in a similar or alternative manner to that already used that there is no rational number equal to $\sqrt{2}$?*

Assume that $\dfrac{a}{b} = \sqrt{2}$, where a and b are relatively prime integers. Hence $a = b\sqrt{2}$ and $a^2 = 2b^2$. Evidently a^2 is divisible by 2. Is a divisible by 2? We know that a has the form $2m$ or $2m+1$ for some integer m. If $a = 2m + 1$, then $a^2 = (2m + 1)^2 = 4m^2 + 4m + 1 = 2(2m^2 + 2m) + 1$, and a^2 is not divisible by 2. Therefore we must have $a = 2m$. Accordingly $(2m)^2 = 2b^2$; that is, $4m^2 = 2b^2$ or $2m^2 = b^2$. Hence b^2 is divisible by 2 and by an argument identical to the preceding one we obtain $b = 2n$. Thus we have arrived at a contradiction, since a and b have been shown to have the common factor 2. Therefore the assumption $\dfrac{a}{b} = \sqrt{2}$ is invalid.

292   Answers to Questions

Alternative proof. Assume that $\frac{a}{b} = \sqrt{2}$, where a and b are natural numbers. Hence $a^2 = 2b^2$. By virtue of the unique factorization of numbers into prime factors we know that a^2 and b^2 will each possess an even number of prime factors. However, there will be an odd number of prime factors in $2b^2$. It is impossible for the product of an odd number of prime factors to equal the product of an even number of prime factors. Therefore this contradiction shows that the original assumption is invalid.

2. *Where does an argument similar to the foregoing fail when applied to $\sqrt{4}$?*

We assume that $\frac{a}{b} = \sqrt{4}$, where a and b are relatively prime integers. We have $a^2 = 4b^2$ and we observe that a^2 is divisible by 4. We know that a must have one of the forms $4m$, $4m + 1$, $4m + 2$, or $4m + 3$. We check all four cases, one at a time, as follows: $a^2 = (4m)^2 = 16m^2 = 4(4m^2)$; $a^2 = (4m + 1)^2 = 16m^2 + 8m + 1 = 4(4m^2 + 2m) + 1$; $a^2 = (4m + 2)^2 = 16m^2 + 16m + 4 = 4(4m^2 + 4m + 1)$; $a^2 = (4m+3)^2 = 16m^2 + 24m + 9 = 4(4m^2 + 6m + 2) + 1$. Hence a could be $4m$ or $4m + 2$. If $a = 4m+2$, then $a^2 = (4m+2)^2 = 4b^2$; that is $4(4m^2 + 4m + 1) = 4b^2$ and $4m^2 + 4m + 1 = b^2$. Hence $b = \pm(2m+1)$, and it is clear that no contradiction exists with $a = 4m + 2$ and $b = \pm(2m+1)$, provided $m = 0$, in which case $a = 2$ and $b = 1$.

Alternative argument. If we assume that $\frac{a}{b} = \sqrt{4}$ and $a^2 = 4b^2$, then, because $4 = 2 \times 2$, we see that there is an even number of prime factors in $4b^2$ as well as in a^2, hence no contradiction exists.

Is the previous statement reasonable? Check by squaring 1.4, 1.41, 1.414, 1.4142, 1.41421.
$(1.4)^2 = 1.96$; $(1.41)^2 = 1.9881$; $(1.414)^2 = 1.999396$; $(1.4142)^2 = 1.99996164$; $(1.41421)^2 = 1.9999899241$.

Can you obtain a polynomial equation with rational coefficients satisfied by $\sqrt[4]{3 + 2\sqrt[5]{7}}$?
Let $x = \sqrt[4]{3 + 2\sqrt[5]{7}}$. Then $x^4 = 3 + 2\sqrt[5]{7}$. Hence $(x^4 - 3) = 2\sqrt[5]{7}$. Therefore $(x^4 - 3)^5 = 7(32) = 224$. If we expand this expression, we obtain

$$x^{20} - 15x^{16} + 90x^{12} - 270x^8 + 405x^4 - 467 = 0$$

Section 3.09
1. *Can you devise some motivation for definition 1?*

If we assume that all rules of algebra hold in dealing with the equation $a + bi = c + di$, then $a - c = di - bi = (d - b)i$ and $(a - c)^2 = (d - b)^2 i^2$. Since $i^2 = -1$, we have $(a - c)^2 = -(d - b)^2$. This equation can be satisfied only if $a - c = d - b = 0$.

2. *Can you determine real numbers, p and q, such that $(a + bi) - (c + di) = p + qi$?*
We will define $(a + bi) - (c + di) = p + qi$ <=>
$$a + bi = p + qi + c + di$$
$$= p + c + (q + d)i$$

Hence
$$a = p + c \quad \text{and} \quad b = q + d.$$
Therefore
$$p = a - c \quad \text{and} \quad q = b - d.$$

3. *Can you determine real numbers, r and s, such that $(a + bi) \div (c + di) = r + si$, where c and d are not both 0?*

We will define

$$(a+bi) \div (c+di) = r+si \iff$$
$$a+bi = (c+di)(r+si)$$

Hence
$$a+bi = cr - ds + (dr+cs)i$$

Therefore
$$cr - ds = a$$

and
$$dr + cs = b$$

We may solve for r and s as follows (see Chapter 6 for a discussion of this procedure):

$$c^2 r - dcs = ac$$
$$d^2 r + dcs = db$$

When we add corresponding sides of the two equations we obtain

$$(c^2 + d^2)r = ac + db$$

and

$$r = \frac{ac+db}{c^2+d^2}, \quad s = \frac{1}{d}\left[c\left(\frac{ac+db}{c^2+d^2}\right) - a\right]$$

$$= \frac{1}{d}\left[\frac{ac^2 + cdb - ac^2 - ad^2}{c^2+d^2}\right]$$

$$= \frac{1}{d}\left[\frac{cdb - ad^2}{c^2+d^2}\right]$$

$$= \frac{cb - ad}{c^2+d^2}$$

4. (a) Is addition of complex numbers (1) Associative (2) Commutative?

(1) $[(a+bi) + (c+di)] + (f+gi) = [(a+c) + (b+d)i] + (f+gi)$
$= [(a+c) + f] + [(b+d) + g]i$
$= [a + (c+f)] + [b + (d+g)]i$
$= (a+bi) + [(c+f) + (d+g)i]$
$= (a+bi) + [(c+di) + (f+gi)]$

(2) $(a+bi) + (c+di) = (a+c) + (b+d)i$
$= (c+a) + (d+b)i$
$= (c+di) + (a+bi)$

(b) Is multiplication of complex numbers (1) Associative (2) Commutative?

294   Answers to Questions

(1) $[(a+bi)(c+di)](f+gi) = [(ac-bd)+(ad+bc)i](f+gi)$
$= [(ac-bd)f-(ad+bc)g] + [(ad+bc)f+(ac-bd)g]i$
$= [a(cf-dg)-b(cg+df)] + [a(cg+df)+b(cf-dg)]i$
$= (a+bi)[(cf-dg)+(cg+df)i]$
$= (a+bi)[(c+di)(f+gi)]$

(2) $(a+bi)(c+di) = (ac-bd)+(ad+bc)i$
$= (ca-db)+(da+cb)i$
$= (c+di)(a+bi)$

5. *Is the multiplication of complex number distributive with respect to addition?*

$(a+bi)[(c+di)+(f+gi)] = (a+bi)[(c+f)+(d+g)i]$
$= [a(c+f)-b(d+g)] + [a(d+g)+b(c+f)]i$
$= [ac+af-bd-bg] + [ad+ag+bc+bf]i$
$= [(ac-bd)+(af-bg)] + [(ad+bc)i+(ag+bf)i]$
$= [(ac-bd)+(ad+bc)i] + [(af-bg)+(ag+bf)i]$
$= (a+bi)(c+di) + (a+bi)(f+gi)$

6. *What complex number plays the role of the additive identity in this number system?*
$0+0i$, since $(0+0i)+(a+bi) = (0+a)+(0+b)i = a+bi$.
Of the additive inverse? $(-a)+(-b)i$, since $[(-a)+(-b)i]+(a+bi) = [(-a)+a]+[(-b)+b]i = 0+0i$.
Of the multiplicative identity? $1+0i$, since $(1+0i)(a+bi) = (1\cdot a - 0\cdot b)+(1\cdot b+0\cdot a)i = a+bi$.
Of the multiplicative inverse? $\dfrac{a}{a^2+b^2}+\dfrac{(-b)}{a^2+b^2}i$, since $\left(\dfrac{a}{a^2+b^2}+\dfrac{(-b)}{a^2+b^2}i\right)(a+bi) = \dfrac{a^2+b^2}{a^2+b^2}+\dfrac{ab-ab}{a^2+b^2}i = 1+0i$.

7. *Are the eleven properties of a field satisfied by the complex number system?*
    Since closure of the set of complex numbers with respect to addition and multiplication is ensured by definitions (2) and (3), the answers to the foregoing six *questions* complete the verification of the field properties.

1. *Can you prove that both addition and multiplication of such number pairs are commutative and associative?*

$(a,b)+(c,d) = (a+c,b+d) = (c+a,d+b) = (c,d)+(a,b)$
$(a,b)(c,d) = (ac-bd,ad+bc) = (ca-db,da+cb) = (c,d)(a,b)$
$[(a,b)+(c,d)]+(f,g) = (a+c,b+d)+(f,g) = ([a+c]+f,[b+d]+g)$
$= (a+[c+f],b+[d+g]) = (a,b)+(c+f,d+g)$
$= (a,b)+[(c,d)+(f,g)]$
$[(a,b)(c,d)](f,g) = (ac-bd,ad+bc)(f,g) = ([ac-bd]f-[ad+bc]g,$
$[ac-bd]g+[ad+bc]f)$
$= (a[cf-dg]-b[cg+df], a[cg+df]+b[cf-dg])$
$= (a,b)(cf-dg,cg+df) = (a,b)[(c,d)(f,g)]$

2. What is the sum, $(a,b) + (0,0)$?
$$(a,b) + (0,0) = (a+0, b+0) = (a,b)$$

3. What is the sum, $(a,b) + (-a,-b)$?
$$(a,b) + (-a,-b) = (a + [-a], b + [-b]) = (0,0)$$

4. What is the product, $(a,b) \times (1,0)$?
$$(a,b) \times (1,0) = (a \cdot 1 - b \cdot 0, a \cdot 0 + b \cdot 1) = (a,b)$$

5. What is the product $(a,b) \times \left(\dfrac{a}{a^2+b^2}, \dfrac{-b}{a^2+b^2}\right)$ where not both a and b are zero?
$$(a,b) \times \left(\dfrac{a}{a^2+b^2}, \dfrac{-b}{a^2+b^2}\right) = \left(\dfrac{a^2 - b[-b]}{a^2+b^2}, \dfrac{a[-b] + ba}{a^2+b^2}\right) = (1,0)$$

6. Is multiplication distributive with respect to addition?

$(a,b)[(c,d) + (f,g)] = (a,b)(c+f, d+g)$
$\qquad = (a[c+f] - b[d+g], a[d+g] + b[c+f])$
$\qquad = (ac + af - bd - bg, ad + ag + bc + bf)$
$\qquad = ([ac - bd] + [af - bg], [ad + bc] + [ag + bf])$
$\qquad = (ac - bd, ad + bc) + (af - bg, ag + bf)$
$\qquad = (a,b)(c,d) + (a,b)(f,g)$

Can you verify the following statements and describe the significance of each?

(1) $(a,0) + (b,0) = (a+b, 0+0)$
$\qquad = (a+b, 0)$

Hence the set $\{(a,0) | a \in R\}$ is closed under addition.

(2) $(a,0) \times (b,0) = (ab - 0 \cdot 0, a \cdot 0 + 0 \cdot b)$
$\qquad = (ab, 0)$

Hence the set $\{(a,0) | a \in R\}$ is closed under multiplication.

(3) $(a,0) + (0,0) = (a+0, 0+0)$
$\qquad = (a,0)$

Hence $(0,0)$ acts as the additive identity for the set $\{(a,0) | a \in R\}$.

(4) $(a,0) \times (1,0) = (a \cdot 1 - 0 \cdot 0, a \cdot 0 + 0 \cdot 1)$
$\qquad = (a,0)$

Hence $(1,0)$ acts as the multiplicative identity for the set $\{(a,0) | a \in R\}$.

(5) $(a,0) + (-a,0) = (a + [-a], 0+0)$
$\qquad = (0,0)$

Hence $(-a,0)$ acts as the additive inverse for $(a,0)$.

(6) $(a,0) \times \left(\frac{1}{a},0\right) = \left(a \cdot \frac{1}{a} - 0 \cdot 0, \, a \cdot 0 + 0 \cdot \frac{1}{a}\right)$
$= (1,0)$

Hence $\left(\frac{1}{a},0\right)$ acts as the multiplicative inverse for $(a,0)$.

(7) $(a,0) \times (0,0) = (a \cdot 0 - 0 \cdot 0, \, a \cdot 0 + 0 \cdot 0)$
$= (0,0)$

This verifies the fact that $(0,0)$ possesses the multiplicative property for the set $\{(a,0) \mid a \in R\}$ corresponding to that possessed by 0 for the set R.

Can you transform $\frac{a+bi}{c+di}$ into the form $r + si$, where a,b,c,d,r,s, are real numbers, with c and d not both 0?

$$\frac{a+bi}{c+di} = \frac{a+bi}{c+di} \times \frac{c-di}{c-di}$$

$$= \frac{ac+bd-adi+bci}{c^2+d^2}$$

$$= \frac{ac+bd}{c^2+d^2} + \frac{-ad+bc}{c^2+d^2}i$$

CHAPTER 4

Section 4.04

Can you give the proof of Theorem 3?

   Proof. Let m be any given line and P any given point not lying on m. Assume that two or more lines pass through P, parallel to m. On each of these lines there is one more point in addition to P by P3 and these latter points must be distinct by P2. Hence there exist at least three points not on m. Since m has two points there would have to be at least five points in all, contradicting P1. Therefore the original assumption is invalid.

Section 4.07.

1. *Can you give the definition of ray $\overrightarrow{AB}$ in set notation?*

$$\overrightarrow{AB} = \overline{AB} \cup \{C \mid C \in \overleftrightarrow{AB} \text{ and } ABC\} \text{ or } = \{F \mid F \in \overleftrightarrow{AB} \text{ and not } FAB\}$$

2. *How does the ray $\overrightarrow{AB}$ differ from the ray $\overrightarrow{BA}$?*

$$\overrightarrow{BA} = \overline{BA} \cup \{D \mid D \in \overleftrightarrow{AB} \text{ and } DAB\}$$

   The points C in *question 1* do not belong to $\overrightarrow{BA}$ and the points D do not belong to $\overrightarrow{AB}$.

3. *How would you describe $\overrightarrow{AB} \cap \overrightarrow{BA}$? $\overrightarrow{AB} \cup \overrightarrow{BA}$?*

$$\overrightarrow{AB} \cap \overrightarrow{BA} = \overline{AB}; \quad \overrightarrow{AB} \cup \overrightarrow{BA} = \overleftrightarrow{AB}.$$

Is $\angle ABC$ contained in $\triangle ABC$, or, in other words, is $\angle ABC$ a subset of $\triangle ABC$?

   No. Rays $\overrightarrow{BA}$ and $\overrightarrow{BC}$ are subsets of $\angle ABC$ but are not subsets of $\triangle ABC$, for that set is only the union of segments.

Section 4.09

What pattern is exhibited by all points that lie two units to the right of the y-axis?
The first coordinate of all such points must be 2.
Similarly three units below the x-axis?
The second coordinate of all these points must be -3.
What are the equations of the two lines in the previous question?

$$x - 2 = 0; \qquad y + 3 = 0$$

CHAPTER 5

Section 5.03

1. *How many significant digits are indicated in each of the following measures?*

    583, 3; 50083, 5; 583.0, 4; 2.18, 3; 2.0018, 5; 0.0015, 2; 0.001500, 4; 0.001005, 4; 0.0010050, 5; 200.00, 5

2. *How would you express the measure 39000 with the proper precision if it is known to have*
    (a) 5 significant digits: 3.9000×10^4
    (b) 4 significant digits: 3.900×10^4
    (c) 3 significant digits: 3.90×10^4
    (d) 2 significant digits: 3.9×10^4 or 39000

Can you write x to the correct number of significant digits, given the following information?
  (a) $197.5 \leq x < 198.5$: 198
  (b) $2.395 \leq x < 2.405$: 2.40
  (c) $2.305 \leq x < 2.315$: 2.31
  (d) $2.35 \leq x < 2.45$: 2.4
  (e) $499.5 \leq x < 500.5$: 5.00×10^2
  (f) $495 \leq x < 505$: 5.0×10^2
  (g) $450 \leq x < 550$: 5×10^2 or 500

Section 5.04

1. *Round the following to three significant digits:* 103499, 103000; 2.3042, 2.30; 0.0097952, 0.00980
2. *Round the following to the nearest tenth:* 10.35, 10.4; 2.3499, 2.3; 979.99, 980.0

Section 5.06

Can you verify the preceding results by reversing the order of the factors in each of the products?

```
       483.26              483.26
       .193 52             .193 52
       966 52              483 26
       24163 0             434 93
       144978              14 50
       434934              2 42
       48326               10
       9352047 52          935 21
       93.520              93.521
```

298   Answers to Questions

Can you verify by short multiplication that $1.872 \times 12.63 = 23.64$ with approximately four-digit accuracy?

$$
\begin{array}{r}
1.8\not{7}\not{2} \\
\underline{12.63} \\
1\,872 \\
374 \\
112 \\
\underline{6} \\
23.64
\end{array}
$$

CHAPTER 6

Section 6.02

How would the graph differ if the universe were the set of integers?

There would be an infinite number of ordered pairs (x,y) satisfying the equation; hence the points of the graph would extend indefinitely in both directions.

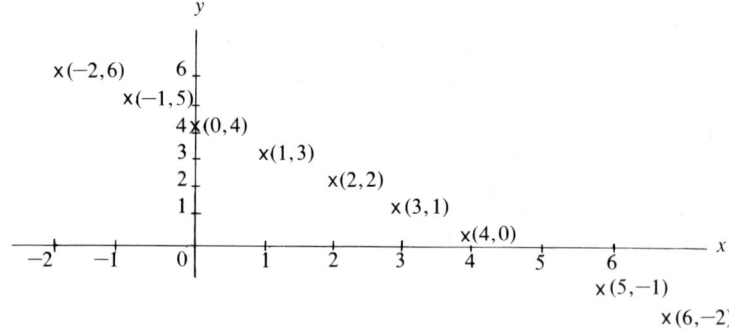

Section 6.03

Can you verify that $x = \dfrac{59}{31}$ and $y = -\dfrac{8}{31}$ satisfy both equations (1) and (2) above?

$$\text{LS} = 3\left(\frac{59}{31}\right) - 5\left(-\frac{8}{31}\right) = \frac{177}{31} + \frac{40}{31}$$

$$= \frac{217}{31}$$

$$= 7 = \text{RS}$$

$$\text{LS} = 5\left(\frac{59}{31}\right) + 2\left(-\frac{8}{31}\right) = \frac{295}{31} - \frac{16}{31}$$

$$= \frac{279}{31}$$

$$= 9 = \text{RS}$$

1. *Can you verify that* $x = \dfrac{df - bg}{ad - bc}$ *and* $y = \dfrac{ag - cf}{ad - bc}$ *are indeed the solution set of these two equations?*

$$LS = a\left(\dfrac{df - bg}{ad - bc}\right) + b\left(\dfrac{ag - cf}{ad - bc}\right)$$

$$= \dfrac{adf - abg + bag - bcf}{ad - bc}$$

$$= \dfrac{adf - bcf}{ad - bc} = \dfrac{(ad - bc)f}{ad - bc}$$

$$= f = RS$$

$$LS = c\left(\dfrac{df - bg}{ad - bc}\right) + d\left(\dfrac{ag - cf}{ad - bc}\right)$$

$$= \dfrac{cdf - cbg + dag - dcf}{ad - bc}$$

$$= \dfrac{dag - cbg}{ad - bc} = \dfrac{(ad - bc)g}{ad - bc}$$

$$= g = RS$$

2. *What happens if* $a = 0$?

Since $ad - bc \neq 0$, therefore $bc \neq 0$; hence $b \neq 0$ and $c \neq 0$. From the equation $by = f$ we obtain $y = \dfrac{f}{b}$. Substitution of this result in $cx + dy = g$ gives

$$cx = g - \dfrac{df}{b} = \dfrac{gb - df}{b}$$

Hence solution is $x = \dfrac{gb - df}{bc}$, $y = \dfrac{f}{b}$. In the example $y = \tfrac{7}{2}$ and $x = \tfrac{1}{3}(11 - 14) = -\tfrac{3}{3} = -1$.

3. *What happens if* $ad - bc = 0$?

In this case we no longer have a unique solution. We may have the empty set or an infinite set as the solution set. These two situations are illustrated in the examples:

(a) $\qquad\qquad\qquad 3x + 4y = 5$
$\qquad\qquad\qquad\quad\; 6x + 8y = 9$

These two lines have the same slope, $-\tfrac{3}{4}$, but are distinct lines, for the first passes through $(0, \tfrac{5}{4})$ and the second through $(0, \tfrac{9}{8})$. Hence there is no point common to both lines and the empty set is the solution set for the two simultaneous equations.

(b) $\qquad\qquad\qquad 3x + 4y = 5$
$\qquad\qquad\qquad\quad\; 6x + 8y = 10$

Since the second equation is obtained by multiplying both sides of the first equation by 2, the two equations are equivalent and have the same solution set. Hence each point satisfying either equation is a common solution of the two equations.

4. *What happens if $a = 0$ and $ad - bc = 0$?*

Since $a = 0$, then $bc = 0$ and either $b = 0$ or $c = 0$. If $b = 0$, our first equation is not true, unless $f = 0$. Hence we will assume $b \neq 0$, from which it follows that $c = 0$. In order to have two equations we must also have $d \neq 0$. In this situation we again have either the empty set or an infinite set as the solution set. Here, however, the lines in both cases are parallel to the x-axis.

Can you obtain $y = \dfrac{ag - cf}{ad - bc}$ by eliminating the variable x in the manner described?

$$ax + by = f$$
$$cx + dy = g$$
$$-acx - bcy = -cf$$
$$acx + ady = ag$$
$$\therefore (ad - bc)y = ag - cf$$

and
$$y = \frac{ag - cf}{ad - bc}$$

In the language of geometry what can we say about the point $\left(\dfrac{df - bg}{ad - bc}, \dfrac{ag - cf}{ad - bc}\right)$?

This ordered pair of numbers is the intersection of the sets of points represented by the equations $ax + by = f$ and $cx + dy = g$.

Can you obtain the solution set for the equations

$$3x + y - z = -3$$
$$x + 2y + z = 0$$
$$2x - 4y - 3z = 5$$

by working only with the augmented matrix?

$$\begin{pmatrix} 1 & 2 & 1 & 0 \\ 3 & 1 & -1 & -3 \\ 2 & -4 & -3 & 5 \end{pmatrix} \rightsquigarrow \begin{pmatrix} 1 & 2 & 1 & 0 \\ 0 & -5 & -4 & -3 \\ 0 & -8 & -5 & 5 \end{pmatrix} \rightsquigarrow \begin{pmatrix} 1 & 2 & 1 & 0 \\ 0 & -5 & -4 & -3 \\ 0 & -3 & -1 & 8 \end{pmatrix}$$

$$\rightsquigarrow \begin{pmatrix} 1 & 2 & 1 & 0 \\ 0 & 1 & -2 & -19 \\ 0 & -3 & -1 & 8 \end{pmatrix} \rightsquigarrow \begin{pmatrix} 1 & 2 & 1 & 0 \\ 0 & 1 & -2 & -19 \\ 0 & 0 & -7 & -49 \end{pmatrix} \rightsquigarrow \begin{pmatrix} 1 & 2 & 1 & 0 \\ 0 & 1 & -2 & -19 \\ 0 & 0 & 1 & 7 \end{pmatrix}$$

$$\rightsquigarrow \begin{pmatrix} 1 & 2 & 0 & -7 \\ 0 & 1 & 0 & -5 \\ 0 & 0 & 1 & 7 \end{pmatrix} \rightsquigarrow \begin{pmatrix} 1 & 0 & 0 & 3 \\ 0 & 1 & 0 & -5 \\ 0 & 0 & 1 & 7 \end{pmatrix}$$ which represents

$$1 \cdot x + 0 \cdot y + 0 \cdot z = 3 \qquad \text{hence } x = 3$$
$$0 \cdot x + 1 \cdot y + 0 \cdot z = -5 \qquad y = -5$$
$$0 \cdot x + 0 \cdot y + 1 \cdot z = 7 \qquad z = 7$$

Section 6.04

What is the solution set for the sentence $ax^2 + b = 0$, $(a \neq 0)$?

$$ax^2 + b = 0$$
$$ax^2 = -b$$
$$x^2 = -\frac{b}{a}$$
$$x = \pm\sqrt{-\frac{b}{a}}$$

Hence solution set is $\left\{i\sqrt{\frac{b}{a}}, -i\sqrt{\frac{b}{a}}\right\}$.

What is the solution set for the sentence, $x^2 + (a+b)x + ab = 0$?

$$x^2 + (a+b)x + ab = 0$$
$$(x+a)(x+b) = 0$$

Hence
$$x + a = 0 \quad \text{or} \quad x + b = 0$$

Therefore, solution set is $\{-a, -b\}$.

Can you factor $2x^2 - 5x - 12$?

$$2x^2 - 5x - 12 = (2x + 3)(x - 4)$$

Can you carry through this procedure for the equation $ax^2 + bx + c = 0$, if $a \neq 0$?

$$ax^2 + bx + c = 0$$
$$x^2 + \frac{b}{a}x + \frac{c}{a} = 0$$
$$x^2 + \frac{b}{a}x + \frac{b^2}{4a^2} = -\frac{c}{a} + \frac{b^2}{4a^2}$$
$$\left(x + \frac{b}{2a}\right)^2 = \frac{-4ac + b^2}{4a^2} = \frac{b^2 - 4ac}{4a^2}$$
$$\therefore \left|x + \frac{b}{2a}\right| = \sqrt{\frac{b^2 - 4ac}{4a^2}}$$
$$\therefore x + \frac{b}{2a} = \pm\frac{\sqrt{b^2 - 4ac}}{2a}$$

Hence

$$x = \frac{-b}{2a} \pm \frac{\sqrt{b^2 - 4ac}}{2a}$$
$$= \frac{-b \pm \sqrt{b^2 - 4ac}}{2a}$$

Therefore the solution set is

$$\left\{\frac{-b + \sqrt{b^2 - 4ac}}{2a}, \frac{-b - \sqrt{b^2 - 4ac}}{2a}\right\}$$

1. Can you determine the point(s) of intersection of the parabola $y = 2x^2 - 5x + \frac{25}{8}$ and the x-axis?

Answers to Questions

We wish to find the solution set for the equations

$$y = 2x^2 - 5x + \frac{25}{8}$$

and

$$y = 0$$

Hence we have $2x^2 - 5x + \frac{25}{8} = 0$. We may factor the left side as $\left(2x - \frac{5}{2}\right)\left(x - \frac{5}{4}\right) = 0$ or we may proceed as follows:

$$x^2 - \frac{5}{2}x + \frac{25}{16} = -\frac{25}{16} + \frac{25}{16}$$

$$\left(x - \frac{5}{4}\right)^2 = 0 \qquad \therefore x = \frac{5}{4}$$

Hence by either procedure the solution set is $\left\{\left(\frac{5}{4}, 0\right)\right\}$, in which case we say that the parabola is tangent to the x-axis.

2. *What is the solution set of the sentence $2x^2 - 5x + 4 = 0$?*

$$2x^2 - 5x + 4 = 0$$

$$x^2 - \frac{5}{2}x + \frac{25}{16} = -2 + \frac{25}{16}$$

$$\left(x - \frac{5}{4}\right)^2 = \frac{-32 + 25}{16}$$

$$\therefore \left|x - \frac{5}{4}\right| = \sqrt{\frac{-7}{16}}$$

$$\therefore x - \frac{5}{4} = \pm\frac{\sqrt{-7}}{4}$$

$$= \pm\frac{i\sqrt{7}}{4}$$

Hence solution set is

$$\left\{\frac{5 + i\sqrt{7}}{4}, \frac{5 - i\sqrt{7}}{4}\right\}$$

Can you fill in the four vacant spaces in the table at the right with the proper adjectives, when a, b, and c are assumed to be real numbers?

Discriminant	Roots Real or Nonreal	Roots Equal or Unequal
Negative	Nonreal	Unequal
Zero	Real	Equal
Positive	Real	Unequal

1. Can you write a quadratic equation for which the sum and product of the roots are $\frac{2}{3}$ and $-\frac{5}{3}$, respectively?

We want $-\frac{b}{a} = \frac{2}{3}$ and $\frac{c}{a} = -\frac{5}{3}$. These conditions are satisfied if $a = 3, b = -2$, and $c = -5$.
Hence a suitable equation is $3x^2 - 2x - 5 = 0$.

2. Can you find in two ways a quadratic equation whose roots are $-\frac{2}{3}$ and $\frac{3}{4}$?

One such equation is $\left(x + \frac{2}{3}\right)\left(x - \frac{3}{4}\right) = 0$. If we multiply both sides by 12 the equation may be rewritten as $(3x + 2)(4x - 3) = 0$ or

$$12x^2 - x - 6 = 0$$

Alternatively, the sum of the roots
$$= -\frac{2}{3} + \frac{3}{4}$$
$$= -\frac{8}{12} + \frac{9}{12}$$
$$= \frac{1}{12} = -\frac{b}{a}$$

and the product of the roots
$$= \left(-\frac{2}{3}\right)\left(\frac{3}{4}\right)$$
$$= -\frac{6}{12} = \frac{c}{a}$$

These conditions are satisfied by $a = 12, b = -1, c = -6$ and an equation with the proper roots is $12x^2 - x - 6 = 0$.

3. What value should be given to a in the quadratic equation $ax^2 + 6x - 4 = 0$ in order that one of the roots will be twice the other?

Let us call one root r and the other root $2r$. Then the sum of the roots $= 3r = -\frac{6}{a}$ and the product of the roots $= 2r^2 = -\frac{4}{a}$. Hence we have $r = -\frac{2}{a}$ and $r^2 = -\frac{2}{a}$.
Since $r = r^2$, then $r^2 - r = 0$ and $r(r - 1) = 0$ and r is either 0 or 1. Since the sum of the roots $\neq 0, r \neq 0$; hence $r = 1$ and $a = -2$.

Section 6.07

Can you employ the Principle of Mathematical Induction to verify this result for the sum of n terms of the arithmetic progression?

Let $P(n)$ represent the statement $S_n = \frac{n}{2}[2a_1 + (n - 1)d]$, where

$$S_n = a_1 + (a_1 + d) + (a_1 + 2d) + \cdots + [a_1 + (n - 1)d]$$

Let S be the set of numbers n for which $P(n)$ is true. If $n = 1$, then $S_1 = a_1 = \frac{1}{2}(2a_1)$, hence $1 \in S$. Assume that $k \in S$. Therefore

$$a_1 + (a_1 + d) + (a_1 + 2d) + \cdots + [a_1 + (k - 1)d] = \frac{k}{2}[2a_1 + (k - 1)d]$$

We wish to prove that $k + 1 \in S$, that is, that
$$a_1 + (a_1 + d) + (a_1 + 2d) + \cdots + [a_1 + (k - 1)d] + (a_1 + kd) = \frac{k + 1}{2}(2a_1 + kd)$$

304 Answers to Questions

The left side of this equation $= [a_1 + (a_1 + d) + \cdots + a_1(k-1)d] + (a_1 + kd)$

$$= \frac{k}{2}[2a_1 + (k-1)d] + (a_1 + kd) \quad \text{(by our assumption)}$$

$$= ka_1 + \frac{k(k-1)d}{2} + a_1 + kd$$

$$= ka_1 + a_1 + \frac{k(k-1)d}{2} + \frac{2kd}{2}$$

$$= (k+1)a_1 + \frac{k}{2}d(k-1+2)$$

$$= (k+1)\left(a_1 + \frac{k}{2}d\right)$$

$$= \left(\frac{k+1}{2}\right)(2a_1 + kd) = \text{RS}$$

Hence $k+1 \in S$. Therefore we may apply the Principle of Mathematical Induction and conclude that $P(n)$ is true for all natural numbers n; that is, S contains all the natural numbers.

Why did we insert the condition $r \neq 1$ in our discussion of the geometric progression and not require $d \neq 0$ in considering the arithmetic progression?

We wish to have $r \neq 1$, for otherwise the sequence is indistinguishable from the trivial case of the arithmetic progression. There was, however, no reason to eliminate the trivial case in the treatment of the arithmetic progression.

Can you establish the validity of the sum of n terms of the geometric progression by use of the Principle of Mathematical Induction?

Let $P(n)$ represent the statement $S_n = \dfrac{a_1(r^n - 1)}{r - 1}$, where

$$S_n = a_1 + a_1 r + a_1 r^2 + \cdots a_1 r^{n-1}$$

Let S be the set of numbers n for which $P(n)$ is true. When $n = 1$, $S_1 = a_1 = \dfrac{a_1(r-1)}{r-1}$.

Hence $1 \in S$. Assume that $k \in S$. It follows that $a_1 + a_1 r + \cdots a_1 r^{k-1} = \dfrac{a_1(r^k - 1)}{r - 1}$

We wish to prove that $k + 1 \in S$. Hence we must show that

$$a_1 + a_1 r + \cdots + a_1 r^{k-1} + a_1 r^k = a_1 \frac{(r^{k+1} - 1)}{r - 1}$$

The left side of this equation $= (a_1 + a_1 r + \cdots + a_1 r^{k+1}) + a_1 r^k$

$$= a_1 \frac{(r^k - 1)}{r - 1} + a_1 r^k \frac{(r-1)}{(r-1)} \quad \text{(by our assumption)}$$

$$= \frac{a_1 r^k - a_1 + a_1 r^{k+1} - a_1 r^k}{r - 1}$$

$$= \frac{a_1 r^{k+1} - a_1}{r - 1}$$

$$= \frac{a_1(r^{k+1} - 1)}{r - 1} = \text{RS}$$

Hence we have shown that $k + 1 \in S$. The Principle of Mathematical Induction may now be applied and we conclude that S contains all the natural numbers and $P(n)$ is true for all natural numbers n.

How large must n be to make $(0.5)^n < 0.01$? or $(0.5)^n < 0.0001$?

Since $\dfrac{1}{2^6} = \dfrac{1}{64}$ and $\dfrac{1}{2^7} = \dfrac{1}{128} < \dfrac{1}{100}$, we know that $(0.5)^n < 0.01$ for $n \geq 7$ and for no smaller values of n.

Since $\dfrac{1}{2^{13}} = \dfrac{1}{8192}$ and $\dfrac{1}{2^{14}} = \dfrac{1}{16384} < \dfrac{1}{10000}$, we know that $(0.5)^n < 0.0001$ for $n \geq 14$ and for no smaller values of n.

What is the "sum" of an infinite number of terms of the following geometric progression:

$$1, \tfrac{1}{2}, \tfrac{1}{4}, \tfrac{1}{8}, \tfrac{1}{16}, \ldots ?$$

Since $r = \tfrac{1}{2} < 1$, we are able to speak of the "sum" of an infinite number of terms of this sequence. Let this "sum" be represented by S. Therefore $S = \dfrac{a_1}{1-r} = \dfrac{1}{1-\tfrac{1}{2}} = \dfrac{1}{\tfrac{1}{2}} = 2$.

Section 6.08

Can you foresee what form the binomial expansion might assume when n is other than a positive integer?

If we examine the coefficient of the general term

$$\frac{n(n-1)\cdots(n-r+1)}{1\cdot 2\cdot 3\cdots r} a^{n-r}x^r$$

of the binomial expansion, when n is *not* a positive integer, we see that it will never become zero for any value of r, for r is a positive integer. Hence for such values of n the number of terms becomes infinitely great and the expression on the right in the statement of the Binomial Theorem may or may not have a limiting value as $r \to \infty$, depending on the relative values of a and x.

Section 6.09

Can you prove that $n! = n[(n-1)!]$ provided $n > 1$?

Since $n! = n[(n-1)(n-2)\cdots 3.2.1]$ and $(n-1)! = (n-1)(n-2)\cdots 3.2.1$, $n! = n[(n-1)!]$ provided $n > 1$.

1. *Can you employ the Principle of Mathematical Induction to prove that the number of permutations of n different objects is $n!$?*

Let P_n represent the number of permutations of n objects. Let $P(n)$ stand for the statement that $P_n = n!$ Let S be the set of numbers n for which $P(n)$ is true. When $n = 1, P_1 = 1$ and $1! = 1$, therefore $1 \in S$.

Assume that $k \in S$; that is, $P_k = k!$ We wish to prove that $P_{k+1} = (k+1)!$ In arriving at P_{k+1}, let us temporarily set aside one particular object. We know the remaining k objects can be arranged in $k!$ permutations. There are then $k+1$ different positions in each of the $k!$ permutations in which the $k+1$(st) object may be placed, each one producing a different permutation of the $k+1$ objects. Altogether there are $(k+1)[k!] = (k+1)!$ permutations. Hence $k+1 \in S$, and by the Principle of Mathematical Induction we may assert that $P_n = n!$ for all natural numbers n.

2. Can you show that the number of permutations of r different objects, taken s at a time, where $s \leq r$, is $\dfrac{r!}{(r-s)!}$?

Let us consider s positions in a line to be filled from the set of r objects. Consider any one of the s positions. It can be filled in r different ways, that is, by any one of the r objects. When it has been filled in r ways, any other position can be filled in $r-1$ ways. Hence two positions can be filled in $r(r-1)$ ways. We continue this procedure and find that the s positions can be filled in $r(r-1)(r-2)\cdots[r-(s-1)]$ ways. This number may be written as

$$r(r-1)(r-2)\cdots(r-s+1)\dfrac{(r-s)!}{(r-s)!} = \dfrac{r!}{(r-s)!}$$

What is the total number of permutations of $p+q+r$ objects of which p are alike of one kind, q alike of another kind, and r alike of a third kind?

Let P represent the total number of permutations of the $p+q+r$ objects. Let us consider any one of these permutations and imagine that distinguishing marks are placed on each of the p objects which are alike. Then these p objects, now distinct from one another, may be permuted among themselves in the various positions they occupy in all the permutations in $p!$ ways. Hence the total number of permutations is now $(p!)P$. Again consider one of these permutations and similarly place a distinguishing mark on each of the q like objects and permute them in the positions they occupy in all the permutations. We now have altogether $(p!)(q!)P$ permutations. Do the same with the r like objects. Finally we obtain $(p!)(q!)(r!)P$ permutations, but by now we have $p+q+r$ distinct objects permuted in all possible ways. Hence $(p!)(q!)(r!)P = (p+q+r)!$.
Therefore

$$P = \dfrac{(p+q+r)!}{(p!)(q!)(r!)}$$

Section 6.10

1. *Should we expect that $C_{r,s} = C_{r,r-s}$? Why?*

We must have $C_{r,s} = C_{r,r-s}$, for any selection of s objects from r objects automatically leaves $r-s$ objects unselected, and this remaining set thereby constitutes a selection in itself. This may also be seen algebraically as follows:

$$C_{r,r-s} = \dfrac{r!}{(r-s)![r-(r-s)]!}$$

$$= \dfrac{r!}{(r-s)!s!} = C_{r,s}$$

2. Can you show that

$$C_{r,s} = C_{r-1,s} + C_{r-1,s-1}$$

(1) $\mathrm{LS} = \dfrac{r!}{s!(r-s)!}$; $\mathrm{RS} = \dfrac{(r-1)!}{s!(r-1-s)!} + \dfrac{(r-1)!}{(s-1)!(r-1-s+1)!}$

$$= \dfrac{(r-1)!(r-s)}{s!(r-s-1)!(r-s)} + \dfrac{(r-1)!s}{(s-1)!s(r-s)!}$$

$$= \dfrac{(r-1)!(r-s+s)}{s!(r-s)!} = \dfrac{r!}{s!(r-s)!} = \mathrm{LS}$$

(2) Picture the r objects as points within a circle and separate one of the objects from the remaining $r-1$ objects. Now we have two methods of making our selections.

We may decide not to use the isolated object, hence make our selection in $C_{r-1,s}$ ways or we may decide to include the isolated object every time, hence make our selection in $C_{r-1,s-1}$ ways. Therefore $C_{r,s} = C_{r-1,s} + C_{r-1,s-1}$.

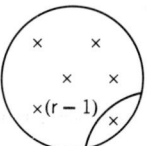

3. *How many diagonals are there in an n-sided regular polygon?*
Required number $= C_{n,2} -$ (number of sides of the polygon)
$$= \frac{n(n-1)}{1 \cdot 2} - n$$
$$= \frac{n^2 - n - 2n}{1 \cdot 2}$$
$$= \frac{n(n-3)}{1 \cdot 2}$$

Section 6.11

When two coins are tossed what is the probability of at least one "head" showing?
Required probability = probability of two heads + probability of one head and one tail.
$$= \left(\frac{1}{2}\right)^2 + 2\left(\frac{1}{2}\right)^2$$
$$= \frac{3}{4}$$

Can you determine the probability of obtaining at least 15 in a single throw of three dice?

A throw of at least 15 may be obtained in the following ways with indicated corresponding probability:

$4,5,6: \dfrac{6}{6^3}$ (4,5,6 may be permuted in 3! ways)

$3,6,6: \dfrac{3}{6^3}$ (3,6,6 may be permuted in 3 ways)

$5,5,5: \dfrac{1}{6^3}$

$4,6,6: \dfrac{3}{6^3}$ (4,6,6 may be permuted in 3 ways)

$5,5,6: \dfrac{3}{6^3}$ (5,5,6 may be permuted in 3 ways)

$5,6,6: \dfrac{3}{6^3}$ (5,6,6 may be permuted in 3 ways)

$6,6,6: \dfrac{1}{6^3}$

Hence the probability of throwing at least 15 is $\dfrac{20}{216}$.

308   Answers to Questions

What is the probability in the foregoing example of drawing one white and two red marbles?

$$\text{Required probability} = 3\left(\frac{10}{15}\right)\left(\frac{5}{14}\right)\left(\frac{4}{13}\right)$$

$$= \frac{20}{91}$$

(Note that there are three permutations of white, red, red).

CHAPTER 7

Section 7.03

How would you establish the preceding statement?

Since a natural number corresponds to every positive fraction, this label or coordinate will merely be reduced by discarding all the fractions equal to some fraction $\frac{p}{q}$ and retaining only $\frac{p}{q}$. It follows that each fraction must still have a particular natural number corresponding to it under this procedure.

Section 7.04

What result do you obtain for N if you write
$N = 1 + \frac{1}{2} + \frac{1}{4}(1 + \frac{1}{2} + \frac{1}{4} + \cdots)?$
$N = 1 + \frac{1}{2} + \frac{1}{4}N$
$\therefore \frac{3}{4}N = \frac{3}{2}$
and $N = 2$,

which has been shown to be correct.

Can you verify by long division that each of the previously obtained fractions has the given repeating decimal as quotient?

```
       .3̇5̇                    2.783̇54̇
  99)350              99900)278076
     297                    199800
     ───                    ──────
     530                    782760
     495                    699300
     ───                    ──────
    →350                    834600
                            799200
                            ──────
                          ┌→354000
                            299700
                            ──────
                            543000
                            499500
                            ──────
                            435000
                            399600
                            ──────
                          └→354000
```

Answers to Questions   309

Can you verify that $.\dot{3}8461\dot{5}$ is equal to $\frac{5}{13}$ by evaluating the repeating decimal fraction?
Let $N = .\dot{3}8461\dot{5}$ (we assume convergence).
Then
$$1{,}000{,}000\ N = 384615.\dot{3}8461\dot{5} = 384615 + N$$
Hence
$$999{,}999\ N = 384615$$
and
$$N = \frac{384615}{999999}$$
$$= \frac{5(76923)}{13(76923)}$$
$$= \frac{5}{13}$$

What result do you obtain by treating $.\dot{9}$ as an infinite geometric progression?
$$.\dot{9} = .9 + .09 + .009 + \cdots$$
Hence
$$.\dot{9} = \frac{.9}{1 - .1} \quad \text{(see Section 6.07)}$$
$$= \frac{.9}{.9}$$
$$= 1$$

Section 7.05
Where does the preceding argument fail when applied to the rational numbers between 0 and 1 when these have been represented as nonterminating decimal fractions?
  We cannot say whether or not the specially constructed number is rational; hence it is not possible to argue that the original assumption has been contradicted.

Section 7.06
Can you prove rules (2), (3), (4), and (5)?
Let $x = \dfrac{m}{n}$ and $y = \dfrac{k}{q}$ where $n > 0$ and $q > 0$; m, n, p, q, integers.

(2) $\therefore b^x \cdot b^y = b^{m/n} \cdot b^{p/q} = b^{mq/nq} \cdot b^{np/nq}$
$$= \sqrt[nq]{b^{mq}} \cdot \sqrt[nq]{b^{np}} = \sqrt[nq]{b^{mq} \cdot b^{np}}$$
$$= \sqrt[nq]{b^{mq+np}} = b^{(mq+np)/nq}$$
$$= b^{m/n + p/q} = b^{x+y}$$

(3) $(ab)^x = (ab)^{m/n} = \sqrt[n]{(ab)^m}$
$$= \sqrt[n]{a^m b^m} = \sqrt[n]{a^m} \cdot \sqrt[n]{b^m}$$
$$= a^{m/n} \cdot b^{m/n} = a^x \cdot b^x$$

(4) We first establish the simpler result, $\sqrt[q]{\sqrt[n]{b}} = \sqrt[qn]{b}$. Let $r = \sqrt[q]{\sqrt[n]{b}}$. Hence $r^q = \sqrt[n]{b}$ and $(r^q)^n = r^{qn} = b$. Therefore $r = \sqrt[q]{\sqrt[n]{b}} = \sqrt[qn]{b}$, by definition, since r is the principal root.
$$(b^x)^y = (b^{m/n})^{p/q} = (\sqrt[n]{b^m})^{p/q}$$
$$= \left(\sqrt[q]{\sqrt[n]{b^m}}\right)^p = (\sqrt[qn]{b^m})^p$$
$$= \sqrt[qn]{(b^m)^p} = \sqrt[qn]{b^{mp}}$$
$$= b^{mp/qn} = b^{m/n \cdot p/q} = b^{xy} \quad \text{or} \quad |b^{xy}|$$

(5) $\left(\dfrac{a}{b}\right)^x = \left(\dfrac{a}{b}\right)^{m/n} = \sqrt[n]{\left(\dfrac{a}{b}\right)^m}$
$= \sqrt[n]{\dfrac{a^m}{b^m}} = \dfrac{\sqrt[n]{a^m}}{\sqrt[n]{b^m}}$
$= \dfrac{a^{m/n}}{b^{m/n}} = \dfrac{a^x}{b^x}$

CHAPTER 8

Section 8.02

Why must two intersecting lines, described in the preceding sentence, lie in the same plane?

We are given two lines r and s, intersecting at A. We may accept the fact that the line r and any point $B(\neq A)$ on s lie in a plane p. However, since A and B lie in p and A and B are points of s, every point of s lies in p. Hence both r and s lie in p.

Can you demonstrate that $\overleftrightarrow{SP}$ is parallel to m if $\angle QPS \cong \angle PQG$?

Suppose that $\overleftrightarrow{SP}$ and m have a common point T on, say the side of k containing G. Then $\angle QPS$ is an exterior angle of $\triangle PQT$ and therefore $m(\angle QPS) > m(\angle PQG)$. This contradicts our hypothesis that the two angles are congruent. Hence our original assumption is invalid and $\overleftrightarrow{SP}$ and m must be parallel.

Section 8.05

1. *Can you deduce that the area of any triangular region is one half the product of the lengths of its base and its altitude?*

In the diagram at the left consider the right triangles $\triangle BDA$ and $\triangle ADC$. Hence area of $\triangle BDA = \tfrac{1}{2}AD \cdot BD$ and area of $\triangle ADC = \tfrac{1}{2}AD \cdot DC$. Since areas are additive, we have

$$\begin{aligned}\text{area of } \triangle ABC &= \text{area of } \triangle BDA + \text{area of } \triangle ADC\\ &= \tfrac{1}{2}AD \cdot BD + \tfrac{1}{2}AD \cdot DC\\ &= \tfrac{1}{2}AD(BD + DC)\\ &= \tfrac{1}{2}AD \cdot BC\end{aligned}$$

The result is already known for the middle triangle, for it is a right triangle.

In the diagram at the right we have area of $\triangle ADB + $ area of $\triangle ABC = $ area of $\triangle ADC$. Hence

$$\begin{aligned}\text{area of } \triangle ABC &= \text{area of } \triangle ADC - \text{area of } \triangle ADB\\ &= \tfrac{1}{2}AD \cdot DC - \tfrac{1}{2}AD \cdot DB\\ &= \tfrac{1}{2}AD(DC - DB)\\ &= \tfrac{1}{2}AD \cdot BC\end{aligned}$$

2. *Can you show that the area of a parallelogram is equal to the area of the rectangle on the same base and having the same altitude?*

Consider the parallelogram $ABCD$ and the rectangle $ABC'D'$, where $\overleftrightarrow{CD} = \overleftrightarrow{C'D'}$. Hence $\overline{BC'}$ represents the altitude of the parallelogram as well as of the rectangle with respect to the common side $\overline{AB}$. The diagonal $\overline{AC}$ separates the parallelogram into congruent triangles, one of which is $\triangle ABC$. The diagonal $\overline{AC'}$ separates the rectangle into congruent right triangles, one of which is $\triangle ABC'$. Both triangles have the same base $\overline{AB}$ and the same altitude $\overline{BC'}$. Hence

$$\text{area of } \triangle ABC = \tfrac{1}{2}AB \cdot BC' = \text{area of } \triangle ABC'$$

Answers to Questions   311

Therefore area of parallelogram $ABCD$ = 2 (area of $\triangle ABC$)
$\qquad\qquad\qquad\qquad\qquad\qquad$ = 2 (area of $\triangle ABC'$)
$\qquad\qquad\qquad\qquad\qquad\qquad$ = area of rectangle $ABC'D'$

Section 8.07

In the second figure at the right how are we certain that the inner quadrilateral is truly a square?

The four shaded triangles are known to be congruent. At every vertex of the inner quadrilateral there are three angles, the sum of whose measures is 180. Because two of these three angles are shaded angles, the sum of whose measures is 90 (since in each triangle the third shaded angle is a right angle), the remaining unshaded angle in each case must have measure 90. Hence the inner quadrilateral, being already a rhombus (four equal sides), must also be a square.

Section 8.08

1. *In the previous construction can you prove*
   (a) *that the circles in question must intersect?*

   The existence of $\angle BAC \cong \angle D$ is ensured by postulate as well as points B and C such that $\overline{AB} \cong \overline{DE}$ and $\overline{AC} \cong \overline{DF}$. Hence $\triangle EDF \cong \triangle BAC$ by (SAS); therefore we know that $\overline{EF} \cong \overline{BC}$ which guarantees that the circle, center A and radius DE, and the circle, center C and radius FE, must intersect at B (as well as at another point below $\overleftrightarrow{AC}$).

   (b) *if they intersect at B, that $\triangle ABC \cong \triangle DEF$?*

   By construction we have $\overline{AC} \cong \overline{DF}, \overline{AB} \cong \overline{DE}$ and $\overline{CB} \cong \overline{FE}$. Hence $\triangle ABC \cong \triangle DEF$ by (SSS).

2. *Can you develop a similar construction procedure for copying a triangle based on the (ASA) congruence theorem?*

   We use the diagram employed in construction (3). Locate point C on the given ray, such that $\overline{AC} \cong \overline{DF}$. In one of the half-planes determined by $\overleftrightarrow{AC}$ we construct two angles, each having one ray lying in $\overleftrightarrow{AC}$. At A construct $\angle D$ and at C construct $\angle F$. We wish to show that the remaining rays of these two constructed angles intersect at a point. We have seen that we may construct $\triangle ABC \cong \triangle DEF$ by SSS construction. Hence we know $\angle A \cong \angle D$ and $\angle C \cong \angle F$ and the rays $\overrightarrow{AB}$ and $\overrightarrow{CB}$ intersect at B. Hence the point B of intersection is known to exist and the constructed $\triangle ABC \cong \triangle DEF$ by (ASA).

Can you complete (4) by proving that TP is perpendicular to m?

We have $\overline{RP} \cong \overline{PS}, \overline{RT} \cong \overline{ST}$ and $\overline{PT} \cong \overline{PT}$. Hence

$$\triangle RPT \cong \triangle SPT \text{ by } (SSS)$$

and therefore

$$\angle RPT \cong \angle SPT.$$

Since $m(\angle RPT) + m(\angle SPT) = 180$, both angles must be right angles and $\overleftrightarrow{TP}$ is perpendicular to m.

Can you complete the proof that $\overleftrightarrow{PQ}$ is the perpendicular bisector of $\overline{MN}$?

By the argument used in construction (4) we are assured of the intersection of the circles, centers M and N and radius $r > \tfrac{1}{2}MN$, in points P and Q. Then we have $\overline{MP} \cong \overline{NP}$, $\overline{MQ} \cong \overline{NQ}$ and $\overline{PQ} \cong \overline{PQ}$. Hence $\triangle MPQ \cong \triangle NPQ$ by (SSS). Therefore $\angle MPQ \cong \angle NPQ$. Let $\overleftrightarrow{PQ}$ and $\overline{MN}$ intersect at C. Then $\triangle MPC \cong \triangle NPC$ by (SAS). It follows that $\overline{MC} \cong \overline{NC}$ and $\angle MCP \cong \angle NCP$, hence $\overleftrightarrow{PQ}$ is the perpendicular bisector of $\overline{MN}$.

Can you prove that $\overleftrightarrow{PH}$ is perpendicular to m?

Since $\overline{RP} \cong \overline{RW}, \overline{RH} \cong \overline{RH}$ and $\angle PRH \cong \angle WRH$, it follows that $\triangle PRH \cong \triangle WRH$ by (SAS). Hence $\angle RHP \cong \angle RHW$. Therefore $\overleftrightarrow{PH}$ is perpendicular to m.

Can you prove that $RP = QP$?

Since $\overline{RH} \cong \overline{QH}, \overline{HP} \cong \overline{HP}$, and $\angle RHP \cong \angle QHP$, we know that $\triangle RHP \cong \triangle QHP$. It follows that $\overline{RP} \cong \overline{QP}$.

Section 8.09

Can you verify that the three pyramids have equal volumes?

Because $PQRSTV$ is constructed as a triangular prism, we know that $\triangle PRQ \cong \triangle TVS$ and that these triangles lie in parallel planes. Hence the perpendicular distance between the parallel planes represents the altitude of each triangular pyramid with respect to the bases $\triangle PRQ$ and $\triangle TVS$, and these triangles have equal areas. Therefore pyramids (a) and (c) are known to have equal volumes.

We know that $\overline{SV} \cong \overline{QR}$. Moreover $\overleftrightarrow{SV}$ is parallel to $\overleftrightarrow{QR}$, for they are coplanar and cannot meet by virtue of lying in parallel planes. Hence $\angle VSR \cong \angle QRS$ and therefore $\triangle SRV \cong \triangle RSQ$. These two triangular regions are coplanar and have equal areas. The two pyramids with these two regions as bases have the same opposite vertex and equal altitudes. Therefore pyramids (b) and (c) have equal volumes. This means that all three pyramids have equal volumes.

CHAPTER 9

Section 9.01

Can you show that Q and R are unique for given N and D?

We have $N = Q \cdot D + R$, where $0 \leq R < D$. Suppose also that $N = Q_1 \cdot D + R_1$, where $0 \leq R_1 < D$ and where $Q_1 \neq Q$ and $R_1 \neq R$. We obtain $Q \cdot D + R = Q_1 D + R_1$. Hence $(Q - Q_1)D = R_1 - R$. Evidently D is a factor of $R_1 - R$. However, we may add corresponding parts of the inequalities, $0 \leq R_1 < D$ and $-D < -R \leq 0$ and obtain $-D < R_1 - R < D$ or $|R_1 - R| < D$. This contradicts the fact that D is a divisor of $R_1 - R$, unless $R_1 - R = 0$. Hence we must have $R_1 = R$. This means that $D(Q - Q_1) = 0$, and because $D \neq 0$ we must have $Q - Q_1 = 0$ or $Q = Q_1$. Hence Q and R are unique for given N and D.

Section 9.02

1. For the function $f = \{(1,2), (2,4), (3,6),...\}$, previously discussed, the domain is the set of natural numbers.

    (a) The range is the set of even natural numbers.
    (b) The "map" of 5 is 10.
    (c) $f(12) = 24$.
    (d) If $f(x) = 42$, then $x = 21$.

2. If $f(x) = 2^x$, can you show that $f(y) \cdot f(w) = f(y + w)$?

$$f(y) = 2^y; \quad f(w) = 2^w.$$

Therefore

$$f(y) \cdot f(w) = 2^y \cdot 2^w$$
$$= 2^{y+w} = f(y + w), \text{ since } f(x) = 2^x$$

for any x in the domain of f.

Section 9.04

Can you verify that the numbers represented by (a) and (b) are equal?

If we expand the expression $2(2[2\{2(4) + (-3)\} + (-7)] + (-4)) + (-9)$, we obtain

$$4(2^4) + (-3)(2^3) + (-7)(2^2) + (-4)(2) + (-9) = 4(2^4) - 3(2^3) - 7(2^2) - 4(2) - 9.$$

Section 9.05

How does $x^2 + x + 3$ factor in the universe of complex numbers?

The roots of $x^2 + x + 3 = 0$ are $x = \dfrac{-1 \pm \sqrt{1-12}}{2} = -\dfrac{1}{2} \pm \dfrac{\sqrt{11}}{2}i$. Hence

$$x^2 + x + 3 = \left[x - \left(-\dfrac{1}{2} + \dfrac{\sqrt{11}}{2}i\right)\right]\left[x - \left(-\dfrac{1}{2} - \dfrac{\sqrt{11}}{2}i\right)\right]$$

$$= \left(x + \dfrac{1}{2} - \dfrac{\sqrt{11}}{2}i\right)\left(x + \dfrac{1}{2} + \dfrac{\sqrt{11}}{2}i\right)$$

If n is odd, what are two proper factors of $x^n + a^n$?

When n is odd, $x^n + a^n = (x + a)(x^{n-1} - ax^{n-2} + a^2 x^{n-3} + \cdots + a^{n-1})$.

Section 9.06

How do you justify lines (8) and (9)?

We have $0 \leq R < b - 1$ from (3) and $-(b-1) < -r \leq 0$ by multiplying both sides of inequality (4) by -1. By adding corresponding sides of the inequalities (7) and (8) we obtain inequality (9)

$$-(b-1) < R - r < b - 1$$

How do you justify the conclusion that $A = 0$?

We have $R - r = A(b-1)$ and $|R - r| < b - 1$; that is, $R - r$ is a multiple of $b - 1$ but at the same time $b - 1 > |R - r|$. This is impossible unless $A = 0$.

Can you prove that if $a \equiv b \pmod{K}$ and $c \equiv d \pmod{K}$ then (1) $a + c \equiv b + d \pmod{K}$?

We have
$$a = b + mK$$
$$c = d + nK$$

Hence
$$a + c = (b + mK) + (d + nK)$$
$$= b + d + (m + n)K$$

or
$$a + c \equiv b + d \pmod{K}$$

(2) $ac \equiv bd \pmod{K}$
Again,

$$a = b + mK$$
$$c = d + nK$$

Hence

$$ac = (b + mK)(d + nK)$$
$$= bd + dmK + bnK + mnK^2$$
$$= bd + (dm + bn + mnK)K$$

Therefore

$$ac \equiv bd \pmod{K}$$

Section 9.07

If a, p, and q are integers and if p and q are relatively prime, can you show that if p divides aq, then p divides a?

Suppose $p = p_1 p_2 \cdots p_m, a = a_1 a_2 \cdots a_r$, and $q = q_1 q_2 \cdots q_s$, where $p_1, \ldots, p_m, a_1, \ldots, a_r, q_1, \ldots, q_s$ are prime numbers. Because p and q are relatively prime, $p_1 \neq q_j$ for any $i = 1, 2, \ldots, m$ or $j = 1, 2, \ldots, s$. Because $p_1 p_2 \cdots p_m$ is a factor of $a_1 a_2 \cdots a_r q_1 q_2 \cdots q_s$, then $\{p_i | i = 1, 2, \ldots, m\}$ must be a subset of $\{a_k | k = 1, 2, \ldots, r\}$. Hence p divides a.

Similarly, if p divides aq^n, does p necessarily divide a?

We now have $p_1 p_2 \cdots p_m$, a factor of $a_1 a_2 \cdots a_r q_1^n q_2^n \cdots q_s^n$. Hence, as before, $\{p_i | i = 1, 2, \ldots, m\} \subseteq \{a_k | k = 1, 2, \ldots, r\}$ and p must divide a.

2. *If we are given that r divides st, where r, s, t are integers and r does not divide t, can you say whether it is necessary that r divide s?*

Again let r, s, and t have the following prime factorizations: $r = r_1 r_2 \cdots r_p, s = s_1 s_2 \cdots s_q$; $t = t_1 t_2 \cdots t_m$. Then $r_1 r_2 \cdots r_p$ divides $s_1 s_2 \cdots s_q t_1 t_2 \cdots t_m$. Since r does not divide t, we must have $r_i \neq t_j$ for some i and j. Hence at least one $r_i = s_k$ for some k. However, this does not prevent some r_i from equaling some t_j. Hence we cannot say whether or not r must divide s.

Section 9.08

What happens to the value of P as the point (x, y) moves

1. *from B to A?* $P (= 120 + 5x + 2y)$ decreases from 182 to 170, for x remains constant at $x = 10$ and y decreases from 6 to 0.

2. *from C to D?* P decreases from 183 to 165. Along the ray $\overrightarrow{CD}$, $2x + 2y$ remains constant and x is decreasing. Hence $5x + 2y [= (2x + 2y) + 3x]$ and likewise P is decreasing.

3. *from B to C?* P increases from 182 to 183. Along the ray $\overrightarrow{BC}$, $6x + 2y$ is constant and x is decreasing. Hence $5x + 2y [= (6x + 2y) - x]$ and likewise P is increasing.

CHAPTER 10

Section 10.05

Under what circumstances could more than one mode occur?

It is quite possible for two distinct items to occur with the same maximum frequency.

Can you explain how nm is obtained in this summation?

$$\sum_{i=1}^{n}(x_i - m) = (x_1 - m) + (x_2 - m) + \cdots + (x_n - m)$$

$$= x_1 + x_2 + \cdots + x_n - \underbrace{(m + m + \cdots + m)}_{n \text{ terms}}$$

$$= \sum_{i=1}^{n} x_i - nm$$

Can you use this approach to obtain the mean of the students' weights in Section 10.03?
Let us take 190 as the trial value. Then

$$\bar{x} = 190 + \frac{1}{31}\sum_{i=1}^{31}(x_i - 190)$$

$$= 190 + \frac{1}{31}(4)$$

$$= 190.13$$

Section 10.06
Can you explain why the above statement in parentheses is true?

$$\frac{1}{n}\sum_{i=1}^{n}(x_i - \bar{x}) = \frac{1}{n}(\sum_{i=1}^{n} x_i - n\bar{x})$$

$$= \frac{1}{n}\sum_{i=1}^{n} x_i - \bar{x}$$

$$= 0 \text{ by definition of } \bar{x}$$

Appendix A
Can you discover the basic discrepancy that underlines the above fallacy?
If the figure is drawn accurately it will be found that the segment $\overline{OC}$ lies outside $\angle FCD$, under which circumstances the fallacy is not present.

Appendix B
Can you obtain the other four expressions, like the two above, and verify that each is equal to $\triangle$?

$$\triangle = a_1 A_1 + b_1 B_1 + c_1 C_1$$
$$= a_3 A_3 + b_3 B_3 + c_3 C_3$$
$$= b_1 B_1 + b_2 B_2 + b_3 B_3$$
$$= c_1 C_1 + c_2 C_2 + c_3 C_3$$

Appendix C
1. *How would you demonstrate that addition of matrices is commutative and associative?*

If we assume, as we wish to do, that the entries in our matrices are chosen from a field, addition of these numbers is commutative and associative. Therefore

and
$$(a_{ij}) + (b_{ij}) = (a_{ij} + b_{ij}) = (b_{ij} + a_{ij}) = (b_{ij}) + (a_{ij})$$

$$[(a_{ij}) + (b_{ij})] + (c_{ij}) = (a_{ij} + b_{ij}) + (c_{ij}) = ([a_{ij} + b_{ij}] + c_{ij})$$
$$= (a_{ij} + [b_{ij} + c_{ij}]) = (a_{ij}) + (b_{ij} + c_{ij})$$
$$= (a_{ij}) + [(b_{ij}) + (c_{ij})]$$

2. *If $b_{ij} = 0$ for all i and j, what can be said about $A + B$?*

$$A + B = (a_{ij}) + (b_{ij}) = (a_{ij} + b_{ij}) = (a_{ij} + 0) = (a_{ij}) = A$$

Hence B is operating like an additive identity.

3. *If $b_{ij} = -a_{ij}$, for all i and j, what can be said about $A + B$?*

$$A + B = (a_{ij}) + (b_{ij}) = (a_{ij} + b_{ij}) = (a_{ij} - a_{ij}) = (0)$$

Hence B is operating like an additive inverse.

1. *Do you believe that multiplication of matrices is associative?*
Yes. Assume that dimensions of A, B, C are m by p, p by q, and q by n, respectively.

$$[AB]C = [(a_{ij})(b_{ij})](c_{ij})$$
$$= \left(\sum_{k=1}^{p} a_{ik}b_{kj}\right)(c_{ij})$$
$$= \left(\sum_{l=1}^{q}\left[\sum_{k=1}^{p} a_{ik}b_{kl}\right]c_{lj}\right) = \left(\sum_{l=1}^{q}\sum_{k=1}^{p}[a_{ik}b_{kl}]c_{lj}\right)$$
$$= \left(\sum_{l=1}^{q}\sum_{l=1}^{p} a_{ik}\left[b_{kl}c_{lj}\right]\right) = \left(\sum_{l=1}^{p} a_{ik}\left[\sum_{l=1}^{q} b_{kl}c_{lj}\right]\right)$$
$$= (a_{ij})\left(\sum_{l=1}^{q} b_{il}c_{lj}\right) = (a_{ij})[(b_{ij})(c_{ij})] = A[BC]$$

2. *Can you demonstrate that multiplication of matrices is not commutative by showing that* $\begin{pmatrix} 1 & -2 \\ 3 & -1 \end{pmatrix}\begin{pmatrix} 2 & 4 \\ -5 & 3 \end{pmatrix} \neq \begin{pmatrix} 2 & 4 \\ -5 & 3 \end{pmatrix}\begin{pmatrix} 1 & -2 \\ 3 & -1 \end{pmatrix}$?

$$\begin{pmatrix} 1 & -2 \\ 3 & -1 \end{pmatrix}\begin{pmatrix} 2 & 4 \\ -5 & 3 \end{pmatrix} = \begin{pmatrix} 12 & -2 \\ 11 & 9 \end{pmatrix}; \quad \begin{pmatrix} 2 & 4 \\ -5 & 3 \end{pmatrix}\begin{pmatrix} 1 & -2 \\ 3 & -1 \end{pmatrix} = \begin{pmatrix} 14 & -8 \\ 4 & 7 \end{pmatrix}$$

3. *What is the special nature of* $\begin{pmatrix} 1 & 0 \\ 0 & 1 \end{pmatrix}$ *as illustrated in the product* $\begin{pmatrix} -4 & 5 \\ 1 & 2 \\ -3 & 0 \end{pmatrix}\begin{pmatrix} 1 & 0 \\ 0 & 1 \end{pmatrix}$ *or*

of $\begin{pmatrix} 1 & 0 & 0 \\ 0 & 1 & 0 \\ 0 & 0 & 1 \end{pmatrix}$ *in the product* $\begin{pmatrix} 1 & 0 & 0 \\ 0 & 1 & 0 \\ 0 & 0 & 1 \end{pmatrix}\begin{pmatrix} -4 & 5 \\ 1 & 2 \\ -3 & 0 \end{pmatrix}$?

$$\begin{pmatrix} -4 & 5 \\ 1 & 2 \\ -3 & 0 \end{pmatrix}\begin{pmatrix} 1 & 0 \\ 0 & 1 \end{pmatrix} = \begin{pmatrix} -4 & 5 \\ 1 & 2 \\ -3 & 0 \end{pmatrix}; \quad \begin{pmatrix} 1 & 0 & 0 \\ 0 & 1 & 0 \\ 0 & 0 & 1 \end{pmatrix}\begin{pmatrix} -4 & 5 \\ 1 & 2 \\ -3 & 0 \end{pmatrix} = \begin{pmatrix} -4 & 5 \\ 1 & 2 \\ -3 & 0 \end{pmatrix}$$

Clearly, $\begin{pmatrix} 1 & 0 \\ 0 & 1 \end{pmatrix}$ and $\begin{pmatrix} 1 & 0 & 0 \\ 0 & 1 & 0 \\ 0 & 0 & 1 \end{pmatrix}$ are acting as multiplicative identities on the right and left sides, respectively.

1. *Is it true, in the foregoing example, that* $AA^{-1} = A^{-1}A = I = \begin{pmatrix} 1 & 0 & 0 \\ 0 & 1 & 0 \\ 0 & 0 & 1 \end{pmatrix}$?

$$AA^{-1} = \begin{pmatrix} 4 & -2 & 0 \\ 0 & -3 & 2 \\ 3 & 2 & -1 \end{pmatrix}\left(-\frac{1}{16}\right)\begin{pmatrix} -1 & -2 & -4 \\ 6 & -4 & -8 \\ 9 & -14 & -12 \end{pmatrix} = \left(-\frac{1}{16}\right)\begin{pmatrix} -16 & 0 & 0 \\ 0 & -16 & 0 \\ 0 & 0 & -16 \end{pmatrix} = \begin{pmatrix} 1 & 0 & 0 \\ 0 & 1 & 0 \\ 0 & 0 & 1 \end{pmatrix}$$

$$= I$$

$$A^{-1}A = \left(-\frac{1}{16}\right)\begin{pmatrix} -1 & -2 & -4 \\ 6 & -4 & -8 \\ 9 & -14 & -12 \end{pmatrix}\begin{pmatrix} 4 & -2 & 0 \\ 0 & -3 & 2 \\ 3 & 2 & -1 \end{pmatrix} = \left(-\frac{1}{16}\right)\begin{pmatrix} -16 & 0 & 0 \\ 0 & -16 & 0 \\ 0 & 0 & -16 \end{pmatrix} = \begin{pmatrix} 1 & 0 & 0 \\ 0 & 1 & 0 \\ 0 & 0 & 1 \end{pmatrix}$$

$$= I$$

2. *Is it true that the multiplicative inverse of* $\begin{pmatrix} 4 & -3 \\ -2 & 5 \end{pmatrix}$ *is* $\begin{pmatrix} \frac{5}{14} & \frac{3}{14} \\ \frac{2}{14} & \frac{4}{14} \end{pmatrix}$ *or* $\frac{1}{14}\begin{pmatrix} 5 & 3 \\ 2 & 4 \end{pmatrix}$?

Yes.

$$\begin{pmatrix} 4 & -3 \\ -2 & 5 \end{pmatrix}\begin{pmatrix} \frac{5}{14} & \frac{3}{14} \\ \frac{2}{14} & \frac{4}{14} \end{pmatrix} = \begin{pmatrix} \frac{14}{14} & 0 \\ 0 & \frac{14}{14} \end{pmatrix} = \begin{pmatrix} 1 & 0 \\ 0 & 1 \end{pmatrix}$$

$$\frac{1}{14}\begin{pmatrix} 5 & 3 \\ 2 & 4 \end{pmatrix}\begin{pmatrix} 4 & -3 \\ -2 & 5 \end{pmatrix} = \frac{1}{14}\begin{pmatrix} 14 & 0 \\ 0 & 14 \end{pmatrix} = \begin{pmatrix} 1 & 0 \\ 0 & 1 \end{pmatrix}$$

Index

Abscissa, 100
Absolute error, 107
Absolute value, 61
Accuracy, 106, 107
Addition, 7, 62, 71, 86
Additive identity, 15, 63, 86
Additive inverse, 61, 75, 86
Algebraic number, 83
Algorithm, division, 25, 197, 201
Analytical, 100
Angle, 98
Approximation, 105
Area, 99, 184
Argument, fallacious, 50
   invalid, 50
   valid, 48
Arithmetic mean, 227
Arithmetic progression, 144
Associative, 9
Augmented matrix, 129, 246
Average, 225
Average deviation, 230

Base, 11, 23
Belongs to, 1
Between, betweenness, 96
Biconditional, 40
Binary operation, 5
Binary system, 24
Binomial distribution, 221
Binomial theorem, 148, 249
Bisector, 192, 193
Broken line graph, 223

Cancellation, 72
Cancellation law of multiplication, 53
Cartesian product, 10, 199
Casting out, 208
Catenary, 90

Cavalieri's principle, 194
Central tendency, measure of, 225
Circuit, 29
Closed interval, 120
Closed set, 8
Closure, 20
Cofactor, 240
Column, 89
Combination, 152
Commutative, 5
Complement, 4
Complex number, 86, 206
Conditional, 39
Congruence, congruent, 175
Conjugate, 88
Conjunction, 36
Consistency, consistent, 93
Construction, geometric, 189
Contained in, 3
Contradiction, 52
Contrapositive, 43, 49, 52
Control, 235
Converse, 43, 50
Convex polygon, 218
Coordinate, 100
Correspondence, 2, 3, 7, 100, 122
Countability, countable, 162
Countably infinite, 162
Counterexample, 73, 92
Counting, 1, 3, 162
Cramer's rule, 242, 248
Critical value, 235
Cyclically permuted code (CPC), 26
Cycloid, 90

Decimal fraction, 78, 164
Decimal system, 23
Dedekind cut, 82
Degree, 201

319

Denominator, 70
Density, 230
Denumerability, denumerable, 162
Denumerably infinite, 162
Descartes, 100
Detachment, rule of, 49
Determinant, 127, 239, 245
Deviation, mean, 230
    standard, 231
Diagonal, 245
Difference set, 6
Digit, 25, 115, 208
Discriminant, 136
Disjoint, 5, 98, 215
Disjunction, 37
Dispersion, 230
Displacement, 58
Distribution, frequency, 220
Distributive, 7, 12
Division, 19, 86, 198
Division algorithm, 25, 197, 201
Divisor of zero, 16
Domain, 200

Element, 1
Ellipse, 90
Ellipsoid, 91
Empty set, 4
Equals, 2, 10
Equal sets, 2
Equivalence class, 66, 80, 159
Equivalence relation, 66
Equivalent propositions, 37, 47
Equivalent sentences, 119
Equivalent sets, 2
Error, 106, 107
Euclid, 53, 91
Euler diagram, 49
Even number, 20
Event, 155, 220
Exponent, 11, 23
Exterior, 98

Factor, 11
Factorial, 150
Factor theorem, 203
Fallacious argument, 50, 238
Fallacy, 50
Family of loci, 102, 103
Field, 84
Finite set, 3

Four-point geometry, 93
Fraction, 67
Fractional exponent, 172
Frequency, 154, 220
Frequency distribution, 220
Frequency polygon, 223
Function, 7, 199, 215
Fundamental theorem of algebra, 134

Geometric progression, 145
Grade point average (GPA), 228
Graph, 119, 221
Graycode, 26
Greatest common divisor (GCD), 21

Half-line, half-plane, 98
Harmonic progression, 147
Harmonic sequence, 146
Histogram, 223
Hypothesis, 48
    null, 235
    testing, 235

Identity, additive, 15, 63, 86
    multiplicative, 10, 64, 86
Illusion, optical, 96
Imaginary part, 86
Imaginary unit, 85
Implication, implies, 45
Independence, independent, 93, 156
Index, 11
Indirect proof, 52, 81
Induction, mathematical, 31–35, 139–141
Inductive set, 31
Inequality, 215–218
Infinite set, 3
Integer, 59
Intercept, 102
Interior, 98
Intersection, 5
Interval, 120, 223
Invalid argument, 50
Inverse, additive, 61
    multiplicative, 74
    operation, 18
Inversion, 239
Irrational number, 83, 84
Isomorphic, isomorphism, 30, 70

Least common multiple (LCM), 22
Length, 99

Limit, 82, 146, 165
Line, 91, 97
Linear equation, 123
Locus, 119
Logic, 36
Logically false, 45
Logically true, 45

Mapping, 7
Mathematical induction, principle of, 31–35, 139–141
Mathematical system, 28
Matrix, 89, 129, 243–248
Mean, arithmetic, 227
Mean deviation, 230
Measure, 99, 104, 225, 230
Measurement, 99, 104
Median, 227, 236
Miniature geometry, 93
Minor, 240
Mode, 226
Model, 93
Modular system, modulo, 28
Modus ponens, 49
Modus tollens, 49
Multiplication, 10, 64, 72, 86
Multiplicative identity, 10, 64, 86
Multiplicative inverse, 74, 86
Mutually exclusive, 155

Natural number, 1, 2
Necessary, 39
Negation, 36
Negative, 59
Neutral geometry, 182
Nim, 26ff
Normal curve, 225
Normal distribution, 224
Null hypothesis, 235
Null set, 4
Number line, 16
Numeral, 9
Numerator, 70
Numerical sentence, 10, 56

Octal, 25
Odd number, 20
One-to-one correspondence, 2, 3, 162
Open interval, 120
Open sentence, 56
Operation, 5

Opposite, 60
Optical illusion, 96
Order, 16, 61, 77
Ordered pair, 5
Ordinate, 100

Pair, ordered, 5
Parabola, 90, 136
Parallel, 95, 128, 179, 182
Parallelepiped 99, 194
Pascal's Triangle, 148, 249
Per cent, 173
Permutation, 149
Perpendicular, 179
Placeholder, 16
Plane, 91
Point, 91, 95, 99–101
Polygon, convex, 218
  frequency, 223
Polygonal region, 99
Polynomial, 201, 209, 212
Positive, 59, 77, 84
Postulate, 92, 93
Power, 11
Precision, 106
Premise, 48
Prime number, 21, 53
Principal root, 171
Prism, 194
Probability, 154
Product, 11
Progression, arithmetic, 144
  geometric, 145
  harmonic, 147
Pronumeral, 10
Property, 1
Proportion, 160
Proposition, 36
Pure imaginary, 86
Pyramid, 195
Pythagorean Theorem, 82, 187

Quality control, 234
Quotient, 25

Radical, 171
Random variable, 235
Range, 200, 230
Ratio, 160
Rationalize, 173
Rational number, 68, 212

Ray, 97
Real number, 83
Real part, 86
Reciprocal, 74
Rectangle, 99, 181
Reflexivity, 66
Region, 99
Relation, 65
Relative error, 107
Relatively prime, 21
Remainder, 202, 205, 208
   theorem, 202
Repeating decimal fraction, 164–168
Right angle, 179
Root, 134, 203
Rounding, 112
Row, 89

Sampling, 233
Scalar, 243
Section, plane, 194ff.
Segment, 97
Self-contradiction, 45
Sequence, 139
Series, 139
Set, 1
Set-builder notation, 1
Short (multiplication and division), 115
Significant digit, 109
Similar, similarity, 185
Slope, 101
Solution set, 43, 57
Sophism, 238
Sorting, 26
Standard deviation, 231
Statistical hypothesis, 235
Statistics, 219
Structure, 1

Subset, 3
Subtraction, 17, 60, 75, 86
Such that, 16
Sufficient, 39
Sum, 7, 144, 146, 243
Superposition, 175
Syllogism, 50
Symmetry, 66
Synthetic division, 204
Synthetic substitution, 205
System, binary, 24
   decimal, 23
   mathematical, 28

Tautology, 45
Testing, hypothesis, 235
Transcendental, 83
Transitivity, 66
Triangle, 98
Trinomial, 133
Truth set, 43
Truth table, 36

Undefined term, 1, 91, 93
Union, 5
Unique factorization theorem, 21
Unit, 99
Universal set, universe, 4, 43, 56

Valid argument, 48
Value, 200
Variable, 121
Variance, 231
Venn diagram, 4
Volume, 99

Whole number, 15

Zero, 15, 59, 100, 203, 212

QA
39
K46

SEP 24 1968